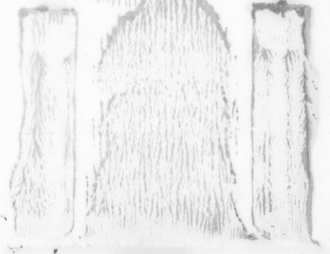

D1058499

THE
OCEAN RIVER

BY HENRY CHAPIN AND

F. G. WALTON SMITH

New York
CHARLES SCRIBNER'S SONS

COPYRIGHT SOURCES QUOTED

Brown, Lloyd A., *The Story of Maps*, Little Brown and Co., Boston, 1949

Chatterton, E. K., *Sailing Ships and Their Story*, Sidgwick and Jackson, Ltd., London, 1923

Haring, C. H., *The Buccaneers in the West Indies in the XVII Century*, Methuen and Co., Ltd., London, 1910

Helps, Sir Arthur, *The Life of Las Casas*, Bell and Daldy, London, 1868

McFarland R., *A History of New England Fisheries*, University of Pennsylvania Press, Philadelphia, 1911

Morison, S. E., *Admiral of the Ocean Sea*, Little Brown and Co., Boston, 1942

Parry, J. H., *Europe and a Wider World*, Hutchinson University Library, London, 1949

Spence, Lewis, *Atlantis in America*, E. Benn, London, 1925

Termier, P., *Annual Report of The Smithsonian Institution*, 1915

Wyndham, H. A., *The Atlantic and Slavery*, Royal Institute of International Affairs, Oxford University Press, 1935

To the Memory of our Friend
HERVEY ALLEN
whose enthusiasm for the subject
led us to write this book.

PREFACE

ECAUSE of the wide scope of this book, it has not been possible to treat many fascinating aspects of the history of the North Atlantic Ocean in as much detail as we should have liked. This is particularly true in regard to the scientific aspects of the Ocean River. At the present time because new additions to our knowledge are being made so rapidly and because the subject is so broad and unsettled, it has sometimes been necessary to give more weight to the older established theories than to the new ideas which are rapidly gaining ground.

We have been indebted to a number of experts in the fields of oceanography and history for their kindness in reading through portions of the manuscript and in offering their comments and criticisms. Although we take full responsibility for any errors in fact or interpretation, we nevertheless wish to acknowledge the generous assistance given by Dr. Maurice Ewing of Columbia University, Dr. Francis P. Shepard and Dr. Walter H. Munk of the Scripps Institute of Oceanography, California, and Dr. Lionel A. Walford of the United States Fish and Wildlife Service.

We are particularly grateful to Dr. Hilary B. Moore, Dr. Ilmo Hela, Dr. Charles E. Lane, Mr. Luis R. Rivas and Mr.

Robert Ginsburg of the Marine Laboratory, University of Miami, and Dr. Virgil G. Sleight of the Geology Department of the University of Miami, for critically reading the manuscript.

Professor Robert G. Albion of the Harvard History Department has made extremely helpful suggestions in regard to the historical matter but is in no way responsible for our opinions or judgments, which have been governed by the particular focus of this book where much, of necessity, has been omitted.

We are also indebted to Colonel and Mrs. Frederick A. Wanklyn whose gracious hospitality in Nassau, Bahamas, provided the necessary seclusion from a busy life in which the first few chapters and outline of the book could be written.

H.C. and F.G.W.S.

MIAMI, *January, 1952*

PREFACE TO
SCRIBNER LIBRARY EDITION

DURING the ten years which have elapsed since we wrote *The Ocean River*, there have been a few new scientific discoveries with direct or indirect bearing upon our subject as well as changes of emphasis in scientific theory. Although they do not materially change the thread of our story, they should be mentioned.

Ideas as to the origin of the earth are still highly speculative but the majority now believe that earth and planets were formed by the accumulation of cold cosmic dust and gases, and that the earth began to heat up only after its formation, due to the effects of compression and radioactivity. Few, if any, now subscribe to the belief that the moon was cast out of a molten earth, a theory still being debated a few short years ago.

On the other hand, the recent discovery of an extension of the mid-Atlantic ridge into the Indian and Antarctic Oceans has given new life to Wegener's theory of continental drift. In 1950, there were about as many scientists against this theory as for it. Today the balance has shifted in favor of the breaking apart of an original single continent.

The origin of sea water is still undecided but there is evidence for a belief that a considerable amount of it is "juvenile," gradually evolved from the rocks as pressure is relieved in geysers or volcanoes.

In the Gulf Stream itself there has been discovered in the west, a deep lying current running in opposite direction to the warm surface water. There is also a deep counter current at the Equator. But most of the advances in our knowledge of the current are not of concern here, since they involve complex mathematical theory.

To these few changes in scientific knowledge and outlook there is little else to add as far as the history of man in relation to the Ocean River is concerned. The giant stream continues along its accustomed path with only minor deviations from year to year.

H. C. and F. G. W. S.

CONTENTS

There shall come worlds in late years, in which this ocean shall enclose the bounds of things and a great land shall appear. Also Typhis shall discover new worlds and Thyle [Thule] shall not be the furthest land.

—SENECA

1

OCEANUS

THE ancients used the word Oceanus, the Ocean River, for a mysterious and dangerous sea which bordered the world as they knew it. The Atlantic Ocean, lying beyond the Pillars of Hercules, was a great unknown of swift malevolent currents and strange monsters compact with dread. Since those days the mysteries of flowing drift and tide, the river of life which began a billion years or more ago, and the complex interweaving of the lives of plants and animals in the ocean today, have all yielded in some measure to the inquiring mind of man. And this, a river of many meanings, is what we write about.

There is a great artery of warm and foreign water which sweeps up the North American coast and across the wide Atlantic, called the Gulf Stream. It is part of a greater system of interlocking currents and drifts that girdle the North Atlantic, a salt stream of life within the salt ocean that helps regulate and sustain the life on land and sea of the Atlantic peoples. This, the Ocean River, sweeps westerly from the Canaries into the Caribbean, thence north along our coasts and easterly to fan out toward Iceland, England, and Norway in the north, and south to the coasts of Portugal and Spain. There are also hidden branches of the River, cold waters sinking in the northern seas, the slow, deep drift to the south, and the lesser streams, the smaller vessels and capillaries of the salt circulation, entering and leaving the main circuit with varying pulse.

The Ocean River brings warmth and energy to northern Europe, which otherwise would remain a subarctic wasteland. As the Mediterranean waters nourished and promoted the

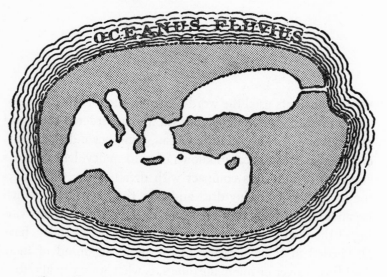

The world, as known in the time of Homer — 1000 B.C.

spread of classic civilization, so our North Atlantic modern world is in great measure a fruit of this watery tree of life, a kind of Igdrasil, whose roots are in the Caribbean and whose branches spread from the Grand Banks to the Baltic. So we can say that Europeans, at home or transplanted across the River to the American continent, are all one people of a river system with its interacting commerce and traffic, and cultural unity.

There is nothing stationary or changeless about this. At one time in geological history things were different, and so again at some unscheduled moment the bounty of this life-giving stream can well be removed from us, its pensioners. It is worth our study. We shall begin at the beginning with the creation of the ocean basin, for the history of the Atlantic is in a way the history of the development of the seas and continents, of the world itself.

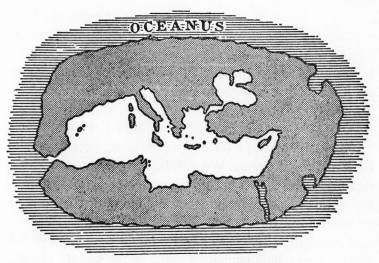

The world, as known in the time of Hecataeus — 500 B.C.

The time of man on earth has been short. If we use as a geological year the time from the creation of the earth as we know it to the present day, the existence of man might measure two minutes. Even thus briefly, with antlike patience and imaginative boldness, man has managed to construct a fairly accurate picture of what the world was like before his own remote ancestry was called forth from the mud and waters of creative chaos. It is a picture of elemental forces in harmony, all stemming from the energy of the sun. The river of the sea in motion reflects an invisible river of the airs above it which act as a great thermal engine geared to the waters beneath. But the waters of the sea do not move in horizontal courses alone, for the sun creates variations of temperature which move the surface waters and the cold depths vertically in actions that make a constant and living unity of the oceans. These actions create conditions favorable to the life within, and so in turn sustain mankind.

So if we look at a current we must look at a climate. If we consider a climate we must consider how it affects the life of man. If we study the depths of the sea we learn not only of the teeming life within the sea, but secrets of subocean geology are revealed that help us to understand our land-bound environment. In other words, there can be nothing unrelated between man and the immediate world he lives in, and it is this that has imposed a certain pattern to our book and made the frame of our picture. We start building the frame with the rock that molds the ocean bed. We watch the waters that move within this foundation and study the forces that drive them on and control their action. We see man put out adventurously upon these waters to new lands and fresh ways of life. We see how certain climates, created by the warmth of these waters and the storms above them, are favorable for the growth of strong civilizations. And finally, looking more closely upon the complex of the Ocean River, we discover a vast new frontier of discovery which the young science of oceanography has just begun to explore. Oceanography in itself is a team of several more restricted fields of scientific inquiry, and is forced to function as a team because man is forced to regard the ocean as a total environment. So we find chemists, meteorologists, biologists, geologists, and students of what is called human geography, all pooling their efforts to solve the mystery of the deep and moving sea.

We know that somewhere, somehow, in the great circle of creation there was a slight punctuation called the globe. Then time, as we count it, began. Just what upheaval set the Ocean River on its course we do not know, but we do know what holds it in its present rhythm, and we are beginning to find out how dependent on this stream the peoples of the Atlantic community are for their climate, their food, and the directions of their development.

Two of the first questions that come to mind are, why is this stream not soon dissipated into the vast Atlantic waters; and what gives it propulsion? Streams as we landlubbers know them run downhill between banks. There is not enough downhill in the ocean, except in a few places, to account for the entire course and powerful drive of the Ocean River, which equals about a thousand times the flood of the Mississippi. There is a power that stirs the whole North Atlantic ocean in a clockwise swirl, with the Sargasso Sea at its center teeming with weed and the special life of its own slow-moving waters. The sun, of course, keeps this wheel of ocean spinning, using as a machine for the discharge of its energy the constant effects of wind and climate and the present fixed conformations of continents and ocean bottom. Under these circumstances the waters of the Great River start on their long journey with a temperature, a density, a salinity, and a pace that creates an entity within the vast surrounding ocean.

We begin to see the measure of the Ocean River, its reach and its constant current carrying the warm tropic waters to the far north. This giant engine, created by climate, distributes and controls climate far from its source. The ocean has well been called a climate in storage, meaning simply that by the nature of salt water it acts as a reservoir of heat energy. But the constituent nature of the sea, the life-giving properties of salt water, are as important to the life cycle of the Atlantic world and its bordering continents as the size or power of the Stream as an engine of climate.

Salt water both in quality and quantity is one of man's best sources of food, as well as his best thermostatic regulator of the fierce energy of the sun. When the Stream wrestles with the Labrador Current from Cape Cod to Newfoundland, a vast mixing of the ocean, slow but effective, creates ideal food conditions by the turbulent stirring of waters rich in the ocean's fertilizer. In these waters the minute vegetable and animal life of the sea called plankton multiplies vastly, and here the numberless schools of fish congregate along the undersea banks. These fishing grounds were almost as early in their pull of venturesome Europeans to the west as Columbus' dreams of the wealth of China or Japan beyond the Gates of Gibraltar; and their wealth has outvalued the treasures of Mexico and Peru. Spanish and Portuguese fishermen, often blown far to sea, kept alive in men's minds the teasing picture of the Fortunate Isles over against the setting sun. Horror and fascination, greed and romance, all drifted against the old continent of Europe from the warm waters of the Atlantic.

The first history of the Ocean River is a combination of rumored voyages and strange legend, and the effect of this on man's mind and imagination must be part of our story. The Phoenicians left no specific log of their bold voyages at the dawn of history, but their deeds have come down to us from other classic sources. Plato, from Solon, an early Greek historian, has written of the legend of the lost Atlantis beyond the Gates of Gibraltar. The early legends of the Fortunate Isles and the Homeric stories all point to persistent rumors of lands in the Sea of Darkness toward the setting sun beyond the known Mediterranean world. So certain first voyages have been accepted as probable, and dates have been assigned to them that mark the beginnings of Atlantic history. Then slowly, as Rome came into power, the voyages westward fell off and the charting and explorations of the western seas ceased for a while.

So used are we in our day to think of the orderly and systematic progress of learning and science as natural that we find it hard to believe that the ruling authority of the Mediterranean world, the early Christian church, for almost a thousand years, helped to suppress scientific inquiry. The dark ages for political Rome were ushered in at about the third century after Christ by the barbarian invasions from beyond the Alps, but the dark age for free intellectual inquiry in Europe was prolonged until the Renaissance broke the spell of repression in the fourteenth century. Map-making in particular suffered because the value of maps as keys to commercial domination was so keenly felt that the utmost secrecy surrounded their making and their use. Even as enlightened a ruler as the Emperor Augustus kept all his charts in secret vaults within his palace. Carthaginian and later Spanish sea captains were sworn to destroy or sink all their charts if threatened by capture. What we might call bootleg map-making by unofficial persons was likely to lead to prison or the torture chamber.

But no amount of restriction or penalty could keep the bold and curious minds of men from probing the mystery of the Atlantic. Merchants and explorers kept pushing back the dark curtain of the oceanic horizon. And the fraternity of pilots and navigators and map-makers by the fourteenth century circulated up and down the coastal ports of Europe and Iceland, to Bristol, to Portugal and France, and even to the harbors of northwest Africa. Before all the others, however, the Norse were the first to break the long inactivity of the dark ages that held the Mediterranean explorers in leash. By the year 1000 the Norse had discovered the American continent at Labrador, and a few years later had pushed succeeding voyages as far south along the North American coast as Cape Cod. The greatest hazard Columbus had was not the physical unknown beyond the sunset but the medieval spiritual darkness of man's superstitious mind.

For the moment this will indicate the reach from Europe out into the uncharted waters dominated by the great Atlantic stream. It is odd that the nature of this perpetual warm current gathering in the West Indies was never evident to Columbus. Had he been aware of the Stream he could have mightily shortened the tedious days of his long voyages back to Spain by taking a northerly route. As a matter of fact, the first recorded word about the Current had nothing to do with scientific inquiry, but crops up in a footnote to the voyages of Sebastian Cabot that the beer stored in the hold of his vessel turned bad and fermented because of unaccountable warmth below decks. This was of course due to a sudden rise in the temperature of the sea as he entered the Gulf Stream.

Just as the first pre-Christian sailors, Phoenician or Greek or Italian, had responded to the legends of Atlantis or the Fortunate Isles beyond the Pillars of Hercules, so now at the thousandth year after Christ the quest for Hi-Brazil, Saint Brandon's Isle, or the new shores of Vineland teased the mind of man. Shortly after this time the men of Spain and Portugal and France and England took up the task of revealing their own western ocean and following down the trail of the strange woods and strange plants that from time to time, riding the whirlpool of the Atlantic, came from the unknown west to European shores. By the fourteenth century the beginning was made that would end with the establishment of a new civilization largely dependent on the bounty of a fruitful western sea and the beneficence of a warm flood of subtropical waters, making possible the successful migration of the landlocked northern European to his new home on a virgin continent.

Intimately associated first of all with this migration, and later with the development of the Ocean River as a great trade highway, has been the evolution of the sailing ship and its ultimate replacement by the modern surface vessel and transocean airplane. Because of the unprecedented upsurge of human activity brought about by the establishment of the Atlantic community, a major share of the world's technological developments in wind-, steam- and oil-powered ocean transport has grown out of the yards and slips and the engineering offices of the River's ports. The ships which have made history in sailing the seven seas have been born of a commercial and technological growth which has had its outposts in Sweden and Texas, Cape Cod and Tyneside, and its center at the center of the Atlantic whirlpool.

With the growth of Atlantic trade there was also a great upsurge of interest in the arts and sciences which began with the end of the Dark Ages, and, coincidentally, with the early western voyages. During the last four centuries of intellectual progress there developed a vigorous new civilization on the western shores of the Atlantic, so that the center of gravity has shifted from the Mediterranean world to the Atlantic Ocean. The civilized world no longer looks only to the eastern rim of the Ocean River for its universities and its centers of art, science, and technology. Today these centers surround the River, and the exchange of ideas takes place across its broad surface, instead of exclusively across the mountains of Europe or the waters of the eastern Mediterranean.

One scientific quest in particular interests us here, since it delves deeply into the very substance of the Atlantic itself, its salty matrix and the creatures which inhabit it. For geographical exploration and conquest of the Atlantic turned out to be only the first phase of discovery in the wide-flowing Ocean River. A new world of discovery began to fire the interest of the scientifically minded, with its horizons extending not merely from shore to shore but also from wave-swept surface to the tranquil mud of the abyssal depth. This special group of the scientific studies which are united in oceanography is today opening up a whole new field of inquiry in all the oceans.

It is not confined to the North Atlantic, yet the Ocean River has received more than its geographical share of attention. The explorations which have gone to the seven seas have more often than not originated from its shores, and the leaders in this new field, with a few important exceptions, have grown up within sight of its waters.

The work of seagoing expeditions is limited to scientific measurements and the collection of material for further study at land-based laboratories. The results of recent scientific exploration have not only extended the foundations of ocean-ography but have also developed laboratories on the sea-coasts. There are many of these of varying importance on both sides of the Atlantic, some devoted to the problems of ocean fisheries and others with wider interests. A great stimulus to the founding of marine laboratories on the eastern side of the Atlantic was the International Council for the Exploration of the Sea. Though primarily concerned with the fisheries of that offshoot of the Ocean River, the North Sea, the Council has had great and good influence on the development of ocean sciences on both sides of the Ocean River, and is symbolical of the international bond of co-operation among modern oceanographers.

When we can chart and fathom and correlate the natural phenomena that create and control the life in the sea along the course of the Ocean River and know the signs and por-tents of the climatic cycles above its waters, we may then be able to predict in advance the weather of Europe and the fluc-tuations of the food supply within the sea. And further, through the modern advance of marine biology and ocean chemistry, new and unpredictable benefits to man will come out of the life-giving waters of the ocean.

With our present knowledge we are beginning to prove out in science the close relationship of basic life and the salt sea. The stable structure of ocean water is the nearest natural compound to the human blood stream. Both the animal kingdom and vegetable life find themselves most at home in the salt waters that were the original home of all life. The sea is biologically independent of the land, but much of the life on land depends for its existence on the bland governance of the sea in controlling destructive extremes of climate. Made by the climate machine, and again manufacturing its own climate and affecting that of the surrounding continents, the Atlantic waters have governed and directed the advance of modern western civilization to a marked degree.

Just what is climate? Let's call it the prevailing conditions of the atmosphere in which we live, controlled by the perpetual adjustments made necessary by the varying capacities of air and vapor, of land and sea, of forest and desert and icecap, to store or transmit the fierce energy of the sun. Man is part of this great thermal rhythm, a minor function of the sun. Climate, in short, is the manifestation of the sun's energy working through what we like to think of as the fixed mechanics of the Earth's physical makeup. It is certain relationships of land, water, and air, charged with heat, and forming a huge invisible engine, that guides the Ocean River.

So, when we think of the term Ocean River, we must think in terms of a balanced and rhythmical system of natural forces of sun and wind and water and the lands surrounding and defining this system. We shall see that coastlines rise and fall, that possibly whole continents drift across the face of the globe, and that the ocean currents wavering in their passage from shore to shore hold the tiny life of man in a delicate balance of elemental phenomena. Around the banks of this life-giving Ocean River is the present home of western man, and an Atlantic community that every year is becoming more clearly defined. If we can put ourselves in tune with this slow, majestic revolve of fruitful waters, if we can so adjust our sense of time that we can fit the past thousand years of historical development into a single unit of expansion for western man, we shall be able to visualize ourselves and nature as a lawful entity, a necessary partnership that has purpose and design in spite of the apparent chaos in the world around us.

No single book such as ours can hope to do more than frame the picture. We hope we have brought the forces and unanswered mysteries of the Ocean River into a brief focus so that from here on the reader may chart his own pathway into the still largely undiscovered country of the frontier of the sea.

2

FIRE, ROCK, AND SEA

THE great circular sweep of the Ocean River — which includes for us the Equatorial Current, the Gulf Stream, the eastgoing Atlantic drift, the north-wending Irminger Current, and the southerly Canary Current — is constrained by river beds and banks sculptured by titanic forces that began their work millions of years ago before ever water flowed. The hand of creation, when a semimolten and elastic globe cooled into a crust, formed the confines and the deep courses of the Ocean River — unlike the beds of some great land streams which have carved their own way by constant erosion from the highlands to the sea. The ocean bed is vastly older than the soil we live on today. It may have been roughly blocked out even before the torrential rains of the infant earth poured ceaselessly on what had till then been a dry surface of heated rock.

In order to understand the beginnings of the Atlantic basin we must therefore know something about the great cosmic convulsions which ended in the birth of a new earth planet. We do know a good deal about this, by many and curious deductions from the study of heavenly bodies and the chemical and physical study of the earth itself. It is not necessary to have been an eyewitness. The methods of scientific inquiry outrank the best detective fiction; but unlike the neat conclusions of fiction the present stage of scientific deduction still holds much of the answer in suspense. The sciences of modern oceanography and geophysics are day by day co-ordinating new discoveries as they accumulate, and modern man can still help solve the story as he reads it.

Over a hundred and fifty years ago a French scientist, the Marquis de Laplace, proposed the now familiar nebula theory of creation, namely that the sun exploded into a huge rotating ball of incandescent vapor or nebula of the kind we see today in parts of the Milky Way. The mass began to contract, and — as Laplace suggested — to speed up in its rotation and then throw off gaseous matter in the form of rings like those that surround Saturn. These rings eventually condensed and formed the planets. Today this theory is not generally accepted, because it does not explain the fact that the planets with a fraction of the sun's bulk nevertheless have fifty times its energy of rotation.

Modern scientists, such as Sir James Jeans and Professor Jeffreys, have suggested that at one time the passage of a great star close to the sun formed tidal waves that pulled away gaseous masses, and that these have split up and condensed into our planets. Still others say this occurred after a direct collision between the sun and another star. None of these ideas is completely acceptable to all scientists, for various mathematical reasons; the question remains open. Most recently it has been proposed by von Weizsäcker that the sun at one time passed through a mass of cold gases and dust particles, such as we know exist in the universe, and that the gravitational pull of the sun collected this mass into a huge whirling disc which later broke up into cores of denser matter. These denser cosmic nuclei continued to attract cosmic dust until the planets formed. We can see that even the best minds have not yet come to agreement. One thing we can be sure of: our solar system is the result of a single gigantic cosmic event resulting in planets, one of which is our earth. As the earth cooled, some say, the surrounding vapor clouds rained down and filled the basins formed in the shrinking crust and thus began our Ocean River. Further, scientists are pretty sure the creation of the earth and the firmament did not take place at 9 A.M. on the 23rd of October, 4004 B.C., as some theologians have precisely determined.

Astronomers have evolved a very accurate scientific clock by their studies of the rate at which the moon appears to revolve around the earth. They use this to try and determine the date when the earth assumed its solid state. Modern physicists more exactly measure the age of the earth's crust by the rate of radiation of such radioactive substances as uranium. But let us first look briefly at the moon.

At the present time the rate at which the moon circles the earth is roughly once in every twenty-five hours. In passing around the earth the moon tends to draw along with it, by means of the gravitational force that exists in all particles of matter, the thin skin of water we call the ocean, and so causes the daily tides. If the surface of the earth were entirely liquid the whole crust would move in this way, but it is solid, and so the water alone moves in a worldwide tidal stream. There are obstacles even to this. The narrow seas, bays, and estuaries in particular hold back the free flow of water with the forces of friction. Though these are relatively small they can nevertheless be estimated. Calculations have shown that in course of time the results of such apparently insignificant obstacles may be nothing short of catastrophic.

Two of these results are of great importance. The first result of the tidal brake is to slow down the moon's period of revolution around the earth by an exceedingly small amount, about one second in 120,000 years, as well as to slow down the rotation of the earth itself. The cumulative effect of this, in billions of years from now, will be that the length of our day

will become a year and that half of the earth would be perma-
nently in darkness.

The second result of the frictional drag is to increase the
moon's distance from the earth, at the rate of about five feet
in each century. This slowing down of the rotation of the
earth and of the revolution of the moon around it and this
movement of the moon away from us become of great importance to our ideas of the origin of the earth and its ocean beds
when we trace them backward in time. It can first of all be
shown that, somewhat earlier than three billion years ago, the
moon may have revolved around the earth in a period of only
four hours and that the earth itself rotated in exactly the same
time. Thus at that distant date there would have been no lunar
tides on the earth. Calculations also show that in this far age
the moon was only 8,000 miles from the center of the earth,
and that a short time before it must have been part of the
earth itself, if we accept the findings of some scientists.

The past now becomes clearer. Somewhere about three or
four billion years ago the earth had not given birth to the
moon. It was rotating every four hours, and tidal effects were
due to the sun alone. This speed of rotation is a particularly
dangerous one for a body the size of the earth, according to the
popular, but now disputed theory of resonance. A familiar
example of resonance is the method we use when we push a
child's swing. If the pushes are given out of time with the to-
and-fro movements of the swing, the movement will be slowed.
If they are given in time with the natural movement of the
swing, they are said to be "in resonance," and the effects of
the pushes will be added to each other and will rapidly build
up as far as or beyond the safe limit of swinging. In the same
manner, if the musical sound of a violin — which is simply
a back-and-forth vibration or swinging of air — should have
the same frequency of movement as the natural period of
a wine glass, the vibrations or oscillations caused in the glass

may sometimes build up to the point of shattering the glass.

The natural period of oscillation for tides on the earth is four hours. The result of the sun's tidal influence about three billion years ago was therefore to build up tidal resonance. Partly due to this, it has been suggested that the tides became ever higher, until the earth was pulled into the shape of a rather long egg, and finally a portion was completely ejected as a colossal drop of matter, to form the moon. The mutual tidal action of earth and moon came into play immediately and caused them to separate very rapidly, so that both were able to reshape themselves into almost spherical bodies. Thus, some say, the moon was born, and they place the time at about three billion years ago.

It has been suggested that when the moon was torn loose, the earth was already losing its liquid state, so that in place of the moon there remained for a while a great void in its surface, a part of which is now the Pacific Ocean basin. It has also been suggested that the remainder of the crust moved slowly to fill this gap, and in drawing apart gave rise to the Atlantic by a splitting process. If this actually took place there could have been at the time little more than a thin skin of solid crust. The perfect spherical shape of the moon could hardly have been achieved if the moon had been torn away when the surface of the earth was in its present solid state. The present shape of the earth, a slightly flattened sphere, must have been molded while all except the outermost crust was fairly liquid, and still able to smooth out the effects of losing the moon.

A more exact way of setting the date when the earth ceased to be molten is based on the great advances made in recent years by researches into radioactive substances. The element uranium is one of these substances found today in the rocks of the earth. It is continually giving off radiations of various kinds at a steady rate. These radiations include alpha particles, which are the positively charged nuclei of helium atoms, beta particles or electrons, and gamma rays, which are very penetrating short-wave X-rays. The rate at which the various particles are given off has been measured in the laboratory. It is known from this that any mass of pure uranium would, in the course of 4,500 million years, give off radiation sufficient to convert half of it into lead, helium and intermediate products. Before the molten rocks of the earth became crystallized, the helium produced by the steady degradation of the uranium was lost, but after the Earth's crust became solid the slowly accumulated helium and lead remained trapped in the rock. The proportion of helium or lead to unchanged uranium, therefore, when measured under proper conditions, is an index of the age of rocks from the time they congealed. In this way it has been found that the most ancient rocks known on earth are over 1,800 million years old; and it is probable that there are still older, inaccessible rocks buried beyond our reach.

Somewhat later, when the earth had cooled sufficiently, the torrential acid rains began to pour incessantly down upon the hot rocks, in an atmosphere lacking oxygen and life of any form, and in the Stygian gloom of an enormous cloud blanket which shut off the sun's rays. At some still more recent time, the rocks must have cooled sufficiently for the rain, instead of evaporating instantly, to remain upon the earth, and to roll down from the bare hills and collect in the depressions and basins. It is not unlikely that one of these basins was the first bed of the Ocean River — though vastly different in shape from the North Atlantic as we know it today.

Some of the clues from which we deduce the manner in which the Atlantic basin was formed come from the modern science of seismology. When an explosive charge is set off in a deep well or at the bottom of the ocean, or when an earthquake occurs, the geophysicist is able to measure with his instruments the speed at which the vibrations travel through the rocks far below his feet. The speed and nature of these vibrations give definite indications of the type of rock at different depths below the surface. Another tool of the scientist who seeks to learn the structure and life history of the Ocean River basin is nothing more than a glorified pendulum. One of the useful properties of a pendulum is that it swings at a faster rate when the pull of gravity increases. Thus, at points of the earth's surface below which there is more than the average amount of matter, or the rocks are heavier than elsewhere, the pendulum swings will slightly speed up. Where the rocks are lighter or for some reason there is a deficiency of matter, the pendulum slows down.

Using these delicate measuring instruments, the geophysicist has discovered that the earth consists of three principal layers. The heavy central portion consists of almost pure iron and nickel, at such high temperatures and pressures that it is completely molten. This extends only about halfway to the surface. Above it is a 700-mile-thick layer of very hot semi-liquid heavy rock of the type known as basalt, about one-third the weight of the iron core, or about four times the density of water. It forms a plastic layer which is more liquid toward the inside and becomes more and more viscous until the outer solid crust is reached. Above the plastic basalt and its thin solid outer layer is an upper crust of solid granite about 30 miles thick, lighter than the underlying basalt, with a density less than three times that of water.

According to one theory the layer of granite is believed to have formed a thin but complete crust around the earth at the time the moon was formed. A striking confirmation of this theory of the moon's origin comes from our knowledge of the earth's structure, and from astronomical calculations that show the moon to be made up mainly of materials similar in density to the granite and basalt of the earth's crust. The moon is believed by some to have left a great gap in the earth's surface as the huge mass of granite and basalt was torn away. The outer crust of granite still covered the remainder of the earth's surface, but in the region of the moon's scar the underlying basalt was exposed and immediately began to solidify. The solid granite skin, exposed to great strain, is believed to have cracked in a number of places.

A. Relative position of fragments of Earth's crust immediately after the separation of the Moon, according to one theory.

B. This is how the map of the world might look today if the separation of continents had not been stopped by the congealing of the basalt ocean.

If the underlying basalt had been completely solid at the time, the great moon scar would have remained as a gigantic Pacific Ocean basin, and the Ocean River of the Atlantic might never have come into existence. As it was, it is supposed that the centrifugal effects of the earth's rotation began to pull the masses of granite toward the equator over the still semi-fluid basalt and then to separate them, as shown in the diagram. A striking fact that supports this belief is that the outlines of the present-day continental masses of Africa, North and South America, Eurasia, Australia, and Antarctica are so shaped that they fit together almost like the pieces of a jigsaw puzzle.

As the continents pulled apart the Atlantic basin was finally formed. Earlier seismological research appeared to confirm this by the discovery that whereas the floor of the deep Pacific basin is composed of basalt, that of the Atlantic has a partial layer of granite. This is thinner and less complete than the granite floor of the continents, and could well have been left in the gap as the continents drew apart, particularly since at this time the lower layers of granite must have been soft and plastic. Today there is doubt as to whether there exist any substantial amounts of granite beneath the Atlantic seafloor.

It may be that in some such way as this the moon's birth caused the breaking up of the granite crust and its separation to form the bed of the Ocean River. Since none of the present continents possesses any rocks which could possibly have originated in the deep sea basins, some scientists are sure that there has been no change in the relative positions of continent and deep ocean since the basins were first formed. But there have been many changes in the shape of the shallow ocean borders, and equally great changes in the course of the Ocean River itself. Ocean currents today have nothing in themselves to tell of their past history, so that we are compelled to return to the geologist in our attempt to follow the many different courses which the Ocean River has followed during its life. Fortunately, the River bed and its boundaries have left tell-tale evidence for the scientist to unravel.

During the two billion years or so which have gone by since the earth's crust solidified, the underlying basalt cooled further and a continuous shrinking of the outer skin took place. As a result of this, some geologists believe that the granite skin has been wrinkled up, on as many as ten or twelve different occasions during the history of the earth, into huge mountain chains. During this mountain building, local weakening of the earth's crust brought about periods of great volcanic activity, that poured forth enormous volumes of lava. At the climax of such a period the highlands must often have been covered by enormous glaciers.

After each period of mountain building there was a corresponding and far longer period of mountain decay, according to the older theories. The effects of rain and wind and of alternating heat and cold were to dissolve and break up the rock into boulders. These became still further reduced in size when they fell into streams and were ground together until they washed down the mountain slopes as gravel and sand. Eventually in the lowlands they became mud. Meanwhile the weathering processes greatly reduced the size of the mountains.

Where the rivers emptied into the shallow parts of the seas bordering the continents they deposited their load of mud and sand to form layers of sediment. Even today, millions of years after the last great mountain growth, the rocks of the United States alone are losing by this kind of erosion 800 million tons every year. The results of erosive action have been to deposit layers of sediment up to a thickness of thousands of feet in a single period between the times of mountain building. Each inch of this layer represents an average of two centuries of time.

As the mountains disappeared, the accumulated sediments

must have displaced a considerable volume of water and so brought about a rise in sea level. The enormous weight of the sediment also played its part in lowering the land by depressing the margins of the continents into the underlying basalt, which even today is still plastic. A further process was also taking place, during at least some of these periods. The immense amount of water locked up in glaciers was released as they melted during the later times of subsidence, and this alone was sufficient to raise the water level by as much as 250 feet. The result of these different processes was a widespread raising of the water level relative to the land, so that the ocean waters invaded the continents and formed shallow seas well inside the former continental edges.

The records of these changes are to be found today in the rocks themselves. Since we live in a geological age when the continents are all well above water, we are able to inspect a great part of the rocks formed by earlier periods of sedimentation. Not only are we able to discover something of the long history of alternating mountain building and inundation by a study of the sedimentary rocks, but the ancient marine sediments also trace out for us the old margins of seas. These strata are not, of course, continuous from continent to continent. The marine sediments of land origin were laid down only in the shallow seas and on the continental margins. It is their very absence from the deep sea floor that leads us to believe that the greater part of the bed of the Ocean River, the deep Atlantic basin, has not in recent time formed part of the continents.

Lack of continuity of sediment layers across the ocean floor cannot prevent us from linking together in a proper time sequence the events that have taken place on both sides of the ocean. The use of radioactive methods of measuring the age of rocks has already been mentioned. But life in the ocean is the main key to the synchronization of these long-past events, for, as the sediments formed, crabs and fishes, the coral reefs and the tubes of worms, all manner of hard skeletons of animals, became buried in the slowly hardening muds, and today we see them as fossils. Each successive era of submergence and sedimentation had, as the evolution of sea creatures took place, its own types of marine life. Thus we are able to place together in the geological scale of time, as far back as hundreds of millions of years, the corresponding rocks of such distant places as the Appalachian Mountains and the Himalayas, both of which at one time were under the waters of a vastly extended Atlantic Ocean.

Written in the sediments which have become today's limestones and sandstones — and even in the quartzites, marbles, and schists to which these have been converted by the tremendous pressure of overlying rock — in these alone can we find the recorded history of the River bed. Earlier periods of mountain uplift and of continental flooding are probably recorded in rocks that have not yet become available to us. We can only surmise that the Atlantic Ocean, on five separate occasions during a period between one and two billion years ago, spread itself across Europe and Asia and across a great part of northern America, and that it receded during the intervening times of mountain building to become a much more restricted ocean than it is today.

Somewhere before 500 million years ago we can see the story in greater detail. Another great succession of wrinkles in the granite crust, known as the Pre-Cambrian revolution, took place, causing the continents to rise up out of the sea and the oceans to withdraw from their margins. The Ocean River may have pursued a shorter course in its circular passage than it does today, since some scientists say that most of the continental shelf of eastern North America, the West Indies, and the Gulf of Mexico became part of a continuous land mass, which united North and South America into a single continent. It is possible that Europe and Asia, on the eastern banks of the Ocean River, were joined together with Africa, when the Mediterranean Sea did not yet exist. From Europe an extension of the continent stood in the place of the present shallow sea between the British Isles and Greenland; this is called Atlantida.

During the next 150 million years of the Paleozoic era the steady action of wind and water wore down the mountains, and the continental blocks of granite once more sank back into the plastic basalt beneath them. The North Atlantic Ocean again spread itself over its borders. Though the Mediterranean Sea did not appear in its present site, a sort of vast ancestral Mediterranean, the great shallow Sea of Tethys, spread over an enormous area between the higher lands of Africa and northern Asia as far east as China and the present site of the Himalayas. On the opposite side of the Atlantic, the ancient American Gulf, well to the northward of the present Gulf of Mexico, flooded the middle of continental North America and reached into Canada. To the south its surf broke upon the land we call Llanoria — southern Texas, Mexico, and the present Gulf of Mexico. The eastern shore of the Gulf was the land of Appalachia, spreading beyond the present Atlantic shores to the edge of the continental shelf; while its western boundary was Cascadia, an ancient land which extended hundreds of miles out into the Pacific Ocean beyond what is now the west coast of America.

Part of the Ocean River at that far distant time may have flowed through the ancestral Gulf of Mexico into the Arctic Sea, and thus have brought warmth to the far northern lands. There is confirmation of this in the strange fact that fossils of temperate and even subtropical life have been found in Alaska and Greenland, though this may be partly due to movements of the earth's axis of rotation and therefore of its poles. Branches of the Ocean River may also have joined the Pacific

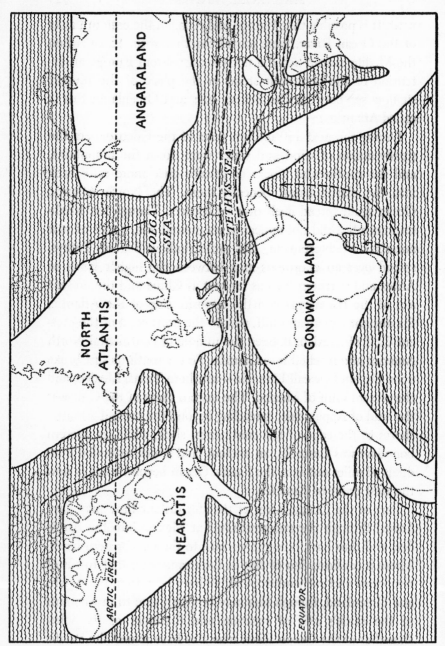

The Atlantis Ocean and its great continental extensions, 200 million years ago. Scan is shaded, land is

Ocean, for the northern part of South America and much of Central America was under water, and the central sea of North America, the ancestral Gulf, broke through to the west. During all this and later periods of submergence a number of minor movements took place, so that the ocean borders and inland seas were constantly changing. Some say that only the deep Atlantic basin, in common with the other deep oceans, remained unchanged, though this is a question yet to be settled.

We have written of the Paleozoic, the 300-million-year era of geological time which began when life became abundant in the primeval seas. Two more eras bridge the dim stretches of time to the present day: the Mesozoic, which ran for 100 million years or so, and the Cenozoic, the era in which we are at present living. With these as the framework for our story we can follow the great pulses of expansion and contraction which have spread the waters far across the continents, and which have at other times withdrawn them into narrower channels. The slow breathing of the earth giant lifted its crust into mountain chains once more during the 300 million years of the Paleozoic era, and then again at the start of each of the two later eras. After each great uplift the crust relaxed, the mountains were worn down by wind and rain, and streams and sediments were formed.

The Caledonian mountain chains of the later Paleozoic rose up from Europe to North America across the northern North Atlantic where Greenland now stands, and formed the land bridge of Eria and so cut off the Arctic Seas. Heaving upward millions of years later, at the end of the Paleozoic were the earlier Appalachian Mountains, great ramparts folding the east coast of North America as far as Texas and then rising from the land westward and northward in an earlier Rocky Mountain chain.

Long after the older Appalachian Mountains had subsided,

the last of the great earth movements began 30 or 40 million years ago in the Cenozoic, when the present-day Himalayas slowly rose higher out of the old Sea of Tethys. Part of the new revolution of the land was the modern range of the Appalachians, smaller by far than their monumental predecessors, and the present range of the Rocky Mountains. Some 20 million years later the Alps arose and the great Tethys Sea shrank, until all that now remains of it beyond the Atlantic Ocean are the Mediterranean and Caspian and Black Seas. A final slow heave brought Central America above water and severed the Atlantic from the Pacific, as the Gulf of Mexico began to dwindle to its present size.

For a while the island of Cuba was joined to Yucatan, and the Ocean River was barred from the path it now takes through the Caribbean. When this connection foundered the Stream poured into the Gulf of Mexico and across the shallow Florida Sea to the Atlantic, and sediments accumulated around the shallow margins of the Gulf of Mexico to a depth of 13,000 feet on what is now southern Louisiana and 5,000 feet or more on the future land of Florida. Less than a million years ago, after emerging for a while as an island, Florida became a peninsula, and the River was confined in its present course.

So, for between one and two billion years the Ocean River, its eddies and tributaries, have flowed along their many courses, sometimes branching out to flood places where mountains or great cities now stand, reaching out across the entire North American continent to the Polar Sea or to the Pacific Ocean, and across Europe and Africa to China and Malay; flowing where ancient cities were later to flourish and die and where the great Himalayas and Alps now stand. At other times — and today is the most recent of ten or more such occasions — the flow has been restricted to a circular path around the deep Atlantic basin. It has been confined for millions of years at a time on its northern border by the lands of Scandia, Eria, and Atlantida, and on the south by a land bridge or at least by a chain of islands between Africa and South America, which separated the River from southern Atlantic waters.

Not all geologists agree that the Atlantic basin has existed for the entire period in the way we have described it. Some have suggested that up until about 200 million years ago, or even later, there existed a great continent where the North and South Atlantic oceans now rest. Although some of the geological evidence is in favor of a more permanent Atlantic Ocean, such as the one we have described, there are a number of queer facts which have never been satisfactorily explained.

When land plants and animals and fresh-water fishes are separated by impassable boundaries of ocean water, without land connections of any kind, they usually evolve along distinct lines, so that in each separate locality a different group of species is found. Thus the North American fossils of the later Paleozoic and early Mesozoic eras, which lived from about 400 million years ago down to about 100 million years B.C., are of a type distinct from those of South America. On the other hand, it has been found that there are striking similarities between the fossils of South America and those of Africa, India, and the Antarctic continent. Since these could not have reached South America by any other route it is believed by some that there must have been a southern land connection, along which fossil forms spread from the other continents as they appeared in the course of evolution. Wegener's highly controversial theory of continental drift holds that a single great land mass, the super-continent of Pangea, was the forerunner of all the present-day continents and that it provided the necessary connection.

It is supposed that Pangea existed until the latter part of the Paleozoic, 200 million years ago, and that only then did it split apart. The separate granite blocks of the continents are supposed to have drifted away from each other over the underlying basalt in much the same way that objects will slowly move on the plastic surface of apparently solid asphalt in hot weather. It has been pointed out that the outlines of the present-day continents fit together like a jigsaw puzzle, and that the mid-Atlantic Ridge may have been left when the continents broke apart. But this is equally well in accord with the description we have already given of a continental splitting over a billion years earlier.

Others have supposed that the ocean basins were formed at a relatively late date by the sinking of former granite continents into the basalt beneath, thereby forming the ocean floors. A number of geologists believe that, long after Pangea was supposed to have split apart, there still remained a continental connection across the South Atlantic. Today there are only a few islands, such as St. Paul, South Georgia, and the Falkland Isles, and the submerged connecting ridges; but it is said that until less than 50 million years ago there was here a great continent, Gondwanaland, in which South America, Africa, and Australia were joined. It remained so until the earlier part of the Cenozoic, the geological era which is still running its course today. At that time either the continents drifted apart, or great masses of land sank to form the floors of the Atlantic and Indian Oceans. While Gondwanaland was in existence it is also supposed, by believers in the more recent origin of oceans, that a second continent connected North America with Europe, and that when this also foundered in the Cenozoic there was left only the mid-Atlantic Ridge, the Azores, Madeira, and — until early historical times some extremists say — the lost land of Atlantis.

There are very few scientists today who will support the extreme view that an Atlantic continent foundered, taking with it an ancient civilization, in about 10,000 B.C. We are therefore compelled to regard the legend of Atlantis as perhaps an extremely ancient and exaggerated myth based on relatively small sinkings of land like those which now separate the British Isles from the continent of Europe, and which are known to have occurred within the time of man's existence on earth. Against the Atlantean legend is the fact that plant life on the Azores and other oceanic islands of the North Atlantic has little in common with that of the mainland. The results of this kind of comparison, based on our knowledge of the past evolution of plants, rule out any land connections during the past 30 or 40 million years, much less the 12,000 years since Atlantis is supposed to have foundered.

Mute evidence against the lost continent also comes from the sea floor itself, in the microscopic shape of one of the smallest of living creatures. Globigerina, as it is called, grows and reproduces in countless billions in the ocean water. As each tiny individual lives out its short span it leaves behind a small but delicately fashioned globular shell. The slow, steady, never-ending rain of these tiny shells upon the sea floor over monotonous centuries of time has built up a carpet of fine mud or ooze on the sea floor in moderate depths away from the land. Since different species have appeared at different times, and since the layers of Globigerina ooze were interleaved with different types of deposit during glacial periods, we are able to read the history of the ocean in its sediments. The tale we read from the sea floor where some say Atlantis now rests tells us of deep water above it since a time well before the last glacial period, so that it could not have sunk at a later date than 100,000 years ago. Nevertheless, a lingering doubt remains with many, for there is much from literary and ethnological sources that brings credence to this idea of a lost continent and a lost people. We shall return to this when we deal with the legends of the River.

While geologists unite in believing that there has been no

Atlantean continent during the time of man, the earlier history and origin of the ocean floor is by no means settled in the minds of modern scientists, and there is today a new upsurge of interest in the whole problem. As recently as September 1950 the British Association for the Advancement of Science held a special symposium of the leading European scientists at Birmingham, England, to discuss the question. As it turned out, the followers of Wegener's theory of continental drift, and his opponents led by the Dutch scientist J. H. F. Umbgrove, were in almost equal numbers, and there were nearly as many arguments pro as con.

The amazing similarity in shape of the continental outlines on opposite shores of the North and South Atlantic has already been mentioned. That they should fit so neatly into each other seems hardly a coincidence. We have also mentioned that some biologists require a fairly recent transatlantic land connection in order to account for the similarity of plants and animals in Africa and South America. Wegener's theory of the westward drift of the American continents away from Europe and Africa at a relatively late date offers a solution satisfactory to the biologists, but it is far from satisfying to many geologists. No one has been able so far to give a universally acceptable explanation of how the lighter continental masses have managed to move through the less easily melted and heavier basalt beneath them, though many different mechanical interpretations have been put forward, the pros and cons of which are too technical for discussion here. If the continents are plowing westward through underlying semiplastic rocks we should expect to find a submarine accumulation of rock or at least of sediment along the westerly edges of the continents, much as a blunt-nosed ship raises the water ahead of its bow. There are no signs of it. Again, we might expect that the sediments would be thinned out to the east of continents as they drifted away, but this is not noticeably true.

Umbgrove and others prefer to think of a more permanent ocean floor; and some scientists think that the ocean floor has folded in somewhat the same way that the continents have. Thus, just as the land was thrown into huge mountain ranges during the great revolutions or periods of uplift, so folds of the deep ocean floor may have been raised to the surface during the past and have enabled plants and animals to become dispersed along island chains or intercontinental connecting ridges like the Isthmus of Panama. It is unlikely that very great changes have taken place in the total amount of sea water in the oceans over the past hundred million years. If this is so, then large areas of deep-sea floor could not have been raised above the surface without a simultaneous and equally deep submergence of large areas of the continents. But none of the sediments typical of the deep-sea floor have ever been found for sure in the rocks of the present continents, and so there is no evidence that the present continents have ever formed part of the deep-ocean floor. If this is so, then it is unlikely that large and widespread uplift of the deep-sea floors has happened except in the very distant past.

Hans Pettersson, leader of the Swedish Deep-Sea *Albatross* Expedition during 1947 and 1948, was able to bring back new evidence obtained with some of the recently invented instruments for probing the secrets of the deep-ocean floor. The results were surprising, though they are capable of different interpretations. Underwater depth charges were used in order to study the thickness of sediment layers in deep water. Echo-like reflections of the explosive shot were carefully recorded, so that the time required for them to return to the ship from the sea floor was known. Part of the explosive wave passes through the sea floor into the sediment layer and is then reflected from the underlying rock. The time taken for this second echo to return to the vessel on the surface is used to estimate the thickness of the sediment layer. By this ingenious method Pettersson calculated the layers of ooze in a few parts of the Atlantic to be nearly 12,000 feet thick. From our knowledge of the present rate at which the slow rain of plankton skeletons and other minute particles are added to the sediment carpet of the ocean floor, some have estimated that this thickness represents a period of several hundred million years during which the ocean floor has been submerged.

Our story of the long history of the sea floor is perforce scattered with ifs and buts. No one was present in the distant past to leave an eyewitness account, and the deductions we draw from the evidence of rocks are based on all too few observations. The sea floor at a depth of several miles is only now beginning to yield up its secrets to such indirect probing as the use of explosive depth charges. One of the newer tools which enables us to observe the ocean bed more directly is the deep-water camera; and even television has been used in moderate depths. The coring tube, a long metal pipe with complicated attachments, has been lowered in depths of thousands of feet and has penetrated into the mud and ooze by as much as 70 feet. The material brought to the surface by this device may give a record of the sediment rain for a hundred thousand years or more, depending on the rate at which it was deposited. Seismological stations throughout the world record the time of earthquake shocks, so that we may calculate their speed of travel through the earth's crust and so, by a process of deduction, form some idea of the distribution of heavier and lighter rocks. The pendulum, which we have already mentioned, tells us where gravity force is greater or less than the average, so that we are able to find out something of the gigantic strains that are warping the earth's crust.

In recent years much of the widespread interest in the ocean floor has become centered on the mid-Atlantic Ridge which runs southward beneath the seas like a great 7,000-mile submarine mountain chain from Iceland in the north to Bouvet

Island, where the South Atlantic and the Indian and Antarctic Oceans meet. In places this gigantic ridge rises to a height of nearly two miles above the ocean floor, though the restless ocean waves roll a mile or more above its peaks. Only in a few places do the higher portions break the surface — at the Azores, at lonely St. Paul's Rocks near the equator, and at Tristan da Cunha, Gough Island, and the Bouvet Islands in the South Atlantic. We do not know its full extent. It may even continue northward across the little known depths of the cold Arctic basin to the shores of Russia.

This mighty chain, wider by far even than the Andes, divides the Atlantic Oceans into eastern and western basins. Those who follow Wegener believe that it was left behind when the continents separated, a submarine remnant of the old connection between the Old and the New Worlds. A newer but equally fascinating proposal has recently been advanced by J. P. Rothe, who believes that the mid-Atlantic Ridge is really the old submerged Atlantic coastline of Africa and Europe, now sunk beneath the waves. The western basin is thus the true ocean, while the eastern basin is really part of the sunken mainland.

The marked resemblance of the outline of the Atlantic coasts of North and South America to the Atlantic edge of Africa give support to Wegener's theory; but the American coast follows the outline of the mid-Atlantic Ridge just as closely, so that, if a continental drift has occurred it may just as well have been over the shorter distance between the Ridge and the American shores. The fact that so many of the submarine earthquakes of the Atlantic originate in the Ridge is in favor of this, because it is a characteristic of continental edges. Rothe also points out that the minor ridges and basins of the eastern Atlantic look remarkably like continuations of the structure of the African continent. Older ideas that the entire Atlantic floor rests on a layer of granite, similar to but thinner than that of continents, are no longer unchallenged, for Rothe brings forward evidence from seismological records to show that earthquake shock waves travel more rapidly in the western bed of the ocean than in the eastern part. These waves travel faster in the heavier types of rock; thus it appears that the western part of the Atlantic is floored by the same heavy basalt rock which underlies the Pacific, whereas the eastern half has a granite foundation, and is more like the continents.

Explorations made by Ewing, Tolstoy, and others aboard the research vessel *Atlantis* in co-operation with the National Geographic Society during the past two or three years, only partially support Rothe's ideas. Most interesting perhaps was the discovery that the Ridge is carved into valleys, and that in these valleys are extensive flat terrace-like plains. They bring to mind the smaller terraces characteristic of valleys exposed to the air. They are unlike river valleys, however, and more needs to be known before we may draw any definite conclusions. On the other hand, it was also discovered that over 4,000 feet of sediment rests upon the slopes of the mid-Atlantic Ridge, and this suggests a considerable period of submergence. Another surprising haul from the deep ocean bed between Woods Hole and Bermuda showed the presence of coarse sandy material. Sands of this kind have been until now considered typical of shallow waters near shore, and the startling discovery of such material in deep offshore water will at least bring about a considerable revision of our ideas, although it fits in with what is now known about the deep canyons which extend outward from the land along the seafloor.

Although modern submarine investigations have not proved anything conclusively, they have begun to obtain new evidence from the relatively young science of marine geology. A new period of interest and accomplishment in undersea exploration has begun, and the spirit that activated Columbus' discoveries on the surface is now being revived on the ocean floor, with all the new equipment that modern technical development is making possible.

We have seen how the great earth movements molded the rocky confines of the River, at least as far as it has been revealed by probing into its depths and into its past with man-made instruments. With this part of our frame in place we shall piece out in our next chapter the story of the stream of evolution which has moved along with it in time, and which links the geological past with the web of life within and around the ocean today.

3

RIVER OF LIFE

THE peoples whose cities line the River's banks, the pioneers who ventured into the unknown sea in vain search of a passage to the Orient, the birds flying above and the fish swimming beneath its waters, all have a close kinship with the Ocean, for it was here that life itself began, and it is in the ancient sea floors over which the Atlantic waters once flowed that we read the story. Millions of years have passed and there have been many steps and changes of evolution since the first fish-like animal left the security of water for life on land. A far greater period separates us from the chance microscopic event whereby an aggregation of molecules first took on the new properties of life which accompanied their new pattern of organization. Yet we still retain many evidences in our bodies of our former shapes and of our former submarine existence. Not only does the human embryo, at various stages of its growth, possess modified gill slits and other reminders of the fishlike stages of past evolution, and not only does the human embryo live in an amniotic sea of its own, but it may even be said that, in a sense, the River still flows in the bloodstream of man.

Human blood, in common with that of other vertebrates, still has the same ratio of dissolved salts as the ocean water, though in lower concentration. This is no coincidence. Marine animals low in the scale of evolution are simply aggregates of cells, bathed on all sides by sea water, which is at the same time a supplier of food and a source of oxygen. As larger and more elaborate bodies were evolved, the internal body cells became shut off from direct access to salt water, but they nonetheless still required life-giving oxygen and food. This vital need was provided by the evolution of circulating body fluids which carried food and oxygen from cells in contact with the outside world to those buried deeper in the body. These fluids — and blood is one of them — were in effect an internal sea. Since such fluids as blood have taken over the functions of sea water it is not surprising that they closely resemble it in composition.

During the long course of evolution in the early seas, several groups of marine animals have independently been able to adapt themselves first of all to life in fresh water, and later, in a fewer cases, to life in air. These adaptations to new surroundings were remarkable achievements, since before they could occur it was not only necessary that the animal should be able to carry its own sea water with it, in the form of the bloodstream, but also that it should have a system of chemical control which would keep the salts at a constant strength and so prevent a fatal upset of the body chemistry. When the early ancestors of land animals left the sea, first for fresh water and later for the land, they thus carried with them a permanent sample of the ocean.

Although the salts of sodium, calcium, potassium, and magnesium in the blood of human beings and of most vertebrates are in the same ratio as in the modern ocean, they are in about half the concentration. This difference, paradoxically enough, is in perfect accordance with our thesis. Many believe that the salts of the ocean may have originated as a solution of materials derived from the erosion of the land and brought into the sea by rivers. Heated by the sun and constantly blown over by winds, the ocean surface continually evaporates, leaving the accumulated salt behind and giving up fresh water to the clouds. When these release their rain upon the land the cycle is completed. The net result would be a continual slow increase in saltness of the ocean, but there is no general agreement among scientists as to the rate of this increase, or even whether it has occurred at all. It has been suggested, however, that at the time when our remote ancestors were beginning to acquire an improved chemical control system, their body fluids became stabilized at the same strength and chemical composition as the ocean in which they lived, and that the ocean was at that remote period only half as salt as it is today. Thus the blood coursing through our bodies today may well be a chemical reminder of the earlier ocean stream which bathed the body surface and permeated the tissues of our far ancestors.

Life in the Ocean River has not always been the same. Though the oceans have probably existed in their various forms for nearly 2,000 million years, there were no fish of any kind until less than 400 million years ago, and even the smaller shellfish and crustacea did not come into being until after the earth had reached at least three-quarters of its present age.

Our knowledge of this ancient sea life is drawn from the sediments deposited in the shallow seas and on the submerged continental plains during those periods when the land was inundated and the course of the River changed so radically. These deposits now form limestones and other rocks thousands of feet thick in various parts of continental Europe and North America. Similar sediments were laid down in other parts of the world, when other oceans spread their borders over the continents. But the great bulk of our knowledge of past life in the ocean has come from the fossilized beds of Tethys, the ancestral Mediterranean Sea, from the great gulfs and continental seas of North America, and from other ancient branches of the North Atlantic over which the Ocean River and its tributaries may once have coursed. These have laid the foundations of our present understanding of evolution and the history of life, for trapped among the sediments are the skeletons and sometimes even traces of the soft parts of the strange sea beasts of the past. From these we piece together a history of life within the River, much as we seek ancient ruins and old manuscripts for evidence of human history along the banks of the River.

Nobody can say for sure what the first living creature was like. It was certainly very small and without a skeleton, so that it would scarcely leave a recognizable fossil to survive the millions of years of enormous pressure due to thousands of feet of overlying rock or the twisting of earth movements. The first abundant animal fossils known are comparatively far along in evolution and nearly all possess skeletons of some kind. We are therefore driven to indirect evidence and speculation in trying to piece out the history of early life in the ocean.

The beginnings of life were probably made possible by the presence in the ancient sea of small amounts of organic chemical compounds, known as hydrocarbons. These were formed when the world was still hot, by the interaction of water and such simpler carbon compounds of rock origin as the carbides. The hydrocarbons and their derivatives may have formed increasingly large and complex molecules with the peculiar properties of what chemists call colloids. Though such colloidal particles are certainly not alive, they possess fascinating properties that have a striking resemblance to the behavior of living protoplasm. Under certain conditions they grow, and when they reach a certain size they tend to divide or reproduce and so become unstable. They have other important properties similar to those of protoplasm, though they do not possess the organization that is characteristic of living creatures. It is also true that one organism, the tobacco virus, has been obtained in the form of nonliving protein crystals. It is at least possible that life originated from colloids during the first few hundred million years of the ocean's existence, when a chance combination of favorable circumstances presented itself and caused the molecules to rearrange themselves in a life-giving pattern.

Almost certainly life began in the hot and somewhat brackish seas, a billion years or more ago. It is also very possible that the first forms of life were not true plants or animals, but somewhat akin to bacteria or possibly viruses. True plants are able to feed on simple salts and the carbon dioxide in air or water, and are able, by means of chlorophyll, their green coloring matter, to use the energy of sunlight and so manufacture their carbohydrate and protein food within themselves. Life may have started when the earth was surrounded by a continuous blanket of clouds, stormy with thunder and lightning and almost completely shutting out the sunlight that plants must have. Since animals are dependent on plants for their food they could not have existed under these conditions. Moreover, the atmosphere in the early days of the ocean may quite likely have contained such gases as nitrogen, chlorine, and ammonia, though lacking oxygen. Bacteria, unlike plants, are able to live in the absence of sunlight, and some of them, like the present-day iron and sulphur bacteria, are able to feed on the simple chemical substances that must have been plentiful in the early ocean. They alone among living creatures are able to extract from such simple materials the energy needed to support life.

Whatever form life took in the young ocean, it must have gone through a long course of evolution before the first recognizable fossils were formed. Long before this, as the seas cooled and the dense cloud blankets began to disperse, sunlight broke through and it became possible for chlorophyll or its early prototype to develop in some of the primitive bacteria-like organisms. Thus plant life came to the ocean. The evolution of plants, even though they were still microscopic, provided the opportunity for a great surge of life. No longer restricted, as the bacteria were, to their specialized chemical foods, which were relatively limited in amount and distribution, the minute prototypes of our modern plant world must have burst into a great profusion of growth as a result of their new-found ability to use the food salts and carbon dioxide in the ocean. This in turn allowed some descendants of the original life form to evolve as animals, which need ready-made plant or animal material for their food.

The first animals were most probably very simple creatures drifting in the water. The growing powers of movement, characteristic of animals, were soon encouraged by the greater ability to catch food which greater mobility provides, and by the greater resultant energy. The increase in size and complexity over millions of years must also have brought these primitive creatures to a point where those that began to develop a supporting skeleton had a great advantage over the others. Not only do larger bodies need support and protection, but muscles work more effectively when attached to a firm framework. As soon as this hard body framework or a protecting shell was formed, the sea creatures began to leave their remains within the sediments for mankind to study hundreds of millions of years later.

Thus it is hardly surprising that the first well-defined forms of life found in the uplifted rocks of the ancient Cambrian sea floors are not simple microscopic creatures. All these early fossils, buried in the sediments which accumulated over 400 million years ago, when the Pre-Cambrian mountain building had died down, possess some hard parts that have defied the destruction of time. With the exception of certain rather doubtful remains, the geological record begins not with bacteria but with corals, sponges, worms, and above all the trilobites which were the dominant forms of those early days. The Cambrian seas were not like ours. No schools of fish swam in search

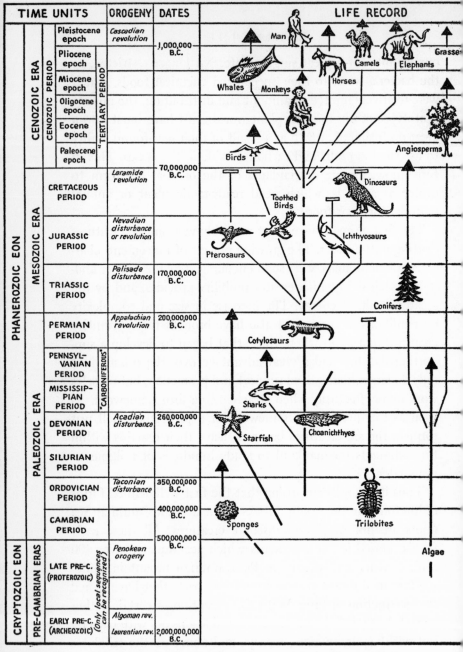

Geologic Time Chart. Ascending lines indicate the range in time of most of the chief groups of animals and plants. If the line ends in a crossbar, this denotes the time of extinction; if it ends in a dart, the group is still living.

of food or broke the surface of the water. Not even crabs or lobsters existed. Instead, the trilobites, forerunners of the crustacea, crawled, burrowed, or swam sluggishly in the shallow waters, looking somewhat like smaller three-lobed varieties of the horseshoe crab, which lives today along the Atlantic coast of North America, almost a living fossil itself.

The trilobites, which existed in a great variety of species, were at times enormously abundant, and were at least as common on the sea floor as lobsters and crabs are today. Yet, after more than 200 million years, they finally ceased to exist, in the Permian, before the start of the Appalachian uplift. Just what happened in those far distant days to bring about the complete annihilation of entire classes of animals is something we shall probably never know for sure. The trilobites had certainly survived fluctuating movements of the sea floor, and were adapted to a variety of temperatures. Perhaps, some think, a race of animals may grow too old for continued adaptation to changing conditions, and may no longer be able to compete with more variable, more adaptable, and more vigorous races. Another probable factor in the case of the trilobites was the appearance, in the period before their extinction, of an abundance of voracious fishes and of the powerful carnivorous relatives of the octopus and squid.

Other ancient forms of sea life have appeared in the changing pattern of life in the ocean, have flourished for a greater or lesser time, and have become extinct. Relatives of the trilobites, the sea scorpions or eurypterids, lived for nearly 100 million years and vanished. Some of them reached the colossal length of nine feet before finally disappearing. Before making their exit, however, it is believed that these monstrous creatures left behind them a group of air-breathing descendants from which came the scorpions and millipedes of today.

Still other groups of creatures have existed without radical changes from the Cambrian to the present. Early in the story

of marine sediments, two great classes of molluscs, the gastro-
pods or conchs and later the bivalves or clams, made their
entrance in turn on the floor of the continental seas, and have
persisted in varying abundance to the present day. Compared
to other groups of sea creatures these clams and conchs have
changed remarkably little over the three to four hundred million years since they first appeared. Had human beings existed
during Jurassic time, about 120 million years ago, they would
have found oysters growing in the shallow seas which were
then intruded upon the continents. Though distinctly different
from present-day oysters, they were unquestionably oysters,
and large ones at that. The fishlike reptiles and ancient squids
and belemnites of that far period were not limited to a diet
of oysters, however, but could well have feasted upon the first
crabs and lobsters, probably descended from the by then
extinct trilobites, as they swam in seas where midwestern
farmlands now exist and in the ancient Sea of Tethys where
parts of which is now Europe stand.

Some of the early groups of sea creatures, more persistent
than others, have repeatedly tried to dominate the marine
communities with new changes in their basic pattern. Each of
these variations in turn enjoyed its period of success and swam
in great numbers through those ancient seas. But each in turn
finally failed to meet the test of adaptation to changing conditions and was replaced by a new outgrowth of the parent
stock. More active than the clams, oysters, and conchs are
those other molluscs, the cephalopods, which include the
squids, cuttlefish, and other relatives of the octopuses. Perhaps
because of their more dynamic way of life they underwent
greater changes as one experiment in evolution after another
failed to survive. The first to appear were housed in long,
straight, slightly tapering tubes or shells, gas-filled for buoyancy.
They sometimes reached a length of 12 feet or more. The
long shells were a considerable handicap for an active animal,

so it is not surprising to find that as evolution progressed their tips became more and more coiled. Thus they gave rise to a group known as the ammonites, whose coiled shell reached a diameter of several feet. Altogether they flourished in the oceans for over 250 million years, but today the coiled cephalopods are represented only by the pearly nautilus. During the period when ammonites were still very numerous the belemnites also appeared. These voracious predators, unlike the others, possessed an internal shell. In their present-day successors, the squids, this is reduced to a mere rudiment. Like the squids, the belemnites swam by jet propulsion, squirting the water from their respiratory chamber. With ammonites the belemnites disappeared by the end of the Cretaceous, 400 million years ago, and today their representatives, the squids, survive as comparatively minor creatures of the sea.

It is true of life in the seas, as of men and nations, that those who over-specialize and thereby lose flexibility to meet changing conditions have within themselves the seeds of their eventual downfall. The lampshells or brachiopods — shelled animals with a superficial resemblance to bivalves — were once enormously successful. The excessive conservatism of this group of sea creatures was reason enough for their decline. Today they are represented by a few localized species. On the other hand, one of them, lingula, well adapted to its life in the mud and subjected to little competition, has remained unaltered for over 400 million years since Ordovician time. It is probably the oldest creature alive today which has survived so long unchanged — well called living fossils.

The starfish, sea urchins, and sea cucumbers are well distributed in the seas and oceans today, both in shallow and in deep water. This is far from true of their flower-like relatives, the stalked crinoids or sea lilies. They are unquestionably animals but well merit their name, for they are attached by stalks to the muddy sea floor, and from their uppermost part there extends a flower-like rosette of brilliantly colored arms. These bizarre creatures, the most colorful features of the shallow waters of Paleozoic seas, were so plentiful that the limy joints of their stalks form almost the entire mass of some of the limestone rocks laid down in the continental seas over 200 million years ago. Today the stalked sea lilies are rarely found in shallow water, though there are large groves of them off the north coast of Cuba and they have been dredged from deep waters in many parts of the ocean.

There would have been no rise and fall of nations on the River's banks and no early explorations to tell of unless, very early in the story of the sediments, a small worm-like creature had not embarked on a path of evolution which was to revolutionize the living world by making possible the later appearance of all the higher animals, including man himself. Nobody can be certain how this began. Some have imagined that the vertebrates originated from the horseshoe crabs and the sea scorpions, the eurypterids. Others believe that the start was made among worms similar to the sea worms or the ribbon worms of the present day, and there is some evidence to support these beliefs. There has even been a curious and fanciful suggestion that insects could readily have evolved into vertebrates if they had turned upside down and their legs had become ribs. Today a much more likely theory is accepted.

We can at least be fairly certain that the remote vertebrate ancestor began its long path of change and development very early in the history of the sea floor, at a time when most of the present-day invertebrates were only beginning to leave their traces in the sediments. This soft-bodied, wormlike forebear was perhaps related to the bilaterally symmetrical ancestor of the now five-rayed sea cucumbers, sea stars, and sea lilies. When a nonbony stiffening rod began to form along the length of the body and so provided a rigid basis of attachment for muscles, the scaffolding of the vertebrate backbone was laid;

but there must have been a long period of evolution before this became cased in bony vertebrae.

Before the vertebrate evolution could follow its full course it was necessary for the plant life of the ocean to set the stage by blazing a new trail away from the waters of the ocean. Although the primeval seaweeds, being soft and usually without skeletons, have only rarely left their story in the sediments, we can imagine that they gradually became accustomed to the intermittent drying out of the intertidal zone or of the fresh waters into which they may have spread. Some of the more vigorous, when their spores were washed up above the water line, became adapted to life completely out of the water. This was a momentous step forward. Without land plants there could be no land animals. With gradual increase in complexity and abundance they provided the necessary food, so that insects, and finally vertebrates, were able to follow them in a slow progress to the land.

The long-drawn-out migration of the vertebrates started when the worm-like prototype adopted swimming habits and became a primitive fish, with a bony shield covering its head but without jaws, and in some ways much more like its degenerate descendants, the lampreys, than any other fish today. These early jawless fish, the ostracoderms, began life as far back as the Ordovician period. It is believed by some that their start was made in fresh water or in the brackish lagoons of a low swampy coast, so that the chemical control system that made possible the move to land was already there, stabilizing their bloodstreams in the chemical image of the sea from which the wormlike ancestor had originally started.

Whether the start was in the seas or in fresh water streams we cannot be sure; but for a while evolution returned to salt water, where it produced the primeval sharks, once the dominant fishes of the ocean. These were followed by three important groups of fishes: the armoured fishes, represented today

by the garpikes and sturgeons; the lung fishes; and their relatives, the lobe-fins. The few remaining lung fishes are found in
the streams of South America, Africa, and Australia, where
their air-breathing lungs permit them to survive the dry seasons
when the streams disappear and they are forced to estivate in
the drying mud of the river beds. It is from the ancestral lobe-
fins, inhabitants of the Devonian streams and lagoons, that
there evolved not only the successful groups of bony fishes
which populate both sea and river today but also the entire
line of four-legged land animals and birds and man himself.
Some of the lobe-fins, the coelacanths, returned early to the
sea but were generally thought to have died out in Mesozoic
time, 100 million years ago. When, in 1939, a fisherman hauled
his trawl off the South African coast at East London and
found a living coelacanth in his net, he was looking at a sur-
vivor of the age of dinosaurs.

The air-breathing lung of the lobe-fins and lung fishes was
an outgrowth of the gullet, modified to permit the breathing
of air. When some of the ancient lobe-fins began to develop
into the fishes which dominate the seas today, the one-time
lung lost its air-breathing function and became a hydrostatic
organ or swim bladder, which enables a fish to adjust itself to
the changes due to the varying depths of water in which it
swims. Other lobe-fins, venturing into strange territory, left
the fresh water entirely to live on land. We can imagine that
the seasonal drying up of lakes and streams during the Devonian period did much to hasten this process. As the descendants
of these venturesome fishes began to live upon land, the skeletons of their pelvic and pectoral fins became modified to
permit them to act, first as flippers and later as legs. In some
such fashion as this the fishes gave rise to amphibians and they
in turn to reptiles.

The oceans and seas today are inhabited by the many surviving forms of life whose long evolutionary paths during
periods of hundreds of millions of years were confined solely

to salt water. But they are not alone. Some of the reptiles and their mammalian descendants have returned to their ancestral home after an intervening period of evolution on land, and are conspicuous members of present-day life in the sea. Others, returning to the oceans from the land, flourished for varying periods before they finally became extinct.

The struggles of the lobe fishes to survive in the face of stagnant or drying watercourses or swamps led to the evolution of amphibia, the first true land-living creatures. They were still tied to the water, for without it their eggs cannot develop. By Permian time, however, as the continents which began to rise above the oceans foreshadowed the Appalachian mountain growth, not only had some of the amphibia successfully left the water behind but the early reptiles that arose from them had burst into a new profusion of life. A great variety of these bizarre creatures now took over the new land kingdom. Some were fierce, sharp-toothed carnivores, such as Dimetrodon, with a fin along its back like the sail of a sailfish. Others with crushing teeth fed on shellfish; while still others fed largely on plants. A few had already begun to adapt themselves once more to life in the rivers and seas, and one small group, the theridonts, had begun to undergo the evolutionary changes that led to the mammals.

The next 50 million years was the great age of reptiles, the Mesozoic era, when 30-ton dinosaurs, giant stegosaurs, 75-foot brontosaurs or thunder lizards, and frightful two-legged tyrannosaurs, each for a time held sway. Returning to their ancestral home other reptiles developed into ichthyosaurs, large porpoise- or sharklike creatures that gorged themselves on fishes and on the squidlike belemnites. The voracious appetite of these fierce carnivores is gauged by the fact that in one fossil ichthyosaur alone the remains of nearly 200 belemnites have been found.

The ichthyosaurs were soon joined by numerous seagoing turtles, including Archelon, which measured over 11 feet from flipper to flipper. Still more fearsome creatures, the plesiosaurs and mosasaurs, the giant sea serpents of their day, ploughed through the seas with long necks stretched before them, up to 40 feet in total length. There have been many legends and some creditable observations of giant serpentlike creatures in modern seas, but they are usually dismissed as an optical illusion, as a deliberate hoax, or as giant squids, fishes, or porpoises, honestly mistaken for the sea serpent. Anthonie Cornelis Oudemans, in his critical treatise on the great sea serpent, suggests that there may actually be hidden in the oceans today an enormous long-necked sea lion, which has given rise to the hundreds of detailed accounts. The possibility that giant plesiosaurs may still be lurking in the depths of the ocean is not seriously considered, but it cannot fail to give rise to speculation when taken in conjunction with the coelacanth fish, hitherto thought to have died out in the same period as these serpent-like monsters but now known to live in the twentieth-century ocean.

When the age of reptiles came to an end the present age of fishes took its place in the salt seas; and only a few crocodiles, turtles, and small sea snakes now survive to remind us of their former splendor. But the main tread of evolution still continued, and the mammals which inherited the mastery of the land gave rise in turn to offshoots which found their way back to the parent ocean. Seacows which, in spite of their uncouth faces, may have originated the mermaid myth; whales, the largest living sea creatures today, and their relatives, the porpoises, first swam the seas after the Ocean River had drawn back from the rising land movement which gave birth to the Rockies, Andes, and Himalayas. This was in the Eocene, only 30 million years ago. They were followed about 10 million years later, around the time the Alps were formed, by Miocene sea otters, seals, and sea lions, the seagoing cousins of the carnivorous cats, dogs, and bears.

There are smaller movements going on today between the

sea and the land. Climbing perches are leaving the streams
for the air, and tropical crabs have learned to climb trees. But
the great evolutionary changes of the future will pursue their
courses over enormous periods of time, just as the great
changes of the past have taken million of years to complete.
The rest of our story is concerned with the legacies of the past
and with the brief second of time which is the present.

The marine sediments in which we have thus traced the
River of Life bring us legacies of more immediate practical
value than fossils and the story of evolution we read from them.
Along the ancient margins and shallow continental extensions
of the seas into which the eddies of the River flowed in the
dim past there were plants and animals which lived and died
and left behind their chemical traces. These traces, vastly
altered, provide us with the fuel whereby the ships and air-
planes of today are propelled across the waters of the River.
The origin of oil-bearing rocks, the precise alchemy of nature
that transformed the original remains of plants and animals
into oil, and the ways in which this oil became concentrated
in its underground reservoirs are still not fully understood,
despite the great economic importance of the problem and the
considerable amount of scientific research that has been devoted to it over the past century. Nevertheless the problem is
gradually yielding to investigation, and we may be fairly sure
of the broad outlines if not the details of these infinitely slow
processes that bring us fuel and energy from the past.

Between the great mountain-building periods, when branches
and eddies of the River circulated over the continents, the
future oil-bearing sediments were laid down in the shallow
seas. Trapped in the muds and sands of the sediments, the
dead bodies of plants and animals that lived and died in the
waters above were gradually buried under thousands of feet of
rock, where a long series of chemical changes converted them
to petroleum. Strangely enough, it is not from fishes, giant
reptiles, voracious squids, and belemnites that we believe the

foundations of today's oil fields began. It is much more probable that the bulk of these organic materials in the oil-breeding
muds of the ancient sea floor came from very much smaller
varieties of life.

Minute animals and plants, drifting helplessly in the salt
waters everywhere, go to make up what we call plankton.
Though small, sometimes even invisible to the naked eye, this
drifting life of the plankton many times exceeds in bulk the
entire mass of fishes, clams, crustacea, and other more obvious
creatures, even though these may individually be thousands
of times larger. The energy of sunlight, trapped by the minute
plants of the plankton, is used through the green magic of
their chlorophyll to build up within their tissues, from the ever-
present carbon dioxide disolved in sea water, the chemical
foodstuffs we call carbohydrates. The teeming microscopic
plants of the plankton and the infinite numbers of small
planktonic animals that feed upon them have lived their short
lives, and their dead bodies have rained ceaselessly down upon
the sea floors throughout the entire history of the fossil sediments, carrying with them the sun's energy transformed into
this chemical energy of the carbohydrates. As they became
buried in the accumulating sediments their bodies decayed
and their substance was converted into the starting materials
from which petroleum is formed.

This process did not take place in all the ancient sea floors.
Parker Trask, Claude Zobell, and others, from their investigations of modern sediments have given us some insight into the
nature of these deposits. It seems fairly certain now that oil
was mainly formed from plankton remains in the sediments of
shallow seas. This was especially true when these seas became
partly cut off from the main ocean, just as parts of the great
ancestral gulfs of North America and of Tethys, the ancient
Mediterranean, were sometimes cut off from the North
Atlantic basin. It seems probable too that, just as today the

bottom waters of the Black Sea are lacking in oxygen as a result of conditions set up by its isolation, so were the waters of some of those bygone inland seas.

Under ordinary conditions the organic remains in sediments are oxidized and their chemical energy is lost, so that they are no longer able to change into oil-producing materials. In the Black Sea today, though, due to the lack of oxygen there is a great increase of bacteria of a special type, and it is these reducing bacteria that bring about a chemical transmutation in the deposits. One effect of this alchemy is to make the bottom waters poisonous to other forms of life; but another effect is to start the sediments along the long chemical road which leads to petroleum. The same lack of oxygen that is believed to be so important in the early development of oil-producing sediments is also found in some of the limestone muds forming today beneath the waters of the River as they circulate in the Gulf of Mexico. Francis Shepard, submarine geologist of the Scripps Institute of Oceanography, and his associates, have begun a detailed study of such deposits in the western part of the Gulf, and the limestone sediments around the Florida Keys are being studied by marine scientists at The Marine Laboratory in Miami. It is likely that these studies of the sea floor will throw new light on the ancient alchemy that brought oil to the sediments of hundreds of millions of years ago.

The principal oil fields of North America were mostly formed in the later Paleozoic period, before the Appalachian mountain uplift, and again before the rising of the Andes and Rocky Mountain systems, and especially during the past 40 million years which we call the Tertiary. The later Paleozoic fields are the final chemical result of plankton which lived in seas covering parts of Pennsylvania, the midcontinental area of Kansas, Oklahoma, and Texas, and parts of Illinois, Indiana, and Kentucky. On the other side of the River and during the same period similar deposits were being formed in England

and Russia. In the same way, in Permian days the foundations
of oil fields in west Texas and New Mexico were laid down.
Most of the oil-bearing sediments of the Gulf states were
formed later during late Mesozoic and Cenozoic time, when
branches and eddies of the River also flowed not only over the
ancient gulf but also over the site of the Venezuelan oil fields.
During the same time the Sea of Tethys deposited its dead
plankton in the future petroleum strata of Rumania, Iran, and
Iraq. The California fields and a number of others throughout
the world were not connected with bygone extensions of the
North Atlantic Ocean, but were most likely formed under
extensions of the Pacific and Indian Oceans.

Though the major production of oil has been from sediments
in the gulfs and bays and inland seas that were formerly connected with the path of the Ocean River, it is also to be expected that similar conditions existed in relation to other
oceans throughout the world, and it is therefore not unlikely
that future exploration will yield oil in such areas as those
between Australia and Asia and around the margins of the
landlocked Arctic Sea. We can still say, though, that our oil
is mostly wrung from the old Atlantic marginal sea floors.

The plankton of ancient seas is known to us mainly by these
important consequences of its existence. No less important to
man are the present-day activities of plankton and the migrations of the fishes which depend on the plankton for food, for
man in turn depends in some measure on fish for his existence.
The story of how man came to live on the Atlantic seaboard
and to migrate in many directions across the River comes first,
however, and this is compounded of many ingredients — part
legend, part unchallenged and documented history, and part
in the making today.

4

ATLANTIC LEGEND

THE progressive creation of our earth as man found it had gone on for many million years before man himself began its discovery. In the long stream of evolution man has been here but the wink of an eye. Early man looking on his world saw chaos where modern man has discovered order. But the necessity for order was part of his mind. The urge to discover harmony between himself and inanimate nature set him apart as Man. He began to think in pictures, stories, and legends — hypotheses formed from the true testimony of his senses tempered with fear and hope. So when we use the word "legend" we do not mean fable or fairy story. True racial legend is a kind of history in the making composed of old memories and inventions to fit facts and events that, as yet, have no orderly recognition in history. Above all it was an effort of the human mind to mold unity out of chaos without the aid of our modern precise instruments or more disciplined scientific method of thought. But, oddly enough, legends often break trail in the dark uncertainty of prehistory and become accepted history in their turn. Troy, we should remember, was once a name in a poem until Schleimann pursued the legend and found the actual city as described in Homer's *Iliad*.

There is a particular and persistent legend connected with our story of the Ocean River — the legend of the lost Atlantis, the civilization and the island empire once presumed to have existed outside the Gates of Gibraltar, about where the present mid-Atlantic ridge rears up a mile or more from the ocean floor east of the Sargasso Sea. Modern science has studied the ocean floor, recorded the travel of earth shock, and drawn up cores of sediment from the depths; and today we can say there is little sure evidence and that Atlantis is merely a legend. Yet the battle of opinion goes on, and a great library of pro and con has accumulated since Plato first reported on Atlantis in his Timeas and Critias dialogues in the third century before Christ. Other ancient writers also have written — but never at first hand — on this mysterious classic world of Atlantis: Homer in the seventh century B.C., Solon in the sixth, Herodotus in the fourth. Today the legend will not down even under the eye of modern science, for strange data keep cropping out of oceanographic research that could use some such scheme of explanation. Our purpose in this book is not partisan for the poets or the scientists, the geologists or the biologists or anthropologists. But we could not write the story of the Atlantic world, nourished on the living stream of its revolving waters, unless we put down what is known and conjectured of Atlantis.

We shall have to plot a beginning point somewhere in prehistoric time in order to frame the environment of Atlantis — if it did exist. Whatever rising or sinking in the earth's crust went on before the final geological period has no relation to the Atlantis we talk of. At the end of the Cenozoic era is the quarternary period, the one in which we now exist, and in this period science is pretty well resolved on a succession of ice ages, with intermediate warm climate when the great ice fields and glaciers were in retreat. Much is supposed to have happened in continental and oceanic changes of level or altitude in these periods. The final retreat of the widespread American and European ice fields occurred in the last thirty thousand years, and established the basic habits of our present geogra-

phy and climate within the time most students now feel sure
modern man existed in the western world. This is called the
holocene period. Some time within this period Atlantis is said
to have occupied a large portion of the eastern North Atlantic
Ocean, with a flourishing and advanced civilization essentially
agricultural and seafaring, with a high degree of artistic development.

How do we come to believe a thing exists that we have not
seen? Scientists, from the study of spectra and a knowledge of
the orderly progression of known phenomena, have successfully deduced the presence of undiscovered planets and metals
and then proceeded to discover them in fact. Doctors diagnose
diseased conditions not otherwise visible to them, just as geologists detect metals and oil beyond sight or reach. One reason
the legend of Atlantis has refused to die is the fact that in
many allied sciences like geology, biology, and anthropology
certain unexplained trails of investigation end around the
shores of the North Atlantic, and a hypothetical Atlantis
fitted into the blank of this puzzle answers many of these
questions in a way that would not be scientifically incredible.

The protagonists of lost Atlantis explain the fact that no
present evidence of the civilization remains, no ruined cities,
no body of art or writing, by arguing that, just as Plato first
reported through Solon from the ancient Egyptian records, a
great cataclysm of flood and earthquake changed the surface
of the lands and waters of the Mediterranean and Atlantic
world sometime about ten thousand years before Christ. They
further point out the broken ends of this civilization in the
earliest beginnings of neighboring civilizations bordering the
shores of the Atlantic. These exist if we will but look, they
say, in England, France, Spain, the Azores, the Canary Isles,
the West Indies, and even in Mayan Yucatan, Guatemala, and
Peru. In all these lands — before the deluge and the fiery
whirlwinds from the sky and the shifting of the very crust of

the earth — there lived other men and women in a good world, in a golden age; and they were not unlike ourselves. True, they had no metals, perhaps, in the original Atlantis, perhaps only tools of bone and ivory; but after all it does not require a knowledge of plastics to insure a high culture or a just civilization.

The main point for us, with no particular theories for sale, is to reopen our modern minds toward the past. We have to accustom ourselves to think that mankind did not start a civilized existence with the Egyptians or the Mayans or the early Hindus. In Europe we now are aware of an artistically mature race of people, the Cro-Magnon, with larger brain areas than our own, who lived in the foothills of southern France twenty-five to forty thousand years ago. The first Egyptian dynasty was less than six thousand years ago. The pre-Inca ruins of Peru, the pre-Mayan cultures of Mexico, all point back before the commonly accepted textbook concepts of historical times. And the farther back in time we trace our ancestry, two important things are emphasized. Firstly there seems to have been a widespread basic common cultural exchange almost encircling the globe in the warm subtropical belt of seas that reach from east of the Mediterranean to west of the Caribbean. And secondly, this dimly observed common cultural ancestry thrived, beyond history as we know it, on the other side of vast geological and climatic catastrophes known to us only as legends in our racial histories from India to Mexico.

The world of Atlantis brings into focus everything that we suspect but that somehow lies just out of reach of memory or easy proof. We shall try to be systematic in this never-never land of conjecture. Plato is father of the story, so we will begin with him. Here, in brief, is what he wrote:

Solon, the Athenian lawgiver, visited Egypt at the great city of Sais about two hundred years before Plato. He learned there from the Egyptian priests the story of Atlantis. This story, as told by Solon to his children and his children's children, came down through Critias to Plato, who was in the act of completing the transcription of the tale when he died. The Egyptian priests, after lecturing Solon on the ephemeral and youthful nature of the Greeks, proceed to tell him of Athenian history in the year nine thousand B.C. They said: "These histories [of ours] tell of a mighty power which was aggressing wantonly against the whole of Europe and Asia, and to which your city put an end. The power came from far out of the Atlantic Ocean, for in those days the Atlantic was navigable; and there was an island situated in front of the straits which you call the Columns of Hercules. The island was larger than Libya and Asia [Asia Minor], and was the way to other islands, and from these islands you might pass through the whole of the opposite continent which surrounded the true ocean, for this sea which is within the Straits of Hercules is only a harbor having a narrow entrance, but the other is a real sea. Now, in the island of Atlantis was a great and wonderful empire, which had rule over the whole island and several others, as well as over parts of the continent."

Then the story of the battle wherein the early Athenians conquered the attacking Atlantean army is recorded, followed by the story of a great natural cataclysm: "Afterward there occurred violent earthquakes and floods, and in a single day and night of rain all your warlike men in a body sank into the earth, and the island of Atlantis in a like manner disappeared and was sunk beneath the sea. And that is the reason the sea in those parts is impassable and impenetrable, because there is such a quantity of shallow mud in the way caused by the subsidence of the island."

Plato then describes the wealth and beauty of the city, its great stone temples to Poseidon, and how canals reached from the sea to an inner harbor well fortified against attack. The harvests of the land were plentiful, with two seasons, one of natural rainfall and one made fertile by waters impounded from the high mountains that ranged along the north of the island. Many wild and tame animals inhabited Atlantis, including elephants. The outermost walls of the citadel were of bronze and others of tin and orichalcum.

Now for many generations of men the Atlanteans maintained almost a divine nature — just, obedient and well-affected toward gods and men. But their wealth brought on a degeneration and they despised virtue, became avaricious, and had no eye to see true happiness any longer. Zeus, seeing that an honorable race was in a wretched state, wished to inflict punishment on them . . . and here Plato's story ends.

If a sudden end came to the Atlantis of Plato, what could have happened sometime as late as nine thousand B.C. or as early as the beginnings of the holocene period, say twenty-five or thirty thousand B.C.? This was about the time the Cro-Magnons came from somewhere southward up the Iberian peninsula to southern France and their cave dwellings.

The answer lies in the recent geological history of the lands beneath the whirl of Atlantic waters from west to east to south, somewhere within the encircling arm of the great Atlantic stream. For a long time it was scientifically convenient to believe that there had been no appreciable change in the great ocean deeps for many hundred thousand years at least; they were labelled as more or less permanent. But research and theory have changed this attitude toward the hidden deeps of the Atlantic Ocean in particular. The plastic surface crust of the earth, thought to be thirty or more miles deep, is now believed to be in a constant state of adjustment to different kinds of strains, internal and possibly external. Occasional acute adjustments occur in the crust, such as the shiver and shake in the Province of Assam in India in 1950 which changed the course of rivers, drained and created lakes, ruined settled communities with quake and landslide, and probably raised the height of the Himalayas close to two hundred feet — all in a blink of time. The slower changes — slow to us — are the westward drift and slow sinking of the Greenland coast while the Swedish peninsula, the Gulf of Bothnia, Finland, and parts of Russia are rising in height several feet a century — this as a release of strain from an icecap that began to disappear more than fifty thousand years ago. In fact the modern world, geologically speaking, is in a period of revolution, with its end not yet in sight.

What happened when the land bridge between England and the continent subsided, or when the two lakes of the Mediterranean basin suddenly rose with the waters coming in at Gibraltar from the Atlantic? The first width of the Straits — as reported by the ancients, according to Forrest — was in 500 B.C. only about a mile; at the time of Christ about seven miles; and in 400 A.D. twelve miles; the present width is fifteen miles. How accurate these early estimates are is open to dispute. But there may have been a slowly continuing separation of the continents there in recent geological time. If a large area of inhabited land went under the waves since the last icecap retreated from Europe, there must be some undersea indications of such a change.

We have spoken in a previous chapter of the mid-Atlantic Ridge, which runs as a gigantic submarine mountain chain from the old continental shelf between Greenland and England to somewhere between the southernmost parts of South Africa and South America. If we assume that it was geologically possible, if not very probable, that a large body of habitable land previously existed west of Gibraltar, there is nothing that we know of climatic conditions at the end of the last glaciation that would preclude reasonably temperate weather in the Atlantic area. At present not more than two percent of the warm waters of the Gulf Stream reach the Arctic Ocean, and yet that two percent accounts for open seas about southern Iceland and the winter Norwegian coast. If, as Brooks in his study of climate believes, there was an optimum warm climate as the last icecap receded to the north, then the warmer-than-present waters of the Arctic Sea would have, according to him, helped maintain an oceanic circulation of warm water from the tropics, and the general Atlantic climate maintained by the great Gyre would have made a very favorable climate for an island of Atlantis, held so to speak in the arm of that oceanic stream. Whether or not the continental shelf of America was above water from Hatteras to the Bahamas and West Indies would have made no real difference in the general Atlantic circulation. There is no exclusive reason why the present Gulf Stream would not still do business much as usual with the Straits of Florida closed to traffic.

With the basic physical problems sufficiently solved to believe that an island continent off Gibraltar was possible some ten to forty thousand years ago, the protagonists of this intriguing theory go on to deduce evidence that it did exist, and that it harbored a culture of which the Minoan, Egyptian, Iberian, and even Mayan civilizations were but later manifestations. In other words, if an Atlantean civilization did exist previous to our knowledge of Minoan, Egyptian, or Phoenician cultures, the weather conditions for a spread of Atlantean culture overseas, west or east to the Mediterranean, would have been as favorable certainly as the conditions that permitted Phoenicians to penetrate the Atlantic southward along the coasts of Africa, northward to the British Isles and the Baltic, and possibly — according to some — as far west as South America.

If such had been the case we would expect to find evidence of these oversea invasions, or of friendly commerce with the Atlanteans, in the legends and stories of the peoples along the Atlantic coast. It is not our purpose to make ours a full case pro or con for Atlantis, so we shall not try to digest the arguments advanced in more than a thousand volumes of this search into the past. But it is well known to most students of literature that the Welsh had their tale of the drowned city of Llion, and the Bretons of the lost kingdom of Lyonesse somewhere undersea off the Point du Raz. The Irish talk of the Island of St. Brandon, of Hi Brazil west, always west, and the Gauls at the time of Caesar said their ancestors came from the sea southwest, off the Iberian coast. Oddly enough the Mayans and other Mexican peoples, even the Peruvian Indians, all have legends of bearded white men who came from oversea bearing their cultures from the East. There certainly would be no particular physical reason why these prehistoric migrations could not have happened. A great belt of good weather and favoring trade winds blow from the Canaries to the Antilles; and from the Azores or Canaries to Gibraltar is a feasible journey. And we might add that the blond Guanches of Tenerife, the pre-Spanish native race, practiced mummification much as did the Egyptians, and claimed ancestry from a source other than the Canaries.

Tracing the rumors of a lost Atlantis is moving inward from a circumference that covers the shores of the whole Atlantic Ocean toward a hub along many spokes, but the spokes slowly disappear under the sea and no hub has yet been found and charted. Yet even certain of the creatures seemed obsessed with this old memory. The familiar story of the lemmings of Norway comes to mind — how these small rodents periodically migrate in great numbers to the Atlantic shore and swim blindly west to their ultimate exhaustion and death. The eels and the salmon also obey a strange concentric instinct in their breeding habits. From both the American and European shores washed by the Atlantic Stream, the mature eels swim back to the neighborhood of the central undersea Atlantic ridge near the Sargasso Sea and there, deep down in this particularly warm and tranquil body of salt water, breed and die.

To this true fish story we can add the observation that certain birds migrating from northern Europe southward over the Atlantic have been observed to pause and circle aimlessly over portions of the ocean west of Gibraltar before resuming their migration, as if they had some kind of instinct for halting where only ocean now exists.

And so also, certain elements of early civilizations and peoples in their legends and customs seem to show an unexplained mid-Atlantic bias. Let us box the compass of this uncharted Atlantis in both time and place. This is here a matter of hints and suggestions, for there is no accurate measure for various cultures that can be universally applied. For instance, the use of bronze occurred at different times in Britain, Greece, and Malay. The advent of written records was likewise varied, in England and France about the time of Christ, in Italy 500 B.C., in Greece a couple of centuries earlier, and in Egypt and Mesopotamia 3,000 B.C. But this is not the end of the story. Earlier records may someday be discovered. But we have very early and excellent examples of art that date back perhaps to 40,000 B.C. in the cave dwellings of France and Spain. The people who dwelt there came from somewhere unknown. The Atlantean enthusiasts think they know. Their argument runs something like this:

There is no trace that the earliest western Europeans came from the East, as has been the general habit of thought about the so-called Aryan migrations. The stone age cultures in the past fifty thousand years have been called Aurignacian, Solutrian, and Magdalenian, in the order of their antiquity, the Aurignacians living at least as long ago as 40,000 B.C. There are other types named by archeologists in the Neanderthal and earlier times, but the people of the lost Atlantean continent were supposed to have been the Cro-Magnons of the Aurignacian period. They brought with them spear-throwers, flint weapons, and a talent for delicate and subtle drawing and sculpture of bulls, bison, and deer that have been preserved to this day in the caves of the Dordogne and in Spain.

It is believed that the Cro-Magnon preoccupation for depicting cows and bulls sprang from certain religious ceremonies not unlike those of the later Minoan culture in Crete. Also these early Cro-Magnons and their successors believed in female witchcraft, and made drawings of women as priestesses or witches, with peaked caps and broomsticks.

Now the analogy which the Atlantean protagonists draw from this is that the spear-thrower and this particular form of witchcraft is also found along the western shores of Africa and in Central America, whereas the Mongolian forms of witchcraft in most other sections of America are apparently derived from male Shamanism. Likewise the practice of the couvade, where the father of a child takes to bed and is treated as if he had suffered the pangs and disabilities of childbirth, have been found, even to this day, in the Basque country, North Africa, and in Central America, and also in the Canary Islands. Archeologists add later evidence from the Solutrian period. This racial migration, dated about 20,000 B.C., is supposed to have come north from Africa into Spain and southern France by a land bridge at Gibraltar or at Sicily. These people made special flints of great delicacy, by pressure rather than chipping, which have been found also in North America in the Gulf of Mexico area; just as recent finds of early skulls in Texas and Florida have been more like the Cro-Magnon type than the Mongolian.

The biologists can add to this kind of evidence certain types of plant life that are found in western Europe and eastern America and on the Canaries and Azores, just as they can point out certain similarly distributed land snails and small animals. This does not specifically prove that this spread of culture, human types, and plant and animal life had to come from a common source inside the radius of this limited distribution, but it makes interesting circumstantial evidence.

Now let us go back a moment to bring this Atlantis time-table up to date. The span is that of the postglacial period. It is held by the scientists that the retreat of the northern icecap began in earnest about twenty-five thousand years ago, though more radical estimates bring that figure down to ten thousand years. Brooks, an authority on climate, tells us that at this time a warm and salubrious Atlantic climatic period set in that enabled the icebound peoples of the Mediterranean areas to move north in the path of the migrating animals they lived on. Though somewhat modified today on the cooler side, this Atlantic period was the beginning of modern climate. Now the geological Atlantis sponsors bring up the fact that world-wide legend tells of radical and widespread changes of the level of the earth's crust in the Atlantic area. Meanwhile the anthropologists give the following rough dates for the south-western European migrations from an undetermined source: the Cro-Magnons in the Aurignacian period some time be-tween 40,000 and 20,000 B.C., then the Solutrian flint workers some time between 30,000 and 20,000 B.C., and after them the Magdalenian peoples with their refined art as the most recent newcomers to Spain and southern France, perhaps as late as 9,000 B.C. Some say these migrations were caused by upheavals in the islands and lands now lost to history which may have existed west of Gibraltar.

Another advocate of the Atlantis legend who brings long years of archeological experience to her task is Mrs. Wishaw, director of the Anglo-Spanish American school of archeology in Andalusia. In 1929 she published a work on Atlantis in Andalusia which set out to prove that the ancient seaport of Tartessos was a center of the lost Atlantis empire. She has made certain interesting finds at Niebla on the Rio Tinto: "My theory, to sum it up concisely, is that Plato's story is corroborated from first to last by what we find here. . . ."

What Mrs. Wishaw found in the neighborhood of the stone-age fortress at Niebla were mines anciently exploited with considerable hydraulic engineering skill dating back somewhere between 12,000 and 40,000 B.C. Her conclusion is that Tartessos and the surrounding area was a colony of Atlantis exporting the wealth of the Rio Tinto mines. She further produces evidence that an Iberian culture existed here long before the Phoenicians settled Gades, and she links up Iberian alphabetic signs with those found in the rock paintings of Libya, and points out that this unique Libya-Tartessian culture must have sprung from an Atlantean source. There is a good deal of other interesting evidence in Mrs. Wishaw's book which at least indicates that there was a very early and highly developed culture beyond the Gates of Gibraltar on the Atlantic shores, predating the Minoan, Egyptian, and Phoenician cultures by several millenniums, and possibly the parent source of those Mediterranean cultures. At any rate she has brought to new life the Tarshish of King Solomon.

Perhaps the man who has made the most thoroughgoing and serious study of the Atlantis question since Donnelly in 1882 published his book, *Atlantis, the Antediluvian World,* is Lewis Spence. Over a lifetime of research this learned Scottish enthusiast has issued the following books: *The Problem of Atlantis, The History of Atlantis,* and *Atlantis in America.* Spence's basic thesis is as follows:

A great continental land mass formerly occupied the major portion of the north Atlantic region and some of the south equatorial region. This land mass, of early geological origin, in subsequent periods underwent frequent submergence and emergence from the surrounding waters. Around a million years ago, in Tertiary times, volcanic activities and shifting of the earth's crust changed the continental nature of this land into island masses. The largest of these was situated west of the Mediterranean entrance, and another island was located in the general area of the present West Indian islands. This large parent is and was called Antillia. There may have been communicating islands in between. These two islands existed until late Pleistocene times or up to about 25,000 years ago, when the western island of Atlantis began to disintegrate. Final disaster to Atlantis is timed at about 10,000 B.C. in conjunction with many of the flood legends. Antillia persisted until more recent geological times, and was supposed to have subsided into roughly the present West Indian chain perhaps as late as 2,000 B.C.

Spence proceeds to make a case for the European and American invasion of culture from an Atlantean source. He quotes Dr. Farrer in his work on language to show that the Basque tongue has no analogy to any other European language, but does have a strong grammatical relationship with aboriginal American languages. And he quotes the great French authority Abbé Breuil on the refreshing influence of new techniques on the Cro-Magnon or Aurignacian civilization, and the smooth flint work of the Solutrians, and states that the later Magdalenian art and culture in this area had new contributions from some unknown source. The final phase of this Spanish-French prehistoric culture, called Azilian from the Mas D'Azil cave in Spain, is a culture that shows a long period of development before it arrived in southwestern Europe. Spence points out an Atlantean origin based on these facts: The Azilians were always buried facing west. They were a seafaring race using big flint fishhooks that indicated a deep-sea occupation. And the date of their arrival along the Basque coast coincides with Plato's date for the sinking of Atlantis.

And now the search to bound the foggy lands of Atlantean culture jumps to America. To recapitulate, the Spence timetable of migrations runs like this: end of the ice age, Cro-Magnon, 23,000 B.C.; Magdalenian second migration, 14,000 B.C.; Azilian-Tardenoisian or third migration, 9,600 B.C.; and finally the last migration westward from Antillia about 200 B.C., when Quetzalcoatl led the ancestors of the Mayans to Central America. Spence has the backing of accepted opinion when he states that about 200 B.C. there are considerable traces of an invasion of America by a highly developed civilization in some respects similar to the Aurignacian culture. The origin of the early Mayas is as much a mystery today as is that of the European Cro-Magnons. It is certain that the culture was well developed if not decadent when it came to Central America There is no evolutionary trace of it in the West.

The most we can say is that some things lead eastward; and the lost sister state of Antillia is used by the Atlantean protagonists as the source of a migration in 200 B.C. It requires no argument to establish the transocean legends of Quetzalcoatl and the Toltec fathers of the Mayan state. Although the Toltec history is in the form of legend, the fact that the description of Tollan, the capital, is like that of Atlantis in the European legend is most interesting. Its end likewise occurred in cataclysmic disaster. It is worth quoting Spence here from his book, *The History of Atlantis*: "From the shores of western Europe to those of eastern America a certain cultural complex is distributed and is found on the intervening insular localities, while its manifestations are also to be discerned in a great measure in North Africa and Egypt on the one hand, and in Mexico, Central America and Peru on the other. This complex is so constant in the region alluded to that it is clear now that a lost oceanic link united its American and European extremities.

"The principal elements which distinguish the Atlantean culture complex are the practice of mummification, the practice of witchcraft, the presence of the pyramid building, the practice of head-flattening, the couvade, the use of three-pointed stones and other minor manifestations springing from a common origin. These are all collectively to be found confined within an area stretching from the west coast of Europe to the east coast of America and embracing the west Atlantic islands and the Antilles. So far as I am aware these elements are not found associated with each other in any other part of the world."

The French savant Termier is one of the few distinguished men of science who exhibit anything but the most extreme caution in regard to this hypothesis of Spence. But Termier is convinced that there is enough geological evidence to put solid ground under the overseas legends. He writes: "Geologically speaking, the Platonic history of the Atlantis is highly probable. . . . It is entirely reasonable to believe that long after the opening of the Straits of Gibraltar certain of these submerged lands still existed, and among them a marvelous island, separated from the African continent by a chain of smaller islands. One thing alone remains to be proved—that the cataclysm which caused this island to disappear was subsequent to the appearance of man in western Europe. The cataclysm is undoubted. Did men then live who could withstand the reaction and transmit the memory of it? That is the whole question. I do not believe it at all insoluble, though it seems to me that neither geology nor zoology will solve it. These two sciences appear to have told all they can tell, and it is from anthropology, from ethnography and lastly from oceanography, that I am waiting the final answer."

Termier is not alone in waiting; though when he states that oceanography may solve the question he cannot help but leave open the geological end of research that he seems to regard as closed. When Termier wrote this résumé of the question, the art of taking cores from the ocean bed, the skill of underwater photography, and the electronic science of sounding abyssal rock by radio and shock waves had not been developed as they are today. The modern oceanographer can reach down two miles into blue water and explore what has long been hidden.

We have summarized elsewhere some of the latest evidence drawn from the bed of the Ocean River by geologists and oceanographers. Though the story written in rock may be of an earlier Atlantis than the legend demands, some of the strange and contradictory facts which have come to light leave doubt even in the scientific mind, and such facts are in accord with the thesis of Termier. Perhaps the results of future sub-marine dredging and the firing of explosive charges and the painstaking reading of delicate instruments will bring new evidence to clinch the matter and finally label the legend as a fascinating myth or fable. Perhaps, though, the reverse may come about, and the future thus bring new life to Atlantis in the mind of man.

This, then, is the picture in legend, in the history of animal and plant migration, and in the dim, far-off picture of our ancestors migrating into Europe and America from unknown sources, carrying elements of cultures we cannot trace, and possibly harassed by world geographic cataclysms we can still see traces of but cannot fix in time or duration. The phoenix was a bird that rose from the ashes of his own destruction and lived again. Let us leave the fascinating field of conjecture with this image of the phoenix, the bird of mysterious ever-lasting life. The Phoenicians derived their very name from this Greek word *phoenix*, "red." They were the early Red Men of the wild western explorations of the Mediterranean world. Strangely, when we come to America, we find the Mayans likewise calling their ancestors who came with beards from the east over the sea the Red Men. It is time now to go on with the actual voyages, from the Phoenicians to Columbus, of those Mediterraneans who dared penetrate and carry the light of bold discovery into the unknown western sea.

5

THE MEDITERRANEAN
LOOKS WEST

PERHAPS as early as three thousand years before Columbus men of the ancient Mediterranean world were probing the limits of their fear and ignorance by courageously pushing their trading voyages ever westward from the settled civilizations of the Aegean Sea. There were many reasons for this searching toward the west, not all motivated by noble intellectual curiosity. The people who did most to open up new paths for civilization to follow and expand were predominantly traders and merchants, the Phoenicians, whose culture was a grab bag of borrowings from the East, from Egypt and from the Philistine remnants of the Crete or Minoan civilization. Nevertheless these tough sailors and traders carried the advance for the men of ancient times, carried the spirit of the pathfinders who were plagued by the challenge of the horizon line and followed new sea paths looking for new worlds.

And they did this in the face of a great barrier of fear and legend that marked the waters beyond Gibraltar as a place of death, an arctic waste, a coagulated sea of mud, in fact the dangerous verge of the world itself, a swift current at the edge of nowhere. It has been truly written that "a dim disquieting sense of the enveloping world formerly haunted the imaginations of men as shown in mythologies, proverbs, legends and superstitious practices throughout the world." But together with this threat beyond the last charted league was also the promise and excitement of renown and riches. And this is all man needs, who of all animals has been led to the edge of knowledge and looked upon the blank unknown. Pressed by the foreknowledge of death, he measures his ambition by the tick of the clock, and thus, self-driven, pursues plans and itineraries forever beyond his reach.

But contrary to the predictions of doom, the first Mediterranean men to stick their high-bridged adventurous noses beyond the straits at the Pillars of Hercules picked up strange news of the West. The great Ocean River, even at this remove, drifted upon the shores of Spain and Morocco occasional reminders of unknown lands. Local fishermen on the Atlantic beaches told legends of the Hesperides and the Fortunate Isles. This warm drift upon the reaches beyond Gibraltar, where the rugged green and red and amethyst of the Spanish mountains rise from the sea, haunted the imagination. There is no venture possible to the mind that will ever lack a volunteer. The West was a magnet even before Homer's day. The Gates of Gibraltar at the same time welcomed the ghosts of the dead and the ships of the living. Nothing could keep the known world from expanding beyond its Mediterranean basin to where the great Atlantic Gyre enlivened and warmed the cold spread of western ocean. New islands and undiscovered river valleys were the goal, for it was from such places the old civilizations had flowered in their time.

So the western Mediterranean and later the western ocean became the wild west of the classic world, and its story was a composite of fact and fiction like that of our own frontier in North America. We have taken some pains to outline in previous pages the legendary history of the Atlantic, because each year we live the historians are revising their textbooks to make room for legends that have caught up with fact. Troy is a city in history which was once a name in a poem. The stay and progress of civilized man in the Americas as well as in Europe is each year being pushed back thousands of years before Christ.

Now who were these Phoenician sailors who took off from Tyre and Sidon for the Pillars of Hercules? They were Hittites, who had migrated overland from sea coasts adjacent to the Persian Gulf, following what is called the "fertile crescent" of hill country stretching northwest from Persia through Syria to the shores of the eastern Mediterranean. One of many such migratory groups, they in particular took to the sea and acted as the carriers and traders to distant lands for the inland peoples of the Near East. The Phoenicians were a tough and hardy race of merchant-adventurers who later developed great artistic skills in metal and glass and weaving to further their grip on the Mediterranean trade with the still barbarous Greek tribes of the Aegean. The Greeks called them the "Red Men" because of their swarthy sea tan. The Red Men of the wild west of the classic world pushed beyond the Aegean, the whole length of the Mediterranean. They were at home anywhere in a bottom with oars and a sail, and like the later Norsemen regarded neither distance nor time so long as they could hound along the coasts and eventually get back with goods and gear.

Although the romantic stories of the Fortunate Isles, of Atlantis and the far Hesperides, were attractive as mere fables, quite probably the bold and experienced Phoenicians regarded such legends as founded on fact and left the literary appreciation to scholars. At any rate, undeterred by fears of landsmen or doubts of the learned, they were out beyond the Straits of Gibraltar a thousand years before Christ. The pull and power of the unknown ocean river was too strong for them.

This was no accidental undertaking. As moderns thinking in terms of steam and engines we too readily presume that long and difficult journeys were impossible before our own immediate time. But this is just a false way of thinking, for "long" means long in time, and the ancient time sense was slower than ours, and danger, to men practiced in their craft of seamanship, was no different from day to day in the Mediterranean than in the English Channel.

For the most part these earliest mariners ran within sight and reach of the coast, but it is obvious that on their longer reaches this was not always possible. We know that the Phoenicians had a basic learning in the astronomy of the time. They were aware that the Great Bear and the Little Bear wheeled around the fixed lodestar Polaris. Other constellations were used by mariners, but it is unlikely that even a rudimentary compass was yet in use — though a simple astrolabe for measuring the angle of the sun above the horizon was a possibility. One thing is sure: Tyre and Sidon were one of the earliest known of the great Thalassocracies or sea powers in any part of the world, and the boldness and efficiency of their seafarers were not equalled for more than a thousand years. Like all the peoples of the warm and relatively calm belt of subtropical waters that girdled the earth, they were among the great travelers in the dawn of historic time, together with the Arabs, the Chinese, and the Polynesians.

To make a little more obvious this necessary point of ancient attitude toward time and distance, let's drop back briefly to the beginning of ships and trace their origin and the spread around the world of ship design and building. Coastal waters and the open seas form the most natural highway in the world. This seaway leads to new lands from harassed or overpopulated areas. Men found their way great distances by raft, by dugout canoes, and in craft whose planks were sewn together with thongs or ropes of vines and hemp. Oars and a square sail were the means of locomotion, in addition to the haphazard use of ocean currents and lucky trade winds, for nothing much was known or charted.

Probably the first craft to leave the shore were rafts such as

Roman Ships of the Third Century A.D. (From Mosaic at Ostia.)

are found in Polynesia, the Nile, and the shores of western South America. Reeds and balsa wood made admirable sea-going platforms in Egypt and Peru, and the earliest legends of the South Pacific tell of men with beards arriving from the land of the sun on great sailing rafts. Oddly enough we have seen that the Central American legends also tell of similar migrations from the east. Without regard to the set opinions of various schools of anthropologists and geographers, it would certainly seem logical that with the craft they had people on the move would most likely go downwind with the trades and be taken willy-nilly with the great east-west equatorial currents. It is also interesting to note that two precisely similar

Portuguese Caravel of about 1450. (From a painting in the church of Madre de Dios, Lisbon.)

methods of making dugout canoes with boiling water to soften
the wood and then with stone adzes are found in Burma and
British Colombia. Also the early drawings of reed boats or
balsa boats from the Nile, from Lake Tshad, and from Lake
Titicaca in the Andes are scarcely distinguishable in design or
methods of tying. How effective even balsa rafts can be in long
sea journeys was recently well illustrated when six young Scandinavian scientists floated on such a raft, the *Kon-Tiki*, a distance of 4,300 miles from Peru to Polynesia.

These reed canoes were probably used in the Mediterranean
about 3,000 B.C. But the Egyptians soon progressed from reed
bundles to pine planking brought down from Lebanon. These
strakes were beveled at the inner edge, holes drilled, and then
bound tightly edge to edge with thongs so as to make a relatively smooth and seaworthy hull. They had upcurling keels
that formed a prow good for beaching or for ramming an
enemy. The design of later Norse craft very closely follows the
early Egyptian craft. Sewn boats were found in Finland, Lap-
land, Norway, and the Shetland Isles as late as the seventeenth
century. An interesting feature of the early Mediterranean
craft in use up to about 1,000 B.C. was the "A" or wishbone
mast made from two spars bound together at the top with the
lower ends fastened at opposite gunwales. This primitive
method of rigging ships growing out of a scarcity of timber in
the earliest times was diffused as far east as Burma and Cochin
China, where ribless construction and A-shape masts were
used possibly as early as 2,500 B.C.

Before leaving the early records of ship construction which
largely have to do with Egyptian sources, it is worth mention-
ing that these Mediterranean craft had eyes painted on the
prows as magic against hostile influence on land and sea. So
had the China ships; and in the Norse sagas at the time of Eric
the Red in Greenland old Eric reprimands Leif his son for not
binding the eyes of the dragon head on his vessel, lest it bring

foreign ill luck to the home port in Greenland. As a matter of record, Chatterton in his *Sailing Ships and Their History* mentions that "there are many points of resemblance of the Scandinavian ships to certain seagoing Phoenician vessels of 1,000 B.C. and there exist Bronze Age rock carvings in Sweden of long boats with figurehead and ramming prow almost identical with East African craft found on Lake Victoria Nyanza."

What does all this prove? Certainly no exact relationship among far distant early peoples that can be called final. But beyond any doubt this and much more available evidence shows that there was a widespread diffusion of similar shipbuilding techniques on a world-wide scale two or three thousand years before the Christian era. This we hope will help the modern-minded man of the age of steam and engines to realize that speed was never an ancient necessity, that safety was relative and not much considered by the pioneers of the dawn of history, and that means were available for clever and adaptable adventurers to coast thousands of miles or even perhaps drift across great distances of open sea in craft that remained afloat and carried sufficient supply for long journeys.

It is possible that Mediterranean man before the dawn of history — let us say the ancestors of the Egyptians — made the long journey downwind, helped by the equatorial current, to far islands in the Atlantic. It is possible, and some think probable, that great island civilizations existed where now Atlantic waters cover the leagues between the Azores and Canaries and our American West Indies. As a studious early Portuguese historian, Antonio Galvano, wrote, "It can not be denied, but that there are many countries, islands, Capes, isthmus and points, which now are grown out of knowledge, because the names of them are found in histories. But the age of the world and the force of the waters have wasted and consumed them, and separated one country from another."

So let's start our Atlantic chronicle of actual discovery with the Phoenicians, who struck out beyond the Straits of Gibraltar at least a thousand years before Christ to sniff out the news of the western ocean. The provincial city of Carthage, outgrowing its parent ports of Tyre and Sidon, made a perfect jumping-off place for further explorations west. About the year 1,100 B.C. the Phoenician traders settled the city of Gades, now Cadiz, beyond the Pillars of Hercules on the Atlantic coast of Spain. They found the neighboring city of Tartessos, or Tarshish, already in existence, but after a few years we hear no more of Tartessos. The hard-bitten traders from the inland sea were in full and exclusive command of the Straits, and like all traders were determined to keep this advantage These men were traders, not much interested in science, literature, or the arts unless they furthered commercial enterprise. But they broke trail for more subtle civilizations to follow. They planted colonies in Sicily, southern France, North Africa, Spain, and possibly as far north as their trade routes in the English Channel. A pretty good case has been made out by Wadell that they founded London and were the real pre-Roman rulers of southwestern England before the Saxons. The image of Britannia can be found on many a Phoenician coin dug up in English soil. Cup markings and Hittite symbols for the sun and of the cross have also been found in England.

The power of Tyre as a great seaport city-state was largely drawn from the western trade in tin from the British Isles and silver and copper from Spain and from the tuna fisheries of the eastern Atlantic shores. The colonies of Phoenicians in western Europe some thousand years before Christ were beginning to suckle on the rich harvests of the great Ocean River that poured its warmth from the far Caribbean along the shores of Spain and France and Cornwall. By the year 500 B.C. Carthage was the complete master of the western Mediterranean and the waters westward beyond the Straits. The last free explorers not under Carthaginian rule to make journeys into the Atlantic were two Mediterranean Greeks. Midacritus coasted along the Biscayan shores to the English Channel, and Euthymenes headed south from the Straits as far as Senegal in the sixth century B.C. Shortly after these voyages two greater expeditions under Carthaginian rule made ready from Andalusia. Himilco and Hanno were governors of this province, and like their Greek predecessors one went north and the other south from Gibraltar.

Himilco, according to Pliny, in 443 B.C. explored with a good deal of care the Atlantic coasts of France, and touched in at the Cassiterides or the Tin Isles off Cornwall. The wide Atlantic even at this early date was becoming familiar to the Mediterranean sailors, though they did not yet venture far from land unless swept out by adverse winds. Hanno, the brother, however, made the most extensive journey, and even established successful colonial cities in his path. This was the most notable voyage into the unknown Atlantic yet attempted. He set out southward with sixty vessels, and thirty thousand colonists who founded the coastal cities of Mehedia, Mogador, and Acre. Hanno reached as far south as Sherbro Island off Sierra Leone, three thousand miles from home, before he turned back. He did as well as many of the first Portuguese explorers some fifteen centuries later, who found it hard to venture too far at a time for fear of the dark beyond and the "Coagulated Sea." It is written of the Canaries that Juba, King of Morocco, sailed there about the time of Christ. The Etruscans planned to settle Madeira in the time of Hanno but were stopped at Gibraltar. Hereafter voyaging south had to wait on the Portuguese.

But the profitable tin trade with Britain still pulled men to the north. A remarkable voyage was made in 300 B.C. by Pytheus, either a Greek or a Phoenician, who set out from Massilia (Marseilles) and pushed on until he had coasted the entire length of northern Europe. As he went, being somewhat of an astronomer, he took observations of the tides and currents, and is said by the historian Eratosthenes, who wrote shortly after the voyage, to have been the first man to note the compass variation between the true and magnetic north pole.

Pytheus was a rare combination of intellectual and bold adventurer. After visiting the Cornish tin mines he went on north of the Scilly Isles to Scotland and the Orkneys, and several days' voyage beyond to an island he called Thule, which very likely was Iceland. In this area he met foul weather that so impressed his Mediterranean senses that he said air, ice, and water formed a kind of turgid mixture he called the "sea-lung." He noted in his log that hereabouts the midsummer night was only two hours long; he must have been off Norway. Coming south he stopped to examine the Frisian coast, where his countrymen were used to pick up amber for the southern trade. On this great journey Pytheus circumnavigated Britain, and three centuries before Christ and seventeen before Columbus covered a distance of some seven thousand miles.

Within a hundred and fifty years after this exploration, Carthage, after a series of disastrous wars, fell before the Roman power and thus ended the Phoenician world of adventurous seapower that first opened up the prolonged but intermittent exploration of the Atlantic waters. Roman power, essentially land power, expanded east and north from the Italian peninsula. All the secret knowledge of closely held trade routes and northern explorations by sea apparently died with the fall of Carthage, and for a while the Gates of Gibraltar were closed.

We can make a kind of picture of just what was lost to the world in Roman times. Though there is no authentic record of the orderly advance of scientific inquiry up to the time the Phoenicians pushed westward from the Gates of Gibraltar, there is a kind of persistent cross reference in the succeeding histories of who said what and when. In fact, much of the intellectual progress of the Mediterranean world — just because its paths and connections were those of seafaring people — is to be found in the history of early map-making. When so little was accurately known, a new map was of necessity a new picture of the intellectual progress or regression of the issuer.

To begin with, as early as the time of Archimedes, an astronomer called Aristarchus hazarded the theory that the earth moved round the sun in a circle. There is only hearsay to prove this — no writing — but it nevertheless suggests that ideas and theories have deep roots in the human mind, even though this was eighteen hundred years before Copernicus made the theory stick as fact. So also we hear of early experimentation with the lodestone or magnetic needle that was the forerunner of the modern compass; and the simple astrolabe from which the modern sextant has developed is first mentioned by Ptolemy in the second century A.D.

What we know of the earliest maps is largely by word of mouth. Parchment was scarce and fragile. Maps were carried by soldiers and sailors and travelers on risky journeys; their chance of survival was slight. Master maps, useful for military or trade purposes, were what would now be called "top secret," and rather than part with them men destroyed them. They were wrapped in sheets of lead ready to be heaved over the side if an enemy attacked.

Many volumes have been written by their contemporaries and later scholars pointing out how faulty and wrong the mapmakers have always been. We should be glad of it, because the bold, imaginative early map-makers were men thinking on paper, drawing what they knew and what they suspected would turn out to be true after fresh discoveries. As much as anyone else the makers of maps were instigators of intellectual advance because they were not afraid to be wrong or haul in an empty net casting for the elusive truth.

One of these pioneers was the great geographer Eratosthenes, born 276 B.C., who figured out, by the crudest kind of sighting the angle of the sun, that the earth was 25,000 miles in circumference. One of the first maps to give a reasonably accurate picture of the European Atlantic coastline was Italian, probably made after the voyage of Pytheus. It shows the Canary Isles labeled as the Fortunate Isles. On a larger scale Eratosthenes, and Hipparchus, another learned Greek who opposed him on many points, both made maps of the world which were more symmetrical than accurate, but nevertheless were the first attempts to measure the land by parallels and meridians. Hipparchus started a mathematical method of geographic studies that was carried forward by Ptolemy. They studied the positions of the stars, the orbit of the sun, and the measurement of sidereal time; and between them might be said to have founded the mathematics of astronomy that was standard for more than a thousand years of the Christian era.

These facts are noted here because there is such a mass of legend and superstition current for the period we write about that the really scientific advance is sometimes overlooked. Of one thing we can be pretty certain — the pilots and navigators of the time were well aware of whatever scientific knowledge was available. The great merchants and the curious and learned minds of the Mediterranean countries, particularly the Phoenicians, were people of the sea. Alexandria, the center of Mediterranean learning at the end of the pre-Christian era, was also the crossroads for all eastern trade, and brought to a focus both practical and scholastic learning. This was a practical age.

But after the fall of Carthage and the advent of the Christian era the religious rather than the scientific mind governed inquiry into the nature of the world. St. Augustine built a kingdom in his head, and men like Solinus collected the fables and tall stories of all time to make a picture for men to marvel at. Sir Charles Beazley in the *Dawn of Modern Geography* speaks of early medieval learning as divided into three cate gories: the "Fabulists," or collectors of narratives and legends; the "Statisticians," who compiled long categories of what were then considered facts; and finally the "Cosmographers," who by chart and map and description tried to draw some feasible picture of the world. All these searchers were pretty wide of the mark, because there was little to encourage any scientific curiosity that might lead men's minds from The Holy City of St. Augustine. Not until the tenth century, in fact, was there much of any free geographical enterprise in the west.

Then came what is called the second period of medieval times, opening with the vigorous burst of voyaging by the Norsemen in the North Atlantic, followed by the sweep of the Crusades in the eleventh and twelfth centuries which stimu-lated the enterprise of the great commercial city-states of Genoa and Venice. The final period, up to the great voyages of Columbus, runs for about two hundred years, largely now under the aegis of the first Atlantic maritime power, Portugal.

As we have pointed out, with the advent of Christianity the sciences were forced into obscurity. Men's minds were obsessed with a new kind of interior world, and taken away from the actual unknown horizons beyond the waters. In addition the Romans built roads in preference to ships. They centralized authority on the political side, and deplored eccen-tricity and individual initiative; just as the church, as it grew in power, put a quietus to any but the permitted authoritarian channels of thought. This block to intellectual freedom and fresh discovery, increasing under the barbarian invasions, per-sisted until the eleventh century, when the great commercial city-states of Genoa and Venice, in developing a European commerce, broke open again the doors of inquiry. At long last the learning and freedom of early Greek and Eastern thought was set free in the Mediterranean, and the heritage of the Phoenicians was taken up by new and equally bold seafarers along the shores of the great Atlantic Ocean. The western world of our own time was ready for creation.

The pathfinders came in the tenth century from the fjords of Norway. The Norsemen took to sea for much the same reasons as the practical Phoenicians. They sought trade, plunder, and renown, and on occasion had to find new lands for their individualistic local governments because of trouble and tyranny at home. In 865 A.D. a group of Norse landowners escaping from the power of Harald Harfarger, the new king, came to Iceland with their families and goods and made a settlement. They found a country not too cold or infertile, with good fishing, and no inhabitants except a few Irish monks. In those days for a period of several centuries the climate created in the north by the Gulf Stream was in one of its periodic warmer spells, as it has been in the Greenland area for the past twenty-five years of our time. There was little or no floe ice to contend with at sea, and the great Greenland icecap was apparently in temporary retreat. Today students of long-range climatic changes believe it possible that the warm period after the last glacial retreat from Europe held on into modern historical times. At any rate the Norse in large numbers crossed the Norwegian Sea and came to Iceland and Greenland in their open vessels. In both these places they picked up foreign woods and drifting seeds and vegetation that came from somewhere over the horizon to the west and south. They did not know of the Gulf Stream as a carrier but they observed its effect, and this no doubt excited their curiosity about unknown lands to the west of the ocean sea.

This advantageous period of climate, coupled with the rising trouble at home, helped to scatter the Norse vessels far and wide to the south and west. Like the Phoenicians of earlier times, the Norsemen were traders and explorers rather than the agents of a new civilization. The best of the Norse tradition of democratic and law abiding organization ripened in remote Iceland. But only at second hand and later, through the Normans, did the Scandinavian north exert any influence on the peoples to the south, and that influence was not great. The Norse explorations, nevertheless, were great steps forward in the revealing of the unknown Atlantic world; and they illustrated once more how bold and skillful men, careless of time, could defy distance in long sea wanderings beyond the charted limits of the world.

First swarming down around the British Isles in the tenth century they settled Dublin, and took over Scotland and the western islands and most of Ireland. Others settled the Norman country of France; and some went still farther south through the Straits of Gibraltar, reversing the Phoenician quest, and hired out to the Byzantine emperor as his Varangian guard. The Ultima Thule of the Phoenicians thus came to the Mediterranean.

So it happened that the western world of North America was made known to the Norse. Eric the Red, the father of Leif Ericson, was a hot-tempered man who became outlawed. He first went from Norway to Iceland. But after a while he got into trouble even there, and set out once more westward looking for asylum. He found a good harbor in southern Greenland in 982, and four years later, with twenty-five ships containing his first colonists, he sailed from Iceland. Fourteen of these ships arrived safely on the Greenland coast. Men had heard rumors of lands still farther west, and these rumors became fact when Biarni Herulfson, a merchant, blown off his course from Ireland, coasted along the rocky wooded shores of a western land and called it Helluland. This he reported in Greenland in 986.

Leif Ericson set out in 1000 to explore further this new western continent, probably coasting as far south as Cape Cod and wintering there before his return to Greenland the next year. Leif's youngest brother, Thorvald, returned to Vinland in 1002 and spent two winters there. Thorvald was killed by the Indians and his company returned to Brattahild in Greenland in 1004. Between the years 1007 and 1010 a further attempt to effect a permanent settlement on the American coast was made by Thorfinn Karlsefni, but it came to no permanence because of dissensions among different members of the expedition. There was nothing miraculous in these voyages. The long, well-modeled vessels of the Norse were probably as good sea boats in their way as those used by Columbus five hundred years later, and there was no insuperable stretch of open sea to deter experienced men. The longest hitch of a voyage from Norway to Vinland would, in fact, be the accustomed leg from Norway to Iceland.

The question naturally arises why this bold beginning was not followed through. In part it was the same kind of trouble that halted the first great Atlantic venture of the Phoenicians. There were bad times at home. Civil wars broke out in Norway, and hard times slowly came on the Greenland colony. Leif Ericson died, and with him the immediate inspiration for further discovery. But beyond the more or less temporary political and economic disruption, as the eleventh century grew older a noticeable change in weather conditions affected the northlands. The long period of warm weather over the far north came to an end. In a later chapter we shall discuss the effect on the European civilizations of fluctuating climate. Here it may be enough to record that the icecap worked down from central Greenland and brought with it new floe ice in

the waters and also a gradual advance of an Eskimo population to compete with the little colony on the tip of Greenland. Fresh recruits from the homelands no longer came to
strengthen the frontiersmen in the west. So, between a troubled Europe and a definite fluctuation in the needed warmth
brought from the equator by the Ocean River, times grew
hard. The hay crop dwindled, and the fishing became more
difficult. There were bold and desperate efforts by the harassed Greenland colony to settle further to the west. In 1121
Bishop Eric of Greenland set out on a missionary exploration
to relocate the early Vinland colony of Leif Ericson. Nothing
was ever heard again of this bold churchman, and in 1124 a
new Greenland bishop was appointed.

In 1135 certain men were said to have settled on the shores
of Baffin's Bay; and there are vague records of attempted settlements on the North American continent again in 1266 and
1285. But in 1347 — according to Icelandic annals — a Greenland ship with eighteen men aboard came in to Straumsfiord
in Iceland from a voyage to Markland or Newfoundland. This
should help us keep in mind that as late as the fourteenth
century the crossing of the North Atlantic by way of Greenland to the American continent was notable but of no special
wonder. By 1364, when Ivar Bardsen came back to Norway
from the Bishop's seat at Gardar, he had nothing to report of
the Greenland colony but bad news. Some life and some little
contact with European sources seems to have lingered on,
however, for as late as 1448 a papal letter referred to the suf-
ferings of the church in this far corner of the Northwest. But
there is one more bit of testimony to the drive of the Norse
discoverers in pre-Columbian days. Within recent years a
most remarkable discovery has been made in Minnesota. At a
little settlement called Kensington a carefully inscribed rune
stone was found telling the story of a small party that came
overland from the sea and how half the party going hunting

returned to find the rest murdered. This stone was made and set up as a final marker — and then there is silence. For a number of years this Kensington stone was not believed to be authentic. But after thorough antiquarian study both in this country and Scandinavia this mid-fourteenth-century stone is now believed to be genuine. A replica of it is on view at the Smithsonian Institution in Washington. Here were actually the first explorers of the North American continent.

All this adds up to a strong impression — for we have no written proof — that the fraternity of pilots, sailors, and navigators of the western continent knew much more before Columbus than the historians like to admit. This in no way detracts from the bold venture of the Italian navigator, but it does indicate that an educated and traveled sea captain of his time probably knew whatever was current in fact or rumor from the ports of Iceland south to Portugal.

It is written that a Danish vessel, storm-driven beyond her course, put in at the old port of Gardar in Greenland in 1450. The Greenland colony no longer existed; but there were traces of an Eskimo invasion, and in a few graves the last of the vigorous descendants of Eric the Red had left remains of woefully undernourished and diseased creatures lying with their wornout iron weapons by their side.

Now it was the turn of another race, under the stimulus of a renewed vigor coming from the Renaissance in the Mediterranean, to take up the never-ending though often interrupted revelation of the wide Atlantic waters. The people of Spain and Portugal in the fifteenth century once more resumed the explorations that had been hampered by the dark ages of the past thousand years. It will always remain an interesting speculation just how much the common knowledge of the fishing fleets of Brest, Dieppe, St. Malo, and the Basque coast ports gave confidence to the learned pilots and navigators who at this time plotted new discoveries. It is true no written record

of fisheries off the Grand Banks of Newfoundland exists before 1500, but we know that for a hundred years before that
time these same adventurous fishermen were plying their trade
in the waters around Iceland and west of Ireland, and it has
been pretty well established that Columbus as a young man
voyaged to Bristol and probably to Iceland.

Having followed the second burst of energy in the far north
of Europe we can go back and pick up in the Mediterranean.
The fall of Rome to the Goths in 474 ushered in the dark
ages of stagnation in the history of modern Europe. The spirit
of scientific inquiry was at least dormant. Successively the
Goths, Vandals, and Mohammedans swept down the Mediterranean. As Antonio Galvano neatly puts it: "In that age all
the world was hurly-burly and all places very tumultuous."
But the undying human flame of curiosity and experimental
endeavor flickered on the fringes of the Old World in Spain
and Portugal.

It is interesting to note that the Crusades inspired by the
Church helped to lift the repression that the Church itself
created in the Middle Ages. Thousands of men pouring down
through the Mediterranean countries to the Holy Land im-
bued with the glory of God — and a little mite touched on the
side, perhaps, with the lust for adventure and the thought of
gain — these adventurers became more and more curious
about the far boundaries of the world. They heard of the
lands of Gog and Magog in the far north of Asia. They saw
how eager the Pope was to find out the kingdom of Prester
John; and they heard their Celtic brethren tell of the heavenly
paradise found by St. Brandon somewhere just over the horizon in the mysterious Atlantic. As late as the sixteenth century Portugal was still sending out expeditions hoping to lay
claim to St. Brandon's Isle. The Church, now an imperial
power, was forced to act as an empire builder, and keep its

hand in with any explorers who might help extend militant Christianity across the world.

Though much of the emphasis of exploration in the twelfth century was eastward into Asia, the Genoese undertook to push their trading ventures westward through the Straits of Gibraltar. In 1270 a Genoese fleet under Lancelot Malocello sailed along the West African coast, rediscovered the long-forgotten Canaries, and called them again traditionally the Fortunate Isles. Twenty years later one of the famous Doria captains, looking for a water route to the Indies for strictly commercial reasons, sailed into the Sea of Darkness as far south as Cape Nun, beyond any previous reach of a European vessel. Within the next hundred years Italian navigators discovered and named most of the Madeiras. For a time the Cape Verde Islands were known as the Islands of Antonio, after Antonio Noli, another Italian.

There is an interesting counterclaim, as reported by Galvano, concerning the discovery of Madeira in the fourteenth century. It concerns a bold and eccentric Englishman named Macham and reads thus: "About the time of 1344 the island of Madeira was discovered by an Englishman called Macham, who sailing out of England into Spain, with a woman of his, was driven out of his direct course by a tempest and arrived in that island and cast his anchor in that haven which now is called Machico after his name. And because his lover was then seasick, he went on land with some of his company and in the meantime his vessel weighed anchor and put to sea, leaving him there. Whereupon his lover, for thought, died. Macham, who greatly loved her, built on this island a chapel or hermitage to bury her in and wrote upon the stone of her tomb his name and hers and the occasion upon which they arrived there. After this he made himself a boat out of a tree, the trees being of great compass, and went to sea in it with men of his company and fell with the coast of Africa. And the Moors, among whom he came, took it for a miracle and presented him to the King of their country and the King also admiring the accident, sent him and his company unto the King of Castile."

But the story of Atlantic discoveries for the hundred years preceding Columbus is dominated by the great figure of the Portuguese Prince Henry the Navigator. Lloyd A. Brown, in his thoroughgoing book *The Story of Maps* puts the Portuguese case very well: "Several factors combined to make Portugal the greatest maritime and colonizing power in Europe during the fifteenth century. Its people comprised a mixture of Moors and Mozarabs in the south, Galicians in the north, and Jews and foreign crusaders everywhere. The most highly developed culture was combined with the most primitive barbarity. The result was a people of unusual courage, ingenuity and greed. They inherited the best in science from the Arabs and acquired by purchase the navigational skill developed in Italy. They were 'outside sailors.' "

Intercourse between Portugal and other European countries was blocked on land by Aragon and Castile. Portuguese goods, therefore, were moved by sea to England, Flanders, and the Hanse towns in northern Europe. Any new markets would have to face the ocean. Moreover, the crusading spirit was still strong in Portugal. The Order of Christ, founded by Diniz at the dissolution of the Templars, was both wealthy and powerful, and the vast resources of the Order, under the direction of Prince Henry the Navigator, were consecrated to the maritime expansion of Christianity.

Up to this time nothing was known of the lands and waters south of the African Cape Bojador. Prince Henry determined to push back the Sea of Darkness in this direction where the very roots of the Atlantic Gyrol commence to move in the equatorial current. By 1441, after several experimental voyages, Antam Goncalvez brought back slaves and gold from the coast of Guinea. Superstitious fear of the Sea of Darkness vanished at the clink of coin.

Near Cape St. Vincent on the Portuguese coast Prince Henry established what might well be termed a maritime university. Here he installed his students of geography and astronomy and his map-makers, and here his venturing sea captains had to check in and report on their voyages of discovery. As a result of this clearinghouse of careful study and practical preparation some twenty-eight years after Henry's death Bartholomew Diaz de Novaes sailed from Lisbon with three ships and rounded the Cape of Good Hope. He was the first man to do this, provided we forget Strabo's mention that it was reported that Phoenicians had circumnavigated Africa from east to west under the Egyptian kings. This great turning of the Cape set Portuguese minds to the eastern trade, which they went on to develop in India and the Moluccas, thus leaving the way open in the sixteenth century for Spain to dominate the western world of Columbus.

No longer did Portugal or the people of the Mediterranean world figure in the uncovering and exploitation of the new world of the great Atlantic Gyre. Spain, England, and France now took over, and began the real unfolding of the River in its streams and drifts and eddies. Many years were to pass before the great Atlantic circulation of salt waters became known as it is today, when we can follow its course on the printed surface of a chart. The growth of a New World civilization and the charting of the River went on side by side, each a history in itself, but each a natural result of the other.

6

CHARTING THE RIVER

I T IS perfectly logical to speak of the Atlantic Ocean as the greatest river in the world. It forms a gigantic pool, with the Sargasso Sea roughly in the center, around which seventy-five million tons of water per second is transported in clockwise fashion. This cold mathematical statistic hides many meanings. The daily flow of the River is nearly one thousand times as great as the Mississippi in flood. Even more important than its size, however, is its function. The circulation of this vast river of warm tropical waters, linked as it is with the North Atlantic climate, has affected both the history and the present pattern of western civilization. Life-giving heat equivalent to the absorption of three million square miles of ocean surface at the equator is carried in constant battle against the encroachment of Arctic waters upon northern Europe.

In his report on the Gulf Stream, written in 1890, Lieutenant John Elliott Pillsbury, of the U. S. Navy, the first to carry out an intensive scientific investigation on this portion of the Ocean River, says: "Man stands with bowed head in the presence of nature's visible grandeurs, such as towering mountains, precipices, or icebergs, forests of immense trees, grand rivers, or waterfalls. He realizes the force of waves that can sweep away lighthouses or toss an ocean steamer about like a cork. In a vessel floating on the Gulf Stream one sees nothing of the current and knows nothing but what experience tells him; but to be anchored in its depths far out of the sight of land, and to see the mighty torrent rushing past at a speed of three to four miles per hour, day after day and day after day, one begins to think that all the wonders of the earth combined can not equal this one river in the ocean."

Only in recent times, since the advent of steam, have ocean travelers ceased to be at the mercy of the direction and force of ocean currents; but even today the steady pace of deep waters working on the hull of a steamer can set her back fifty miles in a day's sailing along the axis of the Gulf Stream. This, of course, has a direct effect both on time and on fuel economy. It is obvious, therefore, that even though we have largely graduated from the age of sail, a thorough knowledge of ocean currents is still of considerable importance for all types of vessels.

In the early days of sailing, especially with square-rigged ships, the importance of currents as an aid or an obstacle to navigation was paramount. Under conditions when wind and stream were both unfavorable a ship might well be set back in its course for many miles, or, at worst, might be lost on the rocks of a lee shore. Though this is still true for all types of sailing vessels it was particularly true of the square-rigged type used in the early Atlantic crossings, because of their limited powers of sailing against the wind. Largely because of this, the existence of great currents and their position and strength have shaped the course of early explorations and the pattern of settlement of the Atlantic shores, first of all in the east and later in the west.

The influence of ocean currents on man, working in various and devious ways, has inspired many scientists from many lands to inquire into their movements and to speculate on their cause. But progress in our knowledge of their position, their strength, and their variations has been understandably slow. Man is not naturally a seagoing animal, and he has been able to live for extended periods on the surface of the ocean only by the invention and development of artificial aids in the form of simple floats, sailing vessels, and later of more elaborate mechanically propelled seagoing hotels. It is a relatively simple matter to take measurements and observations on the rigid platform of land; but to do this on the heaving deck of a small vessel at sea is a very different affair. The problem of measuring and observing the ocean at first hand is neither a simple nor comfortable exercise, even in today's fast and seaworthy vessels. Hence our knowledge of the Gulf Stream, of the Atlantic current system of which it is a part, and of the forces setting them in motion, has only in recent years made rapid progress.

The great Ocean River is, in essence, a vast circular swirl of water complicated by the inflow and outflow of counter-currents, eddies, tributaries, and branches. North of the equator in latitude 15° N. the north equatorial current, under the whip of constant trade winds, runs in a westerly direction toward the American continent, and would thus girdle the globe if it were not turned and channeled by the interposed continents and spun clockwise by the earth's rotation.

The wind starts westward off the African coast behind which lies the great Sahara, and so the waters begin to move by the Canaries and Cape Verde Islands in a great wide flow. Then the west-driving current as it accumulates in its ocean passage is forced in a northerly direction and in a clockwise motion north of the equator. South of the equator is another west-ward-flowing current, and this spins south and to the left, for in southern latitudes the earth's rotation works contrariwise. We spoke of continental interference. The west-driving south equatorial current only in part turns into the southern gyre. The huge shoulder of Brazil acts as a baffle which

catches a goodly portion of it and shunts it north across the
equator to join the north equatorial current on the Atlantic
side of the Antilles or Windward Islands of the West Indies.
Here again part of this great accumulation of warm waters,
known as the Antilles Current, passes north and west outside
the Windward Islands and the Bahamas, until beyond Cape
Canaveral on the east Florida coast it meets the Florida
stream.

Another part of the equatorial drift of waters enters the
Caribbean Sea and finds its way through the Straits of Yucatan between Mexico and Cuba and then through the Straits
of Florida between Florida and the Bahamas. Here we call
it the Florida Current. A side branch of this Caribbean stream
varying in magnitude enters the Gulf of Mexico from the
Straits of Yucatan and returns again near the Florida Keys.

North of the Bahama Islands these two great streams, the
Florida Current and the Antilles Current, reunite to form the
Gulf Stream proper, which soon turns eastward toward the
European continent. As it approaches Europe south of Green-
land along the edge of the north continental shelf and what
is called the Telegraph Plateau, a broad diffuse portion of the
Ocean River turns full circle down by France, Spain, the
Azores, and back to the African coast, but part bathes the
British Isles in a warmth that belies the fact that they stand
in the same latitude as Labrador.

Now just north of Scotland, stretching northwest to Greenland, a rise of undersea land — the Wyville-Thompson ridge
— comes near enough to the surface to stop the deeper southerly drift of heavy, ice-cold arctic waters, but permits about
two percent of the warmer surface waters of the now reduced
Atlantic stream to seep over into the Norwegian Sea. This
mild current keeps open Norwegian ports in the same latitude
as the Greenland icecap, likewise makes Iceland a habitable
place, and even affects the shallow Baltic Sea. A slight but

constant difference in temperature will maintain marked climatic differences. These differences are being traced even today in the Arctic, as we shall later discuss.

The River of the Ocean is not alone. Satellite rivers and countercurrents, clinging to the skirts of the great circular stream, are thrown off from the outer border of the flowing water, while eddies swirl along the inner boundary, small patterns of the Great Gyre itself. Most important of the satellite rivers is a cold mass of arctic water that flows down from the north as the Labrador Current, between the River and the eastern shores of the United States, until it finally disappears beneath the warmer and lighter waters of the Gulf Stream.

Today's charts of the great Atlantic River and its currents were not easily plotted. More than 400 years elapsed after the first recorded Atlantic crossing before even the general outlines appeared in print. Before Columbus' first voyage a few serious speculations had appeared regarding the Atlantic Ocean; but mostly myth had grown up around it, and only an adventurous man would dare advance away from its eastern shores into the sea of mystery. And yet, as we have seen, the conception of the Atlantic as a river is a very ancient one. The Chaldeans imagined that the earth floated on eternal waters, and that a river perpetually flowed in a ditch around it. The Egyptians added their own embellishment to this by picturing a boat that supported the sun, floating in the encircling stream.

The Phoenicians ventured as far afield as the British Isles, but like so many others who followed them in the slow charting of the Atlantic River they guarded their knowledge of navigation as a trade secret and left no maps behind them. With few preconceptions to hamper them, the Greeks who followed were able to speculate without restraint on the nature of the world. Homer considered the earth to be flat and to consist only of the Mediterranean countries he knew.

Outside of this he imagined the Ocean River, as the Greeks so aptly named it, to flow ceaselessly around the world, a living moat of danger and destruction.

The notion of a spherical earth came more than a thousand years before the time of Columbus. Ptolemy had conceived this idea long before, and by the fifth century A.D. his successors were aware that oceans lay to the west and to the south. The map he prepared in 150 A.D. showed only the western ocean between Africa and the Orient; the New World and the Pacific Ocean were still undreamed of. But even this limited knowledge was for all practical purposes lost when superstition and ignorance again took hold during the fifth and sixth centuries. And so, the maps of Bishop Isidore of Seville in the seventh century were far cruder even than the one Homer had made nearly 1,700 years earlier. Bishop Isidore's concept was simple in the extreme. He drew a circle for the earth; cut it into three portions, separated by the Mediterranean Sea and by the two great rivers, the Nile and the Don; and resurrected the Ocean River to form a circular canal connecting the sea and the rivers and embracing the whole.

In the fifteenth century the spirit of exploration blossomed under the encouragement of Prince Henry the Navigator, and Ptolemy's map was brought out of hiding. So it came about that, by the time Columbus was ready to set out across the Ocean River, a great part of the coast of western Africa had been added to the charts. Finally, when Bartholomew Diaz rounded the Cape of Good Hope and found this connection between the Indian and Atlantic Oceans, the extent of the eastern shores was established. The stage was now set for the gradual unfolding of the story of the River itself.

The earlier navigators may not have known that there were steady currents well out to sea, but they can hardly have failed to notice the nearby currents where they ran parallel to the shore. During the century before the westward crossing of Columbus, for instance, the Portuguese had with great perseverance developed a trade route to Guinea along the West African coast; and they therefore knew by hard experience of the Guinea Current, which sets to the south and southeast around Cape Nun on the bulge of North Africa, in places as strongly as three and a half knots. Combined with the north and northeasterly winds, this was a great handicap even to the Portuguese caravels, which, with their fore-and-aft rigs, were much better equipped to sail against the wind than Columbus' hermaphrodite-rigged craft.

Probably the first signs of far-ranging currents in the open ocean were strange objects cast ashore — seeds, branches of trees, and pieces of wood, brought from the western world by the Ocean River to the shores of northern Europe, just as today we find on the Atlantic beaches of North America the glass floats of Portuguese fishing nets, brought there by the Canaries Current, the equatorial drift, and the Florida Current. The presence of these objects from the western world was certainly known to Columbus. The sea-bean — about the size and shape of a horse chestnut — the seed of a West Indian plant, *Entada gigas*, is often thrown on European shores, together with bamboo stems and even an occasional coconut. Particularly large quantities are found on the shores of the Faroe Islands, between Scotland and Iceland. Whether this exotic sea drift influenced the westward migrations of the Norsemen we do not know, but it is certain from their accounts that they met with currents off the coast of North America; names given by them to geographic features of their discoveries make this clear. Among them are Straumsfiord or Bay of Currents, Straummes, Cape of Currents, and Straumsoe, Island of Currents. Unfortunately their writings leave us no way of identifying the exact localities described.

The first well-defined observation of the west-going limb

of the Ocean River was probably made by Columbus during his first voyage, when on September 19, 1492, he became aware of a westerly drift — the Canaries Current. The voyage might easily have resulted in disaster and the entire history of the Atlantic communities might have been changed had it not been for the benign flow of the River. The death of all hands from lack of food and water due to an overextended voyage was prevented by the fact that the Canaries Current and the equatorial current added at times as much as forty miles in a day to his passage.

During the later voyages of Columbus he discovered the Atlantic Stream where it flows into the Caribbean Sea between the Windward Islands and again where it leaves this sea through the Yucatan Channel. He was greatly impressed by the Windward Island currents, and considered them sufficiently powerful to have formed the islands by washing away the land between them: ". . . I hold it for certain that the waters of the sea move from East to West with the sky and that in passing this track they hold a more rapid course and have thus carried away large tracts of land and that from here has resulted the great number of islands." The current flowing along the Honduras coast was a specially difficult one to navigate, and, according to Peter Martyr, he found ". . . the course of the waters so vehement and furious against the fore part of his ship that he could at no time touch the ground with his sounding plummet, but that the contrary violence of the waters would bear it up from the bottom. He affirmeth also that he could never in one day with a good wynde wynn one mile of the course of the waters."

While Columbus was discovering the Caribbean currents, John and Sebastian Cabot crossed the Atlantic in 1497. They rediscovered the coast of Labrador, and then sailed southwest until they reached land somewhere in the vicinity of Delaware. It was here that they noticed the countercurrent running southward between the Gulf Stream and the coast, but even so they were apparently unaware of the Stream itself.

If the Corte-Reals noticed the Gulf Stream in their voyages from Labrador to Cuba between 1500 and 1502 they too failed to leave any account. It was characteristic of the early days of Atlantic exploration that navigators kept their observations to themselves as the Phoenicians had before them and rarely passed them on except by word of mouth, so that they did little to help the orderly development of permanent geographical knowledge. For example, Sebastian de Ocampo circumnavigated Cuba in 1509, taking fully eight months to complete the voyage. It is hard to believe that he did not notice the Stream, because he was almost certainly forced to sail against it when he rounded the western point of San Antonio. But he makes no mention of it.

Once more we turn to Peter Martyr, who gave so much thought and scholarly speculation to the problem of ocean currents. He realized that the stream of water entering the Caribbean must either pass still farther west, through an opening in the mainland into what we now know as the Pacific, or else be diverted to the north. If neither took place then he reasoned that the water must accumulate continuously in the western part of the Atlantic. He mentions a more fantastic possibility, that the westward current might be piled high against the western shores or even absorbed into the depths of the earth, but dismisses it with the remark that such a place had not yet been found. Later he also described an argument between Andreas Moralis, the pilot, and Ouidas, who took opposing sides on the question of a westward passage to the Pacific or a northeastern flow of water back into the mid-Atlantic where the currents were supposed to be completely absorbed:

"As we met thus together there arose a contention between them two as regarding this course of the ocean. They both

agree that these landes and regions pertayning to the Domin-
ion of Castile, do with one continuale tract and perpetual
bond embrace as one whole firme lands or continent all the
mayne lands lying to the north of Cuba and Hispaniola. Yet
as touching the course of the waters they vary in opinion,
for Andreas will, that his violent course of the water be received into the lappe of the supposed continent, which bend-
eth so much and extendeth so farre toward the north, as
we have said, and that by the object or resistance of the
lande so bending and crooking the water as it were, rebounde
in compasse and by the force thereof be driven about the
north side of Cuba and the other islands excluded outside the
circle called Tropicus Cancri, where the largeness of the
sea may receive the waters falling from the narrow streams
and thereby represse that inordinate course by reason that
the sea is there very large and great."

Peter Martyr obviously had not heard of a discovery made
by Ponce de Leon, or rather by his pilot, Antonio de Alaminos.
Though Ponce de Leon is better known for the fruitless quest
of his 1513 expedition, which set out to find the Fountain of
Youth, he has greater claim to fame for leaving one of the
first definite records of the Florida Current. He sailed from
Porto Rico along the northeastern side of the Bahamas, and
somewhat to the north of Cape Canaveral he crossed westward into the Stream. When he turned southward along the
Florida coast he had a good and favorable wind, but he was
powerless to stem the powerful northerly flow. He tells us that
when two of the vessels came into anchor one day, the third,
in water too deep to do likewise, was rapidly carried out of
sight to the north by the fierce pull of the waters.

The Gulf of Mexico was discovered in 1517 and explored
the following year, and this finally disproved the theory of a
break in the North American continent which would allow
the current a westward outlet. Thus it became inevitable that

the great flood of water passing north from Cuba should sooner or later be put to use by the Spanish vessels which were plying in increasing numbers between the Old World and the New. Antonio de Alaminos, pilot first with Columbus and later with Ponce de Leon, was therefore well acquainted at first hand with the Florida Current. He quickly took advantage of it. When sent by Cortez from Mexico to deliver dispatches and presents to Spain, he chose to make his way home by way of the Florida Straits so as to have the benefit of the Stream until he turned eastward toward Spain. From this time onward all sea traffic returning to Spain took advantage of the Current.

In the wake of the great flood of trading voyages and exploring expeditions during the next fifty years, knowledge of the directions and whereabouts of ocean currents began to pile up in the professional gossip of sailors, but nothing further was published; though there were many detailed accounts of the newly discovered lands, people, and vegetation. Because of the value of the cargoes carried by the Spanish vessels, their routes and general navigational knowledge were still held secret for security reasons. The sixteenth century had almost come to a close before Sir Humphrey Gilbert, Martin Frobisher, and others published their observations and confirmed the earlier records of currents in the western ocean.

Now that the idea of a westward passage through the Gulf of Mexico to the rich Orient had finally been disproved, the twin stimuli of greed and curiosity drove merchants and governments to seek a northwest passage from the Atlantic to the Pacific; and the contemporary accounts of voyages reflected this new interest among the more adventurous sailormen. Gilbert, who argued that the Gulf Stream must find an outlet either to the northeast or to the northwest, wrote that the current ". . . runs all along the eastern coast of that continent as far as Cape Freddo, being the farthest known place of the same continent toward the north . . . it must either flow around the north of America into the South Sea or it must needs strike over upon the coasts of Iceland, Norway and Finmark." His desire to prove the existence of the Northwest Passage prejudiced him in favor of the first alternative. Even so he was a careful enough observer to note that, in 50° N. latitude a current carried ice to the southward — the Labrador Current.

Frobisher discovered the northeasterly pull of the Norwegian Current and also saw clearly that there had to be some kind of return path for the currents, a kind of circulating ocean river; but his little knowledge led him to a false conclusion when he wrote: "Sayling toward the northwest parts of Ireland we mette with a great current from out of the southwest, which carried us (by our reckoning) one point toward the northeastward of our said course, which current seemed to us to continue itself toward Norway and other of the northeast parts of the world, whereby we may be induced to believe that this is the same which the Portuguese mette at Capo de Buong Speranza, where, stricking over from thence to the Straits of Magellan and finding no passage there for the narrowness of the sayde Straits, runneth alongue to the great Bay of Mexico, where also haveing a lot of land it is forced to strike back again toward the northeast, as we not only have but in another place also further northward by goode experience this year have found." Though he saw the logical necessity of linking currents into a continuous system, he was unaware that the main Atlantic stream runs southward when it approaches Europe and that the Norway current is only a small branch. And so he produced the fanciful theory of a current that rounded the north of Norway and thence by some unexplained route reached the eastern coast of Africa. By what strange paths it could have reached the Capo de Buong Speranza, or Cape of Good Hope, and so back into the Atlantic he does not say.

As new communities of the Ocean River began to appear in

the west, more and more pieces of the great mosaic of drift and current fell into place. John White, once governor of the colony of Roanoke, repeating Cabot's observation, wrote in 1590 of the satellite swirl which runs to the south and south-west between the Gulf Stream and the shore, and which—as we shall see in our next chapter — has been particularly puzzling to modern oceanographers. He discovered this countercurrent during a voyage from Florida to Virginia, when he found it necessary to stand well out to sea in order to stay within the Gulf Stream and avoid the contrary currents. Shortly afterward Lescarbot rediscovered the south-flowing Labrador Current. The Cabot brothers had noticed this icy stream a century earlier, but a strange result of its head-on collision with the Gulf Stream was not described until Lescarbot wrote in 1612: "I have found something remarkable upon which a natural philosopher should meditate . . . for the space of three days the water very warm, whilst the air was cold as before, but on the 21st of June quite suddenly we were surrounded by fogs and cold that we thought to be in the month of January and the sea was extremely cold." The sudden sharp boundary between the cold Labrador Current flowing to the southwest and the warm Gulf Stream flowing to the northeast is a most striking phenomenon to those who have witnessed it.

Most of the larger drifts and currents that make up the Atlantic swirl were now discovered; but they had not been linked together and no chart had yet been printed to show them. Even so, they were of increasing importance in determining the pattern of the colonization in North America during the early seventeenth century. The northern colonies — what is now New England — were reached by the northern route, for the experienced sailor, in order to avoid the main eastward flow of the River, sailed westward at a latitude of about 40°. The southern colonies, from North Carolina and Chesapeake Bay to the colony of New York, were approached by the southern route by way of the West Indies, to take full advantage of the equatorial drift and the trade winds. In this way the Ocean River continued to influence the practice of navigation to the extent of justifying a course to New York, which was nearly 1,800 miles south of the route taken to the northern colonies only 100 miles away.

Toward the end of the seventeenth century the growing spirit of scientific inquiry began to be felt, and a number of theoretical treatises on ocean currents began to appear. One of these, written by Isaac Vossius in 1663, is worth our mention if only because he showed the true circulatory nature of the Atlantic River and so drew together the separate and unorganized observations of the 150 years that had gone by since Ponce de Leon discovered the Florida Current and the 650 years since Leif Ericson sighted North America. He describes it with admirable simplicity:

"With the general equatorial current, the waters run toward Brazil, along Guyana, and enter the Gulf of Mexico. From there, turning obliquely, they pass rapidly through the Straits of Bahama. On the one side they bathe the coasts of Florida and Virginia and the entire shore of North America, and on the other side they run directly east until they reach the opposite shores of Europe and Africa; from thence they run again to the south and join the first movement to the west, perpetually turning in this manner circuitously."

About this time, too, Athanasius Kircher and Happelius published the first known charts of the Gulf Stream. They were not simple factual records of the known ocean currents, but included a number of greatly exaggerated and half-legendary features like the Maelstrom, the great whirlpool off the Lofoten Islands. Nor were they designed for the practical interests of navigators, but rather to illustrate the real or imaginary scientific questions of the day. But the time was not too distant when the Atlantic currents were to be mapped in careful fashion for the express use of shipmasters, with more attention to fact than to fable.

Most of the ships sailing coastwise along the Atlantic seaboard of North America at this time were delayed as much as three weeks because of their ignorance of the Gulf Stream limits and by not knowing of the countercurrent closer to the shore, and many vessels voyaging between England and New York were likewise set back in their westward course. But gradually the regular coastwise captains were pooling their experiences and evolving a practical system of pilotage. The tremendous expansion of the whaling industry about this time also brought into the western Atlantic a new kind of sailor whose voyages covered a wide area of the ocean and whose observations and experience added greatly to what was already known of the ocean currents. These whaling captains, who were in many ways the founders of the art of modern navigation, traveled in their search for whales from the Bahamas to the Arctic Sea and from the Carolinas to the Azores, and their sea lore quickly spread among the American transatlantic shipmasters. As a result the merchant captains were able to plan a sailing route from Europe that avoided the easterly stream as far as possible, and thus saved themselves in their westerly passage as much as two weeks of fighting wind and stream.

The reasons for selecting this westerly route were apparently unknown to the skippers of the English mail packets, who continued to use the more direct but much slower route. Complaints were made by the Boston Board of Customs to the Lords of the Treasury in London, and brought to the attention of Benjamin Franklin in 1769, at a time when he was Postmaster General for the colonies. He immediately made inquiries in order to discover the cause of the slowness of the mail packets, and discussed the problem with a Nantucket whaler captain named Timothy Folger, who like the majority of his fellows was well acquainted with the currents of the

Atlantic River. With Folger's advice he prepared a chart of the Gulf Stream. This was the first current chart of the North Atlantic designed to aid navigation rather than to support or confound scientific speculation. It is traditionally true that sailormen are conservative and slow to adopt new ideas, and when Franklin's chart was published in 1770 the Falmouth sea captains characteristically refused to use it. Franklin wrote:

"There happened then to be in London a Nantucket sea captain of my acquaintance, to whom I communicated the affair. He told me he believed the fact to be true, but the difference was owing to this, that the Rhode Island captains were acquainted with the Gulf Stream, while those of the English packets were not. We are well acquainted with that stream, because in our pursuit of whales, which keep near the sides of it but are not met within it, we run along the side and frequently cross it to change our side; and in crossing it have sometimes met and spoke with those packets who were in the middle of it and stemming it. We have informed them that they were stemming a current that was against them to the value of 3 miles an hour and advised them to cross it, but they were too wise to be councelled by simple American fishermen. When the winds are light," he added, "they are carried back by the current more than they are forwarded by the wind, and if the wind be good the subtraction of 70 miles a day from their course is of some importance."

Benjamin Franklin marked a turning point in the mapping of salt waters, the plotting of the Ocean River, when he published his chart for the General Post Office. Before this, knowledge of the ocean had grown by the spoken word and by the slow piecing together of scattered information from many sources. But a new impetus was beginning to be felt; and as time went on science was to go about the inquiry in its own logical and methodical way, and to seek not only facts but causes and effects. Yet before we look at the north Atlantic Ocean through the eyes of scientific inquiry we can better understand the reasons for this impetus if we turn for a moment to the growing art of navigation. In coming of age, this art took on a greater accuracy and helped to speed up the ocean map-making and to usher in the infant science of oceanography.

Even today most of the charted facts about the Ocean River are compiled from entries in ships' logs that show how far vessels are carried from their courses by the force of water currents. When the shipmaster knows the direction of his course and the speed of his ship he is able to calculate the apparent position at sea at any time, assuming that no currents are acting. This is his "dead reckoning." If he now finds that his true position is not the same as the dead reckoning, then the difference must be due to the flow of current. Thus, to be able to chart ocean currents we must first be able to measure the speed of a ship and then to find with accuracy its true position.

When Columbus sailed beyond known soundings the crudest kind of dead reckoning prevailed, and men set their course "by guess and by God." The first rude beginnings of measuring speed at sea were by watching by sandglass the speed of a chip of wood released at the bow of a vessel as it drifted astern. After this beginning, a line was attached to a small log of wood and knots along this line were counted, as it paid-out, in relation to a set time. Thus the word "knot" has survived to the present time as a maritime unit of speed, though this kind of measure has long since been superseded by modern instruments.

There were other means of detecting and measuring the pulse of the ocean currents that early explorers could well have used. During his first voyage Columbus, by accident rather than design, made use of a simple but effective way of meas-

uring the surface stream. On September 19, 1492, while becalmed in the southwesterly current, he sounded with the
deep sea lead line. It is not surprising that he recorded no
bottom at 200 fathoms, since on modern charts the sounding
nearest his probable position is 2,290 fathoms, or over 12,000
feet deeper than the length of his line. Nevertheless, at 200
fathoms the water in this locality is relatively motionless. As a
result the weighted end of the line entering the still water
below was held back by friction drag while the ship itself,
being becalmed, drifted with the surface current. Consequently the lead line was pulled a considerable distance from
the vertical. If Columbus had had sufficient knowledge of
physics he could have calculated from this the actual rate of
flow at the surface in relation to the deeper levels. All he actually did was to note the presence of a current carrying him
southwest.

Two important instruments, the modern sextant and the
chronometer, came into use in the latter part of the eighteenth
century and provided navigators and the oceanographers who
came later with tools of greater accuracy for their difficult task
of measuring the Atlantic current. The ship's chronometer,
which became generally available about 1785, was invented by
John Harrison and later developed by Thomas Earnshaw. It
came into use during Franklin's day, and undoubtedly provided a great stimulus to the accurate plotting of ocean currents. Before this it had been impossible to determine the
longitude accurately when out of sight of land, because this
depends on a very accurate measurement of time as well as on
knowing the astronomical position of heavenly bodies.

At the midspring or midfall equinoctials, when the sun is
directly over the equator, the latitude is easily measured from
the sun's noontime altitude or angular height above the horizon, by subtracting this from 90°. At other times of the year,
provided the declination of the sun or its distance from the

equator is known, its noontime altitude may be corrected by this amount in order to determine the latitude. Similar measurements of latitude are made from the moon's altitude. If the polestar is used it is even simpler. The altitude of the polestar, which lies almost on the axis of the earth, is almost equal to the latitude. But the polestar, not exactly on the axis, revolves round the pole; hence certain corrections must be made, and these depend on its place in the circle of revolution. At present the greatest error arising from this is about 1°. At the time of Columbus, however, the polestar was about 3½° away from the true pole.

The movements of the polestar were well known to the ancients during the first century B.C., and they had various methods of making the polestar correction. One of these was to refer to the tables of the astronomers — but these were not always available. Another method, developed later, was the use of a simple hand calculator called the nocturnal. Sailors in Columbus's day also had a simple rule for finding the polestar correction from the position of the other stars in the Little Dipper. Two of these stars, Kochab and Gamma, known as the Guards, are referred to in the *Regimento de estrolabio e do quadrante*, published in 1509.[1] The figure of a little man was marked on the nocturnal, and when held at the proper angle his head pointed above the North Star, his arms were east and west of it, and his feet beneath it. The position of the Guards could then be used for finding the true position of the pole. And here is the *Regimento* as it was used:

This is the Regiment of the North Star

When the Guards are on the West Arm the North Star stands above the Pole one degree and a half.

[1] S. E. Morison: "Columbus and Polaris," *American Neptune*, Vol I, 1941.

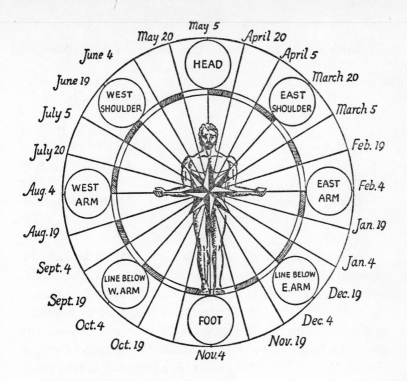

Diagram for telling time from Polaris, 1942.

When the Guards are on the line under the West the North Star is above the Pole three degrees and a half.

When the Guards are at the Foot, the Star is three degrees above the Pole.

When the Guards are on the Line below the East Arm the Star is above the Pole half a degree.

And when you take the altitude of the Star, and the Guards are in some one of these four positions where the Star is above the Pole, from the altitude that you take of the Star, you should know, you subtract as many degrees as the Star is above; and the degrees which remain are as many as you are removed from the equator.

*These are the Four Positions in which the North Star
is below the Pole*

When the Guards are on the East Arm, the Star is below the Pole one degree and a half.

When the Guards are on the Line above the East Arm the Star is three degrees and a half below the Pole.

When the Guards are at the Head, the Star is below the Pole three degrees.

When the Guards are on the Line over the West Arm the Star is below the Pole half a degree.

The measurement of north-south position or latitude by meridian altitude of the sun, moon, or stars is fairly simple, because they apparently move only very slowly in a north and south direction. The measurement of longitude or east-west position is far more difficult, since at the equator the heavens appear to travel at the rate of about 15 nautical miles per minute. Fortunately astronomers have from the earliest times been aware of this, and even in the days of Hipparchus and Ptolemy a great deal was known about the time at which heavenly bodies appeared overhead and the rate at which they moved. Thus the problem of determining longitude really resolved itself into a problem of knowing the exact time taken for the sun or star to reach the longitude of the observer after passing a fixed point. For some time longitude was defined as the distance east or west of Paris, but after some argument on both sides the longitude of Greenwich, England, was generally accepted as the prime meridian, and today longitude is calculated by the time the sun takes to travel from Greenwich to the meridian of the observer.

The first sound proposal for measuring longitude was that of Galileo, who in 1616 suggested that since Jupiter's satellites moved around it with great regularity they formed, as it were, a universal time standard. Thus the time of passage of the sun or star at any place could be compared with the time of meridian passage at Greenwich, by reference to the position of Jupiter's satellites. Unfortunately for Galileo's suggestion, though this observation is perfectly feasible on shore with a firm and level basis for astronomical instruments, it is not a practical possibility aboard a ship at sea. The problem therefore became quite simply that of carrying aboard ship a reliable clock.

The clock used for timing the stars, sun, and planets could not be an ordinary clock. The earth revolves once every twenty-four hours, and the circumference is about 21,600 nautical miles, so that at the equator a mistake of one minute would equal an error of as much as 15 miles. As far as land clocks were concerned the problem was solved by Galileo when he discovered the simple truth that a pendulum of a given length always takes the same time to complete its swing. Using this principle, Christian Huyghens in 1656 constructed the first reasonably accurate clock. But the pendulum principle, like most simple truths, is a good deal more complicated than it first appeared; and it was soon discovered that the time of swing, and therefore the speed of the clock, was different at different parts of the earth and in different temperatures. Moreover, the rolling and pitching of a ship interferes with the movement of a pendulum, so that such a clock is unsuitable as a marine chronometer. For all this, in 1681 the pendulum clock was used along with observations of the sun and Jupiter's planets to make the first longitude determination in the western Atlantic at Martinique and Guadeloupe in the West Indies. It took three years to complete this observation! The method was obviously unsuitable for shipboard use.

The matter was brought to a head at the beginning of the eighteenth century when an admiral and his fleet were lost on account of a gross error in navigation. Sir Cloudesley Shovel, returning from Gibraltar to England, ran ashore on the rocky Scilly Isles, at a time when his navigators thought they were at least a hundred miles farther east. The wreck resulted in the loss of four ships and over 2,000 seamen besides the admiral. Such losses as this, which could have been prevented if a method had been available for measuring longitude at sea, finally persuaded Parliament in 1714 to pass a bill offering £20,000 for an instrument which would be accurate to within two minutes of time, which is equal to about 30 miles at the equator.

Many fantastic solutions were proposed. One, mentioned in Lloyd A. Brown's *The Story of Maps*, is typical. It involved the use of a popular remedy prepared by Sir Kenelm Digby known as the "powder of sympathy." The original purpose of this nostrum was to cure wounds by the imaginative method of applying it not to the wound but to the weapon which had inflicted it. The physician also declared that by merely placing a dressing from a patient's wound in contact with the powder he could cause the patient to jump. The would-be inventor of a longitude method suggested in all seriousness that every ship before sailing be provided with a wounded dog. On shore a trustworthy collaborator, equipped with a good clock and a bandage from the dog's wound, would each hour, exactly on the second, dip the bandage in the powder of sympathy. The dog aboard ship would thereupon mark the exact time with a yelp and so solve the marine clock problem!

John Harrison, without a dog, eventually produced in 1736 the first marine chronometer. It was far from pretty and weighed seventy-two pounds, but it did keep good time at sea. After more than thirty years his fifth clock justified his long labors, for it had the surprisingly small error of less than five seconds in ten weeks. Bureaucracy was the same then as it is now — the prize was awarded to him only after considerable haggling on the part of the Board of Longitude.

The development of chronometers and of more accurate instruments for measuring altitude, like the modern sextant, greatly aided navigators in determining exact positions, and thus helped in the accurate plotting of the direction and strength of currents. With their aid the charting of the Ocean River became more of a science and less an affair of general observation, imagination, and intuition. And so since the time of Franklin the rest of our story is that of the steady growth of ocean science, and the discovery of not merely where, but also why and how fast these salt rivers move in the salt ocean.

7

NATURE OF THE STREAM

I T IS evident from the legends of seafarers long before the time of Christ that men sensed a movement and often a direction in the vast unknown of oceanic waters. We read how men feared the Maelstrom at the edge of the north and the hot coagulated waters south of the Gates of Hercules. In the previous chapter we traced how various currents gradually became known, and saw historical reporting pick up speed with the accumulation of transatlantic discovery, until by the eighteenth century the general idea of the Ocean River as a systematic sweep of water was accepted as a fact. But it was not till after the time of Franklin that any serious study of the nature of the Stream and of the forces driving it was projected.

As the currents became better known, several remarkable theories were put forward to explain the forces behind the Ocean River. A few of these anticipated by guess and intuition some of our modern findings and theories — but not because of any co-ordinated knowledge or disciplined reasoning. Columbus himself, who knew only of the southern portion of the immense Atlantic gyre, was comparatively restrained. He merely suggested that the westerly course of the equatorial waters was due to the *primum mobile,* a bond between the ocean water and the heavenly bodies. It was a contemporary notion that the stars and the air revolved to the westward

about the globe, and Columbus believed that in some mysterious manner the waters were drawn along with them.

Though the speculations of the more thoughtful men of
Columbus' time took into account the westerly movement of
equatorial waters into the Caribbean and their subsequent
passage through the Straits of Florida, yet more than sixty
years later a suggestion was considered which ignored them
completely. Thevet in his *La Cosmographie Universelle* in
1575 put forward a suggestion that the waters entering the
Gulf Stream at the Straits of Florida came from the Mississippi and other rivers emptying into the Gulf of Mexico. This
was an attractive theory because men could see and were
impressed by the majestic flood of the Mississippi; but they
failed to realize that this continuing inflow of water, were it
large enough to be the source of the Gulf Stream, would have
to be accounted for in the ocean. Later, as we know, it was
found that the river volume amounted to a mere one-thou-
sandth part of the flood of the Gulf Stream, and was clearly
insufficient to account for the flow of its current. Moreover, it
left unaccounted for the great flood of equatorial water into
the Caribbean.

To illustrate how long-lived were the myth-making habits of
thought of the Dark Ages, here is a quotation from Merula, a
contemporary of Thevet: "The water flows together near the
Pole, but at the Pole itself is a great Black Rock, 33 leagues in
circumference. Ships which once enter one of these channels
never return, not even with the most favorable winds, and next
to the Black Rock all the water is engulfed into the bowels of
the earth, whence it flows through springs and river sources
once again into the light of day." Yet the same idea in a different guise had been rejected over half a century earlier by
Peter Martyr, who wrote: ". . . which waters I suppose to be
driven about the globe by the incessant moving and impulsion
of the heavens, and not to be swallowed up and cast out again

by the breathing of Demo-gorgon as some have imagined, because they see the seas increase and decrease, flowe and reflowe."

Fortunately, with the slow advance of physical science, it was inevitable that speculation should become more closely confined by the ascertainable facts. Even so, such an unquestionably able scientist as Kepler was handicapped by the limitations of contemporary scientific theory. He saw the equatorial waters being left behind in the west by the eastward rotation of the earth just as a passenger in a rapidly accelerating railroad train finds himself impelled to the rear of the car. Varenius summarized this view when in 1650 he wrote: ". . . the movement of our globe contributes not a little toward it, because the water, not being adherent to the earth, but only in a loose contact with it, cannot follow the quickness of its motion toward the east, but is left behind toward the west, so that the sea does not move from one part to the other, but on the contrary it is the earth which quits or leaves the parts of the sea, one after the other." It did not occur to Kepler and Varenius that even if the earth's movement did generate the westward drift of equatorial waters in this manner it would not fit in with the eastward currents across the northern part of the ocean.

The similarity in westward movement of the Equatorial Current, of the trade winds, and of the apparent movement of the stars, which was so obvious and significant to Columbus and his contemporaries, continued to impress itself on the scientific mind, and a number of conflicting theories were offered to account for it. Isaac Vossius wrote an entire volume, entitled *De Motu Marium et Ventorum*, on the relation of wind and sea. The sun draws the morning mist into rising vapor, and in like manner he believed that its greater tropical heat attracts the equatorial ocean toward it in a long mountain of water whose flanks are steep enough to impede vessels attempting to sail against it. He conceived that as the sun moved westward this great ocean bulge was dragged along beneath it until the obstacle of the South American shores diverted the water coastwise. The sun, of course, does exert a small gravitational force that aids in the periodic swell and movement of the tides; but this is far from being a satisfactory explanation of the continuous current system.

In contrast to this, another theory involved watery valleys instead of mountains, but it too was based on the supposed direct effect of the sun. The French hydrographer Fournier, who started with the perfectly sound principle that the sun evaporates water from the tropical seas, was led into speculations that had little further relation to fact. According to him, the loss of water by evaporation in the tropics is sufficient to leave a prodigious hollow in the sea into which the water is irresistibly drawn. This maritime valley moves from east to west with the sun, the currents naturally follow, and in this simple — and to him completely satisfactory — fashion the North Atlantic circulation is kept in motion.

Thus far, most speculations were focused on a supposed attraction between sun and water. To some this attraction was a complete mystery, while to others it was due to evaporation or to the rotation of the earth; but gradually these explanations were supplanted by others with a little more basis of scientific truth. Athanasius Kircher, who published the first crude chart of the Atlantic River, was among the earliest to realize the importance of the trade winds in causing the Equatorial Current: "This motion touches many things, whether partly from the general motion of the trade winds against the opposing shores of that region and thence again reflected, which they call the Sailor's Current, or from wind storms. . . ." So far he was close enough to modern scientific beliefs, but he fell into error when he advanced a further suggestion that the attraction of the moon produced not merely tides but also continuous currents; and he abandoned science for fantasy when he resurrected the ancient idea that abysses in the sea floor were the ultimate destination of the ocean stream.

During the eighteenth century the communication of observations and ideas began to speed up; hence, most of the later theories had a much greater basis of fact than those of the seventeenth century, and the true nature of wind action became more clearly recognized. Franklin, for instance, was certain that the trade winds were responsible for the Gulf Stream by blowing water westward across the equator and heaping it up against the American continent until it was forced to flow between the islands into the Caribbean and the Gulf of Mexico.

The forces that keep the Ocean River in its great circular path emerged from the world of fantasy with the aid of two separate but interacting factors. There was a gradual appearance of new and improved ways of measuring the flow of water, and at the same time a development of the modern physical sciences that in its turn made possible newer, indirect ways of studying ocean currents. One of the first of the new scientific tools to be applied to the Gulf Stream was the thermometer, and its first user, Benjamin Franklin. Franklin's contributions to ocean science did not rest with making charts and with his belief in a simple wind theory of ocean circulation, but he pioneered in what is still an important field of oceanography when he used a thermometer to locate the Gulf Stream by means of its characteristic warmth. With typical ingenuity he also adapted a wooden barrel by fitting it with valves in order to collect water samples at depths of 100 feet beneath the surface. In this way he was able to show that the deeper waters are colder than those above.

The thermometer was used in navigation for finding the limits of the warm currents — though, as we shall see, even here it may lead to errors. Among those who used it to trace the Gulf Stream in its varying courses during the next twenty-five years were Franklin's nephew, Colonel Jonathan Williams, and Colonel William Strickland, whose temperature observations gave the first certain evidence of the northeastern branch that brings beneficial climate to Norway. They also discovered mysterious and alien water within the Stream itself. During a cruise of the packet *Eliza* from Halifax to England in 1810, pools of cool water were found in the middle of the warm current, as much as 15° colder than the surrounding sea and as much as 200 miles wide. It was suggested at the time that icebergs had drifted into the main current and had melted while trapped within the warmer water. As we shall see later, the true significance of these cold patches has been explained only during the past few years.

The general eighteenth-century concept of the Gulf Stream was that of a fixed and permanent current, but this was seriously disturbed by the observations of Captain John Hamilton. From his air and water temperatures and current records, taken during a series of twenty-six voyages between Europe and the United States, he concluded in 1825 that the River, continually shifting its position, is so unsteady that definite limits cannot be assigned to it. At the same time more evidence was obtained of its northwesterly and southwesterly branches. Somewhat similar conclusions were reached by the celebrated German scientist von Humboldt, and also by Colonel E. Sabine, who were convinced — though without proof — that the Gulf Stream is affected by changes in the strength of the trade winds.

So far, the increasingly clear conception of a great Atlantic system of currents had grown out of numerous independent and scattered observations rather than from a systematic investigation. The close of this period of relatively random observation was marked by two extensive compilations. The first was based on a considerable amount of material collected by the British Admiralty office during the first part of the nineteenth century and carefully summarized by Major James Rennell, whose book and charts, published posthumously in 1832, included courses of currents, wind directions, soundings, and water temperatures. Rennell concluded that the breadth of the Gulf Stream varies more than twofold within a period of little more than two months, and that the variations are independent of seasons. He also found that the south side of the Stream is more unsteady than the north side, and that warm water may be present in the eddies as well as in the main current — thus it became known that temperature is not always a true indicator of its boundary. He also confirmed the presence of cold water masses within the body of warm water, but the true nature of this strange phenomenon was still unsuspected.

The second compilation was made by Lieutenant Matthew Fontaine Maury of the U. S. Navy. While superintendent of the U. S. Naval Observatory he took advantage of an unusual opportunity for studying ocean currents, and in carrying out the tedious work of digesting a great amount of data he laid the foundations for the modern system of ocean charts. He began by collecting all the log books of vessels between 1840 and 1850. The summaries were then published in the form of wind and current charts and as sailing directions of the greatest practical and commercial value. The scope of his contribution to navigation and oceanography became international when he called a maritime conference at Brussels in 1853 in order to devise a uniform system of observations at sea. As a result, the co-operation of a large number of nations was insured, and data were collected from which more elaborate and detailed information could be prepared. Much of the summarized results and the theories he deduced were included in his *Physical Geography of the Sea,* one of the first important hydrographic books to be published. With this as a stimulus and a starting point, the navigators, oceanographers, and meteorologists who studied the Ocean River were now interested not merely in its general features but in its detailed structure and its fluctuations in speed and position.

Benjamin Franklin was responsible for one of the first summaries of navigational knowledge to be published as a chart of the Gulf Stream, and his grandson, Professor Alexander Dallas Bache, was the first to carry out its systematic exploration. When Professor Bache became director of the U. S. Coast and Geodetic Survey he immediately drew up a detailed plan to plot the position of the current and its boundaries, to find out how permanent they are, and also to discover to what depths the current penetrates and how the water temperature changes at various depths.

The brig *Washington* was commissioned in 1845 for this work, but tragedy soon interrupted the investigations. The vessel was small, and during the second year of operation the commander and ten of the crew were lost overboard in a storm off the North Carolina coast. In spite of the great difficulties of the venture, a very large number of observations were made aboard this and other vessels. At the western edge of the Stream a considerable drop of temperature was noticed, called the "cold wall."

Bache's investigations continued for six years. The only method of measuring the currents was by observing the ship's drift, and the methods used for measuring depth were not satisfactory in deep water; but he succeeded in obtaining a great number of observations of temperature. From these he concluded that between Florida and New York the Gulf Stream is not a uniformly simple flow but is divided into alternating hot and cold bands of water, corresponding to the cold-water pools encountered by the packet *Eliza* and later confirmed by Rennell. Bache believed that the cold bands were caused by mountain ranges on the ocean floor, which forced the waters to split apart into separate streams. Later, as instruments improved and more careful soundings were made, these mountains were found to be nonexistent, and today we know that the separate streams or veins are really eddies of the main current.

A simple but very effective aid to the slow and tedious process of investigation was the use of floating indicators and instruments for the direct measurement of currents. In its simplest form this is nothing more than the timing and observation of drifting objects. The floating sea beans which stirred adventurous instincts along the eastern shores of the Great River in the early days of Atlantic exploration were the chance forerunners of a vast quantity of floats of various types that have since been thrown into the sea in the study of ocean currents. The first deliberate use of this kind of measurement was made in 1802, when special bottles with the time and place of release recorded in them were thrown overboard from the English ship *Rainbow*.

The Prince of Monaco eighty years later became not only a patron but an active devotee of the new science of oceanography, and concentrated on a study of the eastern part of the Gulf Stream. He had made large numbers of hollow copper spheres, of which more than 900 were released between the Azores and Newfoundland, over 500 in the ocean off the coast of France, and 139 northwest of the Azores. Their movements provided indisputable proof of branching currents that reached from the western Atlantic to Ireland and Norway on the one hand and to France and Africa on the other. Two of the floats released off the coast of France drifted as far as the West Indies.

A few years later, Professor Mitchell of the Coast and Geodetic Survey invented a system of deep weights and surface floats joined by wires, with which he found that in the Straits of Havana the current flows at full strength even at 400 fathoms. The work of many scientists, both from direct observation and from deduction, was later to show that not only the main Stream runs deep, but that in many places enormous volumes of water move in slow drifts far below the surface, in directions quite different from those of the faster surface currents.

The most extensive single investigation of the Gulf Stream ever to be carried out was begun in 1885 by John Elliot Pillsbury, who anchored his vessel, the *Blake*, in various parts of the Florida Straits. This in itself was a decided achievement considering his limited equipment. Using special instruments devised by himself, he spent two years measuring the currents between Cat Cay and Miami, and actually stayed at anchor in the middle of the Straits for a total of over 1,000 hours. The instruments lowered into the water at each anchorage were based on the simple device of rotating cups driven by the current as an anemometer, or wind meter, operates, with a system of gears attached to a revolution counter to indicate the rate of flow. But anchoring in deep water puts a great strain on the anchor cable and on the equipment. Moreover, the swinging of the vessel about its anchor introduces such difficulties in measuring currents that the method is not widely used in the open sea, though it has considerable value and is very convenient in shallow water.

Pillsbury also measured the current off Cape Hatteras, at a number of places in the Windward Islands passages, between Cuba and Yucatan, and between Cuba and Key West. The results were an unprecedented amount of entirely new data, which added proof that part of the Equatorial Current sidetracks the Caribbean Sea and flows northward outside the

West Indies and Bahamas Islands. The Antilles Current, as it
it called, rejoins the Florida Current north of the Bahamas.

Pillsbury's painstaking study of the fluctuating pulse of the
River was specially useful to merchant vessels plowing their
way against the Stream; and if it were more generally known it
would probably save amateur yachtsmen considerable time in
their races to Havana, Nassau, and Bimini. It was found, for
instance, that the fastest part of the Stream is nearer to Havana than to Key West, but by the time it arrives at Miami it
has shifted to the westward side. It is about 11 miles east of
Fowey Rocks Light, near Miami, or less than one-third of the
way across.

That the speed of the River was continually changing had
been known in a vague manner for a long time. Even the experienced navigator frequently found his vessel set by a greater
current than he expected; but at other times he might find
virtually no drift in a place where he usually made allowance
for several knots. The careful measurements made from the
Blake showed that these changes were not due to any tempera-
mental vagaries of the River but that they seemed to follow a
distinct pattern, which depended on the position of the moon.
The current reaches its maximum about three hours after the
moon's transit, or highest point in the heavens, and thus a
slight increase of up to 1½ knots in flow at the Stream's axis
comes at Florida ports about two hours after mean low water.
Changes also take place during the lunar month. Just after low
declination, when the moon is nearly over the equator, the
current near Miami has a tendency to flow faster in a nar-
rowed stream and in a more easterly direction, whereas at high
declination, when the moon is most distant from the equator,
the current is broader and runs more closely parallel to the
axis.

Using these observations, Pillsbury gives the following advice as to the quickest way in which a vessel may steam south against the current with the least delay: "A steamer bound from Cape Hatteras to Havana or the Gulf ports crosses the Stream off Cape Hatteras. A fair allowance to make in crossing the Stream at right angles is 1½ knots per hour [sic] for a vessel's speed of 5 knots for a distance of 40 miles from the 100-fathom curve. In the run from the southern edge of the Stream to Matanilla Shoal, no allowance for current can be given. Upon sighting the Bahama Bank, time will be saved by running down the Stream on the east side as far as Gun Cay instead of crossing at Jupiter and running the latitude down on the Florida side of the channel. The current is weak on the Bahama side, and on the shoals there is practically none. This route will be difficult and perhaps impracticable until a lighthouse is built at Matanilla, unless the green water of the northwest corner is sighted before dark. Arriving at Gun Cay, Bahama, an allowance of 2½ knots per hour for speed of the vessel of 5 knots per hour will make a course of west good to Fowey Rocks. This is the average velocity of the Stream. The weakest current will be experienced about three hours before the transit of the Moon, and if the crossing is made so as to arrive at the axis at about this hour, time will be saved." Pillsbury advises the navigator of a vessel steaming north to take advantage of the periodic shift in the River's axis: "At high declination he can edge out so as to pass Fowey Rocks lighthouse 7 miles distant, and be sure of a good current, while, at low declination the maximum velocity at this distance will be found much less, and it will be necessary to go 4 or 5 miles farther to the eastward."

The *Blake* investigations have deservedly been called a classic in oceanographic current studies. No similar large-scale survey has been made until recent years, but the work of collecting and summarizing data from the observations of numerous vessels, which was begun by Maury in the middle of the nineteenth century, has continued, and the U. S. Navy Hydrographic Office, which carries out the huge task of co-ordinating all such information, has been able to prepare special charts that give the average currents for each month of the year. These are provided for every one-degree square of latitude and longitude, covering 60 miles in each direction. These modern charts and their remarkably few blank squares are in strong contrast to the scanty and generalized information on charts of less than 100 years ago.

While Pillsbury worked from the American side, several scientific expeditions were made from Europe. Most of them were not organized primarily for current measurement, but they have all contributed more or less to the charting of currents. There were the cruises of the *Lightning* and the *Porcupine*, and later the celebrated cruise of H.M.S. *Challenger* covering 69,000 miles in the Atlantic, Pacific, and Antarctic Oceans between 1872 and 1876, under the leadership of Wyville Thompson. Though he was not principally interested in ocean currents, Thompson succeeded — as a later chapter will show — in laying the foundations for the study of the depths of the ocean floor and of the living creatures of the deep sea. The *Challenger* was followed by the *Michael Sars* in 1910, the *Deutschland*, the Danish *Dana* in 1921, and the British *Discovery* and *Discovery II* between 1925 and 1939. In addition to these were the French vessels *Travailleur* and *Talisman* toward the end of the nineteenth century, and the Danish ship *Ingolf* — to mention only some of the more important.

Our story has shown that the slow piecing together of the experiences of many men was at first hindered by the poor communication of ideas and always handicapped by the technical difficulties of making direct measurements of such large-scale happenings as currents flowing through the restless sea.

Side by side with the steady compiling of data for charts went the growth of physical theory. The logical though partial explanation offered by Benjamin Franklin will serve as a starting point from which to trace its development into the concepts of present-day science.

Franklin's wind-current theory was both supported and extended by Rennell. In his *An Investigation of the Subject of the Currents of the Atlantic Ocean* he distinguished clearly between drift currents produced by the force of winds acting directly on waves, and stream currents which flow as a result of a difference in water level. According to Rennell, the trade winds are responsible for the equatorial currents, which in turn heap water in the Caribbean Sea and the Gulf of Mexico above the general ocean level. The increased height of this water causes a stream current to flow, and this is the Gulf Stream. Since this theory requires the level of these seas to be higher than the general sea level, it became discredited when Arago insisted that they are actually lower. In Poggendorf's *Annalen der Physik und Chemie*, published in 1836, he pointed out that surveying parties between Chagres and Panama on the opposite sides of the Isthmus of Panama had found the sea level of the Atlantic Ocean to be from three to five feet lower than the Pacific. Later these measurements were proved incorrect, but for some time to come this was a serious setback for the wind-current theory.

Arago, with a rival hypothesis, started a battle of opinion that raged throughout the nineteenth century. He thought that the heating of tropical sea water causes it to flow outward from the equator toward the cooler regions round the poles, just as the unequal heating of the air causes the great wind systems of the earth. He also brought in the effect of the earth's rotation to explain why the currents do not run simply from south to north: ". . . the rotation of the earth ought principally to be taken into view, and that this, together with the cooling and warming of the water in the north and south, is the main cause of their more rapid or slower deviation and progress toward the east or west . . . we ought to apply to the ocean the same theory which has already afforded a satisfactory explanation to the trade winds if we will decipher the question of currents."

Maury added his opposition to the wind theory on the grounds that a current caused by winds would cease as soon as the wind dropped, so that permanent continuous currents would be impossible. In opposition to Arago he firmly believed that the different density of sea water in different parts of the ocean, caused partly by unequal heating, is sufficient to account for currents. Perhaps the most striking of Maury's ideas was that the center of the Stream rises to a higher level than the sides. If this were so a surface flow of water would continually run off toward the edges, which is an obvious impossibility.

As the nineteenth century drew toward its end the controversy continued, some arguing for wind causes and some for density causes. Even the scientists of the *Challenger* expedition were divided — Wyville Thompson and W. B. Carpenter held firmly opposed views on the problem. One opponent of the wind-current theory, Zoeppritz, proved to his own satisfaction that wind forces would require hundreds of thousands of years to whip the ocean into continuous deep currents. He was not entirely without reason. If water flowed with perfect regularity and smoothness the wind would disturb only the immediate surface, and this purely superficial motion would with difficulty be imparted to the layers below. But five years later Osborne Reynolds used dyes to cause colored streaks in water, and with this simple device made the apparently unrelated discovery that water in pipes flows as a series of distinct layers and not as a smooth undivided whole. As one layer of water moves over the other an irregular eddy action takes place between them, and in this way motion from one layer is quickly transferred to the next layer and so on. This independent study brought new support to the wind-driven theory of ocean circulation, by showing that the ocean when driven by winds at the surface does not require thousands of years to build up a deep current, but a very much shorter time. The eddies acting on each other engage like invisible gears in mesh — a kind of fluid drive.

Meanwhile another concept of the physicists had for over a century grown independently of oceanography before scientists saw its application to the mysteries of ocean currents: this was the effect of the earth's spin. From the very beginning curiosity about the causes of the Ocean River had led men to a dim realization that the earth's rotation played some part in their movement; but the early ideas of Kepler and others entirely neglected one of the most important effects — the Coriolis force. This was explained mathematically by Laplace as early as 1775, but it was not applied to the ocean until toward the end of the nineteenth century. At first the growing interest in wind and weather inspired men to study the effects of the Coriolis force on the wind systems, and its true relation to water currents was made clear only as late as 1903 by the pioneer oceanographers Sandström and Helland-Hansen.

What is this mysterious Coriolis force that pulls wind and water into a clockwise spin in the northern hemisphere and contrariwise south of the equator? The answer is that in the ordinary sense there is no force. There is simply a tendency for moving objects to continue in the same straight line, combined with the fact that straight-line movements on the earth's surface go in circles. To understand this paradox it is only necessary to spin a cardboard disc slowly on a phonograph turntable, and then, paying no attention to the fact that the disc is turning, draw a pencil across it in a straight line from one side to the other — in any direction. After the disc has stopped it will be seen that the pencil mark is actually a left-handed curve. But the northern hemisphere of the earth moves in the opposite way from the phonograph disc; therefore what would be a straight line to an observer fixed in space is to us a right-handed curve.

The Coriolis effect was noted in a general way by Humboldt in 1814 when he wrote: "Considering the velocity of the fluid elements which, in different latitudes, in consequence of the earth's rotation, is different, one should be tempted to think that every current from south to north ought to have at the same time a tendency to the east, and, *vice versa*, a current from north to south a tendency to the west." One important consequence became obvious toward the end of the nineteenth century when certain mathematical relationships were worked out among water density, current, and Coriolis force. In spite of the mathematics involved this relationship is simple, and it is the basis of a valuable indirect method of measuring currents that has been widely used during the past quarter century.

Whenever a stream flows in the ocean, the Coriolis effect is balanced by a remarkable adjustment of the water layers. Lighter water tends to accumulate on the right-hand side of the stream and heavier water on the left, while the ocean surface actually slopes upward across the stream toward the right. Put into more familiar words, this means that the sea level rises across the Florida Current and that the water level at Cat Cay, in the Bahamas, is nearly two feet higher than at Miami. Moreover, the amount of uphill that a vessel meets in an eastward crossing of these Straits is a measure of the speed of flow of the Stream; and this can be calculated from the important theorem of Vilhelm Bjerknes. The geostrophic relation, as it is called, was a wonderful new tool for oceanographers, but there are practical problems to be overcome in using it.

One cannot sight across an ocean in order to measure the slope of the water, but an ingenious Dane, N. E. Nørlund, solved this problem recently by laying pipes across the Great Belt between the Danish islands of Zealand and Fyn, a distance of about twelve miles, and across the Sound between Denmark and Sweden, a distance of three miles. Water in the pipe comes to the same level at each end, except for temperature and other effects which may be compensated for, and thus a basis of comparison is provided for sea level measurements.

The Danish pipe arrangement, while perfectly feasible over a short distance in fairly shallow water, is beset with formidable difficulties in longer distances and deeper waters. For this reason the direct measurement of sea level has not hitherto been widely applied in the calculation of ocean currents, and the Atlantic oceanographers have used a less direct but more practical application. The displacement of lighter and heavier water layers across the width of the ocean currents, related to the water slope, can be found by lowering thermometers and steel sample bottles to different depths at a series of stations across the current. The density or heaviness of water depends both on its temperature and its salinity, both of which are measured by the deep-sea instruments, and therefore the modern oceanographer uses them indirectly to measure current.

The accuracy of this method was dramatically shown by Wuest in 1924. From temperature and salinity measurements between Miami and the Bahamas made on the *Blake* in 1878 and the *Bache* in 1914, he calculated that a current of over three knots flows at the center of the Stream and that at some places a current extends almost to the bottom. What was of greater interest was that the calculated currents were almost exactly identical with those definitely measured by Pillsbury during his long periods at anchor in the Florida Straits between 1885 and 1889.

The slow but steady growth of information and understanding which sprang from the birth of oceanography along the Ocean River's shores has encompassed not only the surface streams but also another movement, more massive though less obvious, deep down below the surface of the open ocean. We have mentioned in a previous chapter that in every second of time the south equatorial drift carries six million tons of water across the equator into the North Atlantic. There is no appreciable return of surface water to the South Atlantic; hence there would be a continuous piling up of water north of the equator and a continuous loss of water from the southern ocean unless some other path existed for a compensating southward movement. It is now known that deep below the surface such a movement of water does take place. Deep unseen flows of heavy, ice-cold water are fortunately fairly easy to trace, because it has been found that large masses of water differ from each other in their relative degrees of temperature and saltness. Thus, even when it is difficult to measure the rate of flow, oceanographers can still identify the sources of the deep waters by sending down their sample bottles on thin wire cables.

The sample bottles are made of steel tubing, open at both ends, so that on their way down water may pass freely through them. When they reach the required depth a messenger weight, slid down the cable, trips a release catch on the bottle, which then traps a sample of the water. At the same time an extremely accurate thermometer, attached to the bottle, is reversed in such a way that the thread of mercury is interrupted and the temperature of the deep water may still be read when the bottle returns to the surface. In order to save time, ten or more bottles with their thermometers may be attached to the same cable. When returned to the surface the water samples are analyzed to determine their saltness. Though simple in plan this kind of sampling has its difficulties — as for instance, when the steel bottle is by mischance sent down to deep water closed instead of open. This invariably results in the metal being crushed flat by the tremendous pressure, which may in the deepest waters exert a force of over 1,000 tons on an eighteen-inch bottle.

From the thousands of samples analyzed since H.M.S. *Challenger* first began her voyage has come the knowledge that the warm northward surface drift across the equator is compensated for by means of a deep cold southward flow that originates between Iceland and Greenland, where colder waters of the East Greenland Current meet with part of the North Atlantic Drift. The mixed waters are further cooled in winter, so that they become very dense and sink to the bottom at an average rate of 2,000,000 tons per second, and here they begin a slow journey which takes them south of the equator as far as latitude 60° S. An equal amount of cold water sinks in the Labrador Sea. During the several years this massive flow takes to travel from Greenland to the latitude of Argentina it is every second added to by another 2,000,000 tons of water flowing out of the Mediterranean, where the surface is constantly evaporating and becoming saltier and therefore heavier. This dense water pours over the shallow rim of the sea along the bottom of the Straits of Gibraltar and joins the Atlantic Deep Drift, while in return lighter Atlantic surface water flows into the Mediterranean at a rate of over two knots. The entire deep drift of Atlantic water continues south beyond the equator. Thus the South Atlantic water is repaid, and in like manner other currents throughout the oceans are nicely poised and balanced in a continuous circulation.

While the slower submarine rivers of the ocean were giving

up their secrets to the persistent curiosity of oceanographers, meteorologists continued their inquiries into the prime causes of the great surface flow, and as a result the long-continued arguments between adherents of the density theory and of the wind theory are now fairly well resolved. There is little doubt today that the density of sea water, its varying heat and cold and saltness, is a reservoir of solar energy for the rise and fall of water and the slow massive movements deep below the surface. The work of Ekman and others has made it equally certain that the great circular sweep of the surface currents has for its engine the whole Atlantic wind system — the trade winds driving the Equatorial and Caribbean Currents and the westerly winds of the northern part giving movement to the North Atlantic Drift. Today attention is focused on certain other mysteries of the Gulf Stream.

During the past twenty years the major attack on the Gulf Stream has been by scientists from the Woods Hole Oceanographic Institution, which was partly founded for this very purpose. Under the leadership of Columbus O'D. Iselin, a team of scientists has collaborated with other scientific institutions to bring new light to bear on a number of difficult problems. From observations made at sea aboard the Diesel-engined ketch *Atlantis*, it was found that water is added to the Stream along its right-hand edge and an equivalent amount is thrown out intermittently along the western border in the form of eddies. This sideways transport of water across the Gulf Stream has been explained by the mathematical analysis of Carl-Gustaf Rossby, who regards the Current as a wake stream or jet flow forced out of the Straits of Florida into the Atlantic Ocean. He has shown that a necessary characteristic of this kind of stream is that eddies should be formed at the left side while water is drawn in from the right.

Another feature that seems to be characteristic of the water circulation of all oceans is that in the western part the current is concentrated and in the east is broad, slow, and diffuse. Thus the Gulf Stream runs northward through the western Atlantic at a pace which may sometimes exceed five knots, while the Canaries Current, running in a southerly direction, is very wide but barely noticeable. A stronger current in the west is also found in the North Pacific, where the Japanese Current, the Kuroshio, takes the place of the Gulf Stream; in the Indian Ocean, with its strong Agulhas Stream; and in the South Atlantic, where the Brazil Current flows. The only exception seems to be the Humboldt Current in the eastern South Pacific. The explanation for this comes from the work of Henry Stommel, Walter Munk, and others who have studied the balance of forces working on the whole system. And here is Munk's interpretation:

The spin of the winds, which blow outward in roughly spiral fashion from the mid-ocean center of high pressure, keeps the water moving in its circular path, but there are other forces acting that are different on the two sides of the ocean. We have spoken of the Coriolis force and of the right-hand twist it gives to movement in the northern hemisphere. This effect is not constant, but becomes greater in the higher latitudes — it becomes increasingly powerful as the western current flows northward from the equator; whereas in the eastern part of the ocean the Stream runs south and the Coriolis pull becomes less. When the opposing spin of water friction is taken into account, a mathematical analysis shows that the ocean circulation can become stable and balanced only if the current becomes concentrated in the west. Shorn of its technicalities this new wind theory means that there must be a broad, slow Canaries Current in the east and a narrow, fast-flowing Gulf Stream in the west, and that this would be so even if the Caribbean were dammed up and the water no longer forced to flow through the Straits of Florida.

Although Munk's work is the first successful attempt to

calculate in precise mathematical terms the effects of the wind as a motive power for currents, there is much still to be done. These calculations only account in their present form for about half of the water flow. Perhaps, when some of the factors involved here have been studied in greater detail it will be found that the wind is responsible for a much greater part of the Ocean River. The question of how far the heat engine shares the work is not yet solved.

Science advances by steps. From a study of observations and measurements a theory is drawn that seems to explain their working. From a consideration of the practical consequences arising from this theory comes a need for new observations and measurements to test its truth. And from the new observations comes a modification of the theory to make them fit. And so it is with oceanography. The drive of scientific curiosity and the need to fit theory and fact led to a demand for more observations of the detailed behavior and structure of the Gulf Stream.

One important source of the information needed has been the operation of vessels patrolling the area where the warm Atlantic and polar waters meet and where icebergs find their way into the North Atlantic shipping lanes. This is a direct result of the tragic loss of the *Titanic* in 1912 after her collision with an iceberg. As a future safeguard to transatlantic traffic, the U. S. Navy Hydrographic Office suggested the formation of the International Ice Patrol, and this is now in continuous operation, using vessels and men of the U. S. Coast Guard.

The great amount of observation which has gone into the Hydrographic Office pilot and current charts from such sources as the Ice Patrol fails to show the daily pulses and meanderings of the Gulf Stream but instead gives an average view. The faster changes are harder to observe. One of the chief difficulties has been that a research vessel cannot be in two places at once, and by the time it has steamed to another part of the Stream a considerable change may have taken place in the whole system. A complete and synoptic picture of the entire Gulf Stream, seen as it were from a God's-eye view, has long been needed. For this reason during 1950 a concerted effort was finally made to obtain simultaneous observations over a wide area. The Woods Hole Oceanographic Institution, together with the Hydrographic Office, worked out a co-operative plan which became known as "Operation Cabot." Under the direction of Dr. Richard Fleming, the *Atlantis* and the *Caryn* from the Oceanographic Institution, the U.S.S. *San Pablo* and *Rehoboth*, both of the Hydrographic Office, the Canadian naval research vessel H.M.C. *New Liskeard*, and the U. S. Fish and Wildlife Service *Albatross III*, together with a U. S. Coast Guard Ice Patrol cutter and several planes, joined in an unprecedented hunt to track down the true courses of the Gulf Stream.

With the most modern navigating equipment, including loran, to pinpoint exact positions, and with planes to watch from the air, it was possible for the first time in the history of oceanography to study a large area at one time instead of piecing together fragments of information gathered days or even months and years apart. New scientific instruments added greatly to the success of the venture. Among them was the bathythermograph, developed by A. F. Spilhaus during World War II to spot temperature changes in the sea that divert sound waves and interfere with submarine sound detection. Whereas Benjamin Franklin was able to take only one temperature reading at a time, at the surface, the bathythermograph, though it looks like a small and rather simple bomb, is capable of continuously recording temperatures and the depths at which they occur, down to several hundred feet below the surface with the ship at full speed. The enormous increase in speed of observation when this is used instead of the old-fashioned thermometer makes it one of the important new weapons in the arsenal of ocean science.

The most obvious and important thing about a current is that it has a speed and a direction of its own, hence the measurement of these is vital to such an expedition as Operation Cabot. For over five centuries the computing of a ship's drift has been the chief way to measure the pace of the Gulf Stream, and Columbus' practice was improved on only as more accurate methods of navigation were invented. Pillsbury's current meter can be used only by a ship at anchor; and the indirect calculation of currents from density measurements is even more poorly adapted to rapid synoptic observation. But Operation Cabot was able to make use of a brandnew instrument, the geomagnetic electrokinetograph — GEK for short — which gives almost instantaneous information on the direction and strength of water currents.

This new instrument is based on an old principle that has little apparent relation to oceanography. William von Arx, who developed it, used the little-known fact that currents of water in their passage through the salt ocean generate electricity, though in very small amounts. As the electric conductors in a dynamo, passing between the poles of a magnet, produce within themselves a flow of electricity, in the same way sea water, itself an electrical conductor, develops an electric current in its passage across the earth's magnetic field, and the greater the speed of the stream the greater the electricity produced. Von Arx's instrument is simply a delicate recording device that leaves an ink trace on a roll of paper to tell the amount of electricity in water through which the vessel in passing, and thus by simple calculation measures the direction and strength of the water current. Thus the research ship is no longer obliged to anchor or heave to when measuring currents, but may do so when traveling at full speed — and yet get a detailed answer .

During the past century the earlier notion of a gradually widening River in the ocean, with sharp boundaries and a fixed course, has given way before accumulating evidence of changes in position and speed. Operation Cabot brought these ideas into focus and showed that the Gulf Stream is narrow rather than wide, that it does not broaden out, and that a sharp drop of temperature may not necessarily mean the edge of the main current. When it leaves the confining influence of the land after passing Cape Hatteras it continues as a jet stream, and behaves in some ways like the high-speed jet streams that twist across the upper levels of the atmosphere. It begins to curve in wavy fashion from side to side as it moves to the northeast, and the curves grow wider until it looks like the leisurely meander of a slow river through flat country. But the current itself is still little wider than when it left the restraining banks of the Florida Straits, and it still flows at a good pace. Because of its wavy course the general easterly movement of water is slowed down; and we now see why a vessel sailing through this region is unable to judge the speed of the Gulf Stream from its accumulated effect on dead reckoning. A vessel sailing to the east may at one time be set almost to the southeast by a four-knot current, but a few hours later it may again cross the River, which this time might be running as fast to the north.

There is nothing fixed about these waves and curves in the Stream, for they may change their position as rapidly as eleven miles in a day; and they seem to become increasingly great until they reached the neighborhood of longitude 63° W. At unknown intervals of time a loop may twist so far out of line that it remains connected with the Stream only by a long narrow neck of flowing water — which may finally become completely pinched off. When this happens the loop becomes a more or less circular cyclonic eddy, running off on its own to the westward, an isolated swirl of Gulf Stream water. It seems likely that the larger loops bending to the south and enclosing colder northern water within them are identical with the so-called cold pools first described by those aboard the *Eliza* in 1810 and wrongly attributed to the melting of icebergs trapped within the Stream.

South of Labrador, according to F. C. Fuglister, where changing densities show a redistribution of energy within the

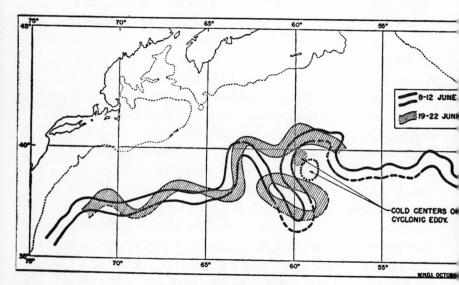

Positions of the warm "core" of the Gulf Stream during the first and last periods of Operation Cabot.

water, there arise two or more new and overlapping currents, and the southernmost streams seem to die away to the east. The exact nature of this triple stream is unknown, but it is at least certain that the Gulf Stream does not divide in the way a tree branches. Another puzzling discovery of Operation Cabot was that the warm water flows in pulses. And so — as always — in attempting to answer its own questions science has found new problems to solve.

Near the headwaters of the Gulf Stream, in the Florida Straits, a new attack is being made. Here the emphasis is on the day-by-day changes in the pulse of the Ocean River. It has already been mentioned that currents may be measured by the uphill slope across the flow, and for this purpose tide stations at Miami and Cat Cay are being operated by the U. S. Coast and Geodetic Survey and by the Miami Marine Laboratory for the continuous information they give about sea level. The Hydrographic Office of the Cuban Navy is also co-operating in a careful accounting of the waters that enter and leave the main course, and the detailed structure of the current is being recorded by the pen of the GEK as its electrodes are towed across the Straits. And here the current has already shown itself to be not a simple steady flow but a turbulent torrent, where fast- and slow-moving bands of water alternate across its width.

With such intensive interest in the Atlantic circulation as there is today the future may bring new understanding of the rhythm of its pulse and of the effects that this rhythm has on the movement of ice in the North Atlantic, on the yield of great commercial fisheries, and on the climate and weather of many places. But this forms a later part of our story.

Enough has been said to give some idea of the circulation of the greatest river in the world, with its headwaters in the Gulf of Mexico, its course the entire North Atlantic. The great wind engine that drives it and the deep slow massive flows of cold water that keep the whole in equilibrium have been studied by oceanographers and meteorologists, so that we now have some idea of the machinery that operates it. But the wind engine has a tale of its own, for it is through the air above us that the energy of the sun is dispensed to bring movement to the oceans and life to the creatures within and around them.

8

THE ENGINE OF THE AIR

ONE cannot talk of the Ocean River as a great circulating system storing and releasing tropical heat throughout the North Atlantic without describing the partner and indeed the motivating force of the currents of the sea — the similar vast, circulating current of air that acts like an immense flywheel powering the Atlantic gyre. Sir Napier Shaw, in a simplification of the North Atlantic weather system, describes the climate as a kind of steam or water-vapor engine, heated by the sun, with the tropic seas as the boiler room and the walls of pressure as the containing boiler. The water vapor of the air, in its ability to pick up and release heat in the piston thrust of the wind, acts as the steam in a world-wide steam engine. In a word, the carriage of heat and its release as wind energy is the powerhouse of the world we live in.

Now if this were a strictly scientific treatise, an exact accounting of the variations in the radiation of the sun, in temperatures, in water-vapor pressures, and in wind velocities, under all kinds of conditions, could be expressed in complicated mathematical formulae. Instead, we shall keep to everyday terms. Where heat is available at the sea surface it gives energy to the evaporation of water into the air. When air is forced aloft, water drops out and heat energy is released. This is convection or the transference of heat. There is nothing but this to act as motive power for every drop of rain that ever fell, and for every wind that ever filled a sail or wrecked a ship since the world began. This is the effect of the climate engine.

A relatively simple explanation of the forces that make the air engine of climate work is given by Rossby in the *U. S. Agricultural Department Year Book* of 1941. It goes like this: The earth's atmosphere is heated not from above but from below, by radiation of heat from the ground, caught largely by water vapor at low levels. The atmosphere acts as a protective blanket to hold and raise the mean temperature of the earth's surface. This heat, trapped before it can radiate into space, is not evenly distributed, and therefore, seeking to establish equilibrium, indirectly creates winds that in turn help create and maintain the heat-circulating system of the Ocean River.

But the power of the engine, the prime source of the earth's radiant heat, is the sun. About sixty percent of the total radiation from the sun reaches the surface of the earth. Though this short-wave radiation passes with little change through the lower atmosphere, it is nearly all absorbed by land and water, turned into heat energy, and eventually radiated back again. The radiations leaving the earth are heat rays with a longer wave length than solar radiation and are easily absorbed by the atmosphere. It is obvious that any changes in radiation from the sun or in its distribution over the earth would be translated into climatic changes. This transfer of heat motivates the constant battle between high- and low-pressure areas partly because gases and liquids expand when they are heated and lose weight and rise — just as when they are cooled they contract and settle.

The land and the sea have very different actions in this machinery of climate. The sun's energy, absorbed by rocks and the soil, cannot penetrate far because they are notably poor conductors of heat and cold — soil is warm below frost, and cool beneath rocks too hot to touch. Therefore this energy is almost at once transformed into heat and returned to the atmosphere; and this is why the land becomes quickly cold at night. But sea temperatures change little from day to night, because the turbulent water quickly passes a share of incoming solar heat to the layers beneath and thus becomes a storehouse, a moving reservoir that can carry heat poleward to parts less well endowed by the radiant energy of the sun.

All that immediately concerns us in following the story of the weather and climate is that the Ocean River carries heat and in turn affects the air above and conditions our lives. People are often concerned lest a change in the Gulf Stream might be responsible for unusual weather in the United States. But this could be so only indirectly, since in the Atlantic States our prevailing weather is continental — coming from inland. Yet an increase of a permanent nature in the warm, humid atmosphere of the Stream might well result in sucking down cold high-pressure waves from the Arctic. Because of this, a radical, warmer change in the Stream, while it would warm Europe, would probably cool off our Atlantic seaboard.

The atmosphere is divided. Up to about six miles above the earth we have the troposphere, then a demarkation called the tropopause, and above that the stratosphere. In the troposphere around and above us the temperature drops as we go higher; above it in the lower parts of the stratosphere the temperature is relatively constant and cold. There is one essential variation in these layers. The stratosphere begins at nearly 10 miles above the equator but is only about 5 miles above the pole. This is because the sun strikes full upon the tropics, whereas at the pole its rays are oblique, spread thin, and poor in heat. With greater warmth from the land and sea below to act on it the tropical air expands and rises; the polar air loses heat and shrinks. The result is that at the equator there is a greater height of air above the tropopause; and this has a tendency to slide down hill toward the pole. At ground level a compensating flow of cold air tends to flow south from the Arctic. This is the prime motive of air circulation in the northern hemisphere, but it is conditioned by other forces that cause variations in the northern hemisphere wind system.

In a previous chapter we have spoken of the effects of the earth's rotation on the flow of water, and now we see related

Diagram showing the heavy, irregular convections, accompanied by cumulus and thunderstorm clouds, that would occur if the sun's heat were applied uniformly everywhere and the earth did not rotate.

NORTH POLE

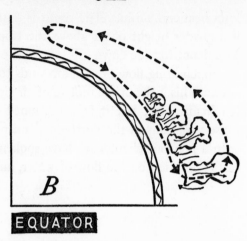

B

EQUATOR

Diagram showing concentration of convection in the vicinity of the Equator, north winds near the ground and south winds aloft, which would occur on a non-rotating earth if the sun's heat were applied mainly in low latitudes, as it actually is on the rotating earth.

effects pulling the northgoing winds to the east and the southgoing winds to the west. If this were all, then the river of air would become a simple flow of west winds aloft and east winds below, with the entire air mass slowly drifting toward the pole at high altitudes and returning toward the equator along the ground. But as the high winds travel north from the tropics the air cools, and as it sinks to the ground in the Horse Latitudes of about 30° N. it spreads out partly toward the pole and partly southward. Still blowing from the west, the poleward branch meets cold east winds moving across the ground from the Arctic, and here in a latitude of about 60° N. it is forced to ride over the heavier air and continue its northward drift as a high west wind, until further cooling at the pole again causes it to sink. There are also differences in radiation from the ocean and the continental land masses and the reflection of radiation from ice, which disturb the symmetry of this elementary circulation.

The net result — short of a technical explanation — is that the simple engine becomes a three-zone system of air be-

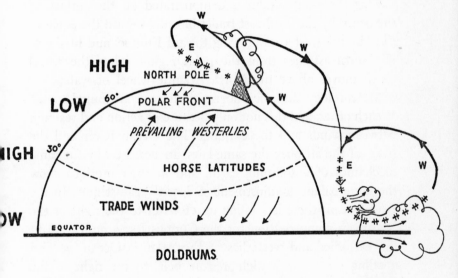

The final result of cellular meridional circulation on a rotating earth; Convection near the Equator, a clear zone of descending air motion north of it in about Latitude 30°, and cloud masses and rain at the polar front in Latitudes 50–60° N.

tween pole and equator. There is a trade-wind zone with rising air near the equator, a polar-front zone with falling air at the pole, and a separating zone in middle latitudes.

The polar-front and trade-wind zones together function as heat engines in which evaporation of water and heating of air takes place at ground level and cause the air to rise, expand, and lose both its own heat and the latent heat of condensing vapor as it moves north. Then it sinks to the ground and moves south to begin the heat cycle again. As we look eastward both of these are seen to be engines with counterclockwise motion working against the brake of contrary movement in the middle latitudes.

This three-cell system is demonstrated on the surface of the ocean by the northeast trades blowing toward the equator, then by the westerlies blowing toward Europe, and finally as the northeasterlies from the polar region. Thus the wheel of air moves above the North Atlantic wheel of waters.

Meteorology and oceanography have contributed much to each other, and this not only because of action and reaction between winds and the currents. The Ocean River and the rivers of the air obey the same laws, are acted on by the same mechanics of a spinning earth, and in their motions show the same balanced adjustment of density against flow. In the Gulf Stream there is a piling up of water to the right of the Stream in compensation for the Coriolis force, and again in the easterlies and westerlies of the Atlantic Ocean we find a piling up of air, a high-pressure belt, to the right of the wind's path. The arrangement of winds across the surface of the ocean is balanced against a high-pressure belt in the Horse Latitudes and another at the pole, with areas of low pressure in the equatorial doldrums and in latitudes between 55° and 65° N.

Convection, the vertical transfer of temperature by air and water, does not work uniformly over the earth because water, earth, and ice reflect heat and conduct, store, and radiate it at different rates. This varying of heat transfer breaks up the belts of high and low pressure into separate areas of low-pressure instability and of high pressure, which is usually cool and fair weather, seeking to fill the low pressure areas. Now in the semipermanent movement of winds over the North Atlantic there are certain areas that remain more or less uniform. There is a central high between the Azores and Bermuda. Opposed to this there is a northward area predominantly low, called the Icelandic low. Again over the Arctic regions high pressure usually prevails.

This gives us a general picture of the big circulations of the engine of our climate. But within this are lesser engines of varying intensity that control the local and more changing aspects of our weather, but that may also have power to influence the major movements. These are the cyclonic storms revolving in a counterclockwise direction that in general move along the paths of equal pressure, the isobars of the weather maps. Cyclones are caused by the fact that any rising current or convection of heat from the earth tends to spin the air into a vortex just as any descending column of air — or water in a drain — will do. Around the edges of the slow revolving flywheel of our engine of the North Atlantic climate, cyclonic weather has its course, and the general path of wind and weather follows the path of the Ocean River coiling slowly around the periphery of waters. This must be, because of the location of pressure areas and because winds follow lines of like pressure, the isobars, with low-pressure areas on their left.

Seasonally the hurricanes — the smaller but more violent cyclones of the tropics — twist up the pathway of the Gulf Stream from the Caribbean and move off across the ocean on this same course. Above the roaring forties of the Atlantic, between these invisible walls of pressure, a series of cyclonic storms in a widely varying path move from the continent northeasterly by the Grand Banks toward England and Europe, and form the invigorating and changeable climate of the north temperate. This path marks what is called the polar front, the conflict between heavy cold arctic air and the warmer moist air from the southwest which rides against it where the polar-front cell touches that of the middle latitudes. The same great turbulence takes place in the ocean where warm and cold waters meet to the south of Labrador and in the oceanic polar fronts of the Icelandic and Barents seas.

The ocean acts as a brake on the perpetual battle between areas of pressure, because the ocean stores more heat and releases it more gradually than the earth. For this reason the most stimulating and livable areas develop around the seaways of the world and breed the healthiest and most energetic civilizations. It is this beneficent and energizing machinery of air and Ocean River that accounts for the rapid development of the second phase of western Christian civilization as an Atlantic community. But there is another characteristic of the climate engine over the northern hemisphere and in particular over the Ocean River, and this is the domination of the polar front in making our weather. Here is the continually shifting battle of the low-pressure areas of the roaring forties and the wall of cold air settling from the north at 60° latitude, and here the cold and drier polar winds meet with the warm moist southwest winds. Wedges of cold air along the polar front push into the low-pressure air and force it to higher levels, where cooling causes it to condense into cloud and give us rain, winter snow and powerful winds. This is the reason the North Atlantic is one of the stormiest and roughest bodies of water in the world.

As any weather map will show, there are succeeding waves of high pressure bellying down from Canada and the Arctic, interspersed with low-pressure cyclonic storm areas. The quantity and the movement of this great permanent mass of arctic air as it pushes down on the temperate zone is today presumed to be the key to short-term and particularly long-term weather forecasting. Any permanent change in the domination of the polar front by the warmer low-pressure cyclonic storms from the south would most certainly be reflected in the delivery of warmer waters to the north by the Ocean River, and the combination of wind and water would affect the Arctic icecap. Some such drastic change is believed to have had a great deal to do with the recession of the great icecaps that overlay North America and Europe thirty thousand years ago. But before we take a look at early climatic changes and the days of the retreating ice, we should first briefly study the nature of a cyclonic storm as an engine of climate.

The king of cyclonic storms in the North Atlantic Ocean is, of course, the hurricane. William Dampier more than two centuries ago gave a good description of the approach of such a tempest. "The clouds," he said, "which precede a hurricane, are different from the North Banks of a norther which are uniform from horizon to horizon. The hurricane clouds tower up their heads pressing forwards and are yet so linked together that they all move alike. The edges of these clouds are gilded with various and afrighting colors, the very edge of all seems to have a pale fire-color, next that of a dull yellow and nearer the body of the cloud is copper color but the body of the cloud itself, which is very thick, appears extraordinarily black." William Gerard de Brahm, one of the first Americans interested in the study of weather and the Gulf Stream, quoted this story of the great Florida storm in 1759: "A heavy gale from the northeast so impeded the current of the Gulf Stream that the water forced, at the same time in the Gulf of Mexico by the trade winds, rose to such a height that not only the Tortugas and other islands disappeared, but the highest trees were covered on the Penninsula of Largo, and at this time the Litbury, John Lorain master, being caught in the gale, came to an anchor, as the master supposed, in Hawke Channel, but to his great surprise found his vessel the next day high and dry on Elliott's Island and his anchor suspended in the boughs of a tree."

As yet modern meteorologists have not figured out a satis-factory relationship between the prevalence or scarcity of the greatest of all our cyclonic storms and the polar fronts; but certainly there is such a relationship, which is gradually be-coming more thoroughly explored. It is even possible that there may yet be charted indirect but consistent relationships between the fluctuations of the Gulf Stream and the incidence of hurricanes storming above its waters from the Caribbean. But these violent storms of late summer and fall roaring along our Atlantic coasts, and occasionally following the Ocean River clear to the English Channel, are important manifesta-tions of the climate engine of the North Atlantic. Some of them are set up at the very roots of the Equatorial Current of the Cape Verde Islands, and make full circle to the Grand Banks of Newfoundland or even back again across the north-ern seas. They travel, as the Stream does, east-to-west-to-north in a kind of end run around the prevailing midocean or Bermuda high pressure area. If they happen at the same time to be pinched from the west by a strong continental high-pressure area as they were in 1938 and 1944, we get increasing intensity, as they come up the coast.

The chances are that a line storm about the time of the autumnal equinox along our North Atlantic coasts is the tail end of a Caribbean hurricane. A cyclonic storm is one where winds blow in a circular direction around a relatively windless center in a counterclockwise direction. These storms have a secondary movement along a directional path controlled by the pull of the earth spin and the pressure isobars of the atmosphere. They can cover hundreds of miles in extent, and are flat in proportion to their depth. The average hurricane or intense cyclonic storm is about a mile deep, but the big ones can disturb the air for at least twice that height above the earth. The revolving winds curve more or less inward toward the center, but vary in different sections of the cyclonic circle. In front of the storm the winds tend to blow directly across the path, and in the rear to follow a more immediate line toward the center.

A consistent feature is the variation of intensity between the right- and left-hand sides of the hurricane. The right side, where the winds blow from the rear forward and around the front, has the added force of the speed of the storm as a whole, which may be considerably more than ten miles per hour. Conversely the winds heading toward the rear on the left side are partly cancelled out by just this forward speed of the whole storm, and are therefore less severe. The forward right quadrant of the storm is where the real business of wind and rain goes on, where winds can rise to 150 miles per hour and rains amount to a terrific cloudburst. Some hurricanes have precipitated as much as two or three feet of rainfall in their passage, or the equivalent of the annual rainfall of Paris or London.

This terrific precipitation is a part of the wind engine that furnishes the energy of the cyclone by the release of heat. Nothing can better describe the workings of a hurricane than the words of I. M. Cline of the U. S. Weather Bureau, who has been a pioneer in the study of tropical storms. This is how the engine works: "The winds in the rear right-hand quadrant blow in the same general direction as that in which the cyclone center is traveling and continue to do so during the life of the storm. These winds with velocities of 40 to 100 miles an hour or more, converge upon the winds of the front right-hand quadrant, which have a variable inclination towards the center but which, within a hundred miles of the center, blow nearly at right angles to the line of advance. The winds in this front right quadrant blow intermittently in sudden local powerful gusts which appear to have a marked vertical component upwards.

"Precipitation occurs mainly in this front right-hand quad-

Structure of Hurricane Winds

At right front, the heaviest rains and highest winds tend to cross in front of storm at right angles to the direction of storm's movement. Winds tend to follow in the rear in the direction of the storm. Central calm core bends winds towards front right quadrant where rainfall acts as energizing center of storm.

rant and almost ceases at any station with the arrival of the minimum pressure. . . . The source of moisture-supply (that furnishes the energy of the cyclone) is through the winds in the rear right-hand quadrant, and the precipitation is due to the forced ascension produced by the convergence of these winds with those of the front right-hand quadrant. The primary cause of tropical cyclones is the convergence of air currents. The cyclone itself persists by continuous redevelopment over the area of the greatest precipitation, and the core of the cyclone is inclined from the area of the lowest surface pressure (or center) forward into the cloud region over the area of maximum precipitation. (The center moves forward to the right in a tilted cone.) As the cyclone travels, the area of low pressure moves towards that of precipitation." The storm tides (which can rise up to twenty feet above normal) that are built up in advance of the cyclone are found only directly in front of the approaching storm or in front of its forward right-hand quadrant.

The hurricane, the cyclonic storm at its greatest intensity, in basic nature varies little from the milder storms we are used to in the so-called temperate zone of the northern hemisphere. Therefore, before we consider how changing climatic conditions in the past have influenced the oceanic heating system and even the destructive rise and fall of ocean levels, it may be a good idea to look at the kind of force a hurricane can exert. The wind strength that defines hurricane weather ranges from above 60 miles an hour to 150 miles an hour — or until the measuring instrument lets go and disappears. This kind of wind strength, customarily associated only with tropical hurricanes, often exists in the high airs of northern areas. Winds as high as 200 miles an hour have been recorded by the Government bureau on top of Mt. Washington in New Hampshire at 6,288 feet. When winds of this strength occur they lift sea and solid alike and change the immediate face of things.

But in addition to the force of the wind or of the rapid advance of tidal waters rising up to twenty feet, the force of the accumulated rainfall is tremendous. In Porto Rico in 1899 a particularly severe storm deposited more than two and a half billion tons of water on that island. This force, plus the violent changes in the barometric pressure of the air, may account for the frequent recordings of earth tremors during the progress of a hurricane. It has been calculated by Brooks that a barometric drop of air pressure of two inches removes a load of two million tons from each square mile of the earth's surface. A ten-foot rise in water would add nine million tons of pressure to each square mile. The time and manner of the combination of these forces might be sufficient to release already existing tensions on the earth's crust. These microseisms have been recorded by the Navy Department of the United States at Guantanamo Bay, Cuba, and indicate that the approach of severe storms can sometimes be detected by the increase of earth tremors when the storm center is still a thousand miles away. The elements walk with a giant's tread.

In our northern hemisphere in the middle latitudes the airs move generally from west to east across the Atlantic to Europe north of the thirtieth parallel. The air currents and the currents of the Ocean River are companion systems that control and influence each other. Between them for ages past they have determined the English and European climate. In conjunction with other forces, the climate of sea and air formed the great age of glaciation that ushered in the time of modern historic man; and they could again bring on an age of ice.

Now that we have looked briefly at the nature of the climate engine we can drop back in time and see what it has done to foster or hinder the development of our present-day life on earth.

There has been a distinct evolution of climate as we know it today since the last icecap at about 30,000 B.C. — the time of Cro-Magnon man. In geological time this icecap is a modern phenomenon. The history of modern man begins with the recession of the cap about 15,000 years ago. How modern this is from a geological point of view is best stated by measuring the entire period of the earth's existence from the Archean or earliest geological times as one year. This would give a value of only a little over a minute to the existence of historic time, or the last 8,000 years; hence we can feel very much up-to-the-minute in starting the history of modern weather conditions over the Ocean River with the recession of the most recent icecap, which extended through the Great Lakes to Boston and covered England just south of London and extended thence through the Baltic.

Today we live in a glacial climate — as defined by the presence of icecaps at the poles. But this kind of climate is not normal if we consider the calendar of geological time: glacial climates have existed less than one percent of that total time. Our planet has experienced these periodic times of ice because the greater part of it is covered with water which in the polar regions never varies far from freezing temperature. A relatively slight variation in the uniform temperature of the ocean due to the tipping of the earth's axis, a warmer current from the tropics due to increased solar radiation, or sudden geological changes in the earth's crust, could make the difference between a shrinking or expanding icecap and thus affect the climate of the whole world.

R. J. Russell, of the Soil Conservation Service, explains the fluctuation of an icecap — according to Brooks — as follows: "As long as winter temperatures remain above 28 degrees F., the approximate freezing point of ocean water, the polar seas remain open. At slightly lower temperatures, the ice frozen during the winter melts again in the following summer, and the seas remain effectively open. But if the winter temperature falls about 5 degrees F. lower than the freezing point of ocean water, an icecap will form. Its growth will be slow at first . . .

but after its radius has reached about six hundred miles, the growth of the icecap becomes rapid because the ice itself has a cooling effect on surrounding areas and the rate of summer melting is reduced. Growth continues until the ice extends so far from polar areas that its margins encounter temperatures sufficiently high to stop further extension. Rising temperatures cause retreat of the ice and the modifications of climatic patterns. The cooling effect of the icecap is so great that retreat is slow until the ice has diminished in area to its critical point, a radius of about 600 miles, after which the ice disappears very rapidly."

This kind of a retreat from a maximum extension set in just before the time of historic man; that is, before the time of factual records of man's existence in a civilized community. We know that since this retreat the level of the seas and the level of land areas has risen and fallen, sometimes in response to the release of the pressure caused by the mass of the icecap. Today the Gulf of Bothnia is measurably rising in a release of pressure and Greenland appears to be sinking. Just what combination of conditions actually existed at the advance or retreat of the icecap has never been determined. But three main factors, singly or together, are probably the cause, namely: the variation of the orbit of the earth in its distance from the sun; the transmission of tropical heat by winds and ocean currents to the north; and sudden radical geological changes in the topography of the earth's crust. Without getting caught in the lively scientific battle of theories we can look at the evidence in this order.

When the earth, traveling in its orbit around the sun, is nearest the sun it is called in perihelion; when most distant, in aphelion. At perihelion the earth travels along its orbit more rapidly than at aphelion; therefore, the season that coincides with perihelion will be shorter and warmer than the season that coincides with aphelion. At present the northern hemisphere has its winter in this shorter season. Because of the slow cosmic forces of the sun and moon, the earth takes about 26,000 years to complete the cycle of variations of its orbit, so that approximately every 13,000 years the earth will pass through its perihelion, with its northern and southern hemispheres alternately turned toward the sun. This is called the precession of the equinox. In addition to this change, during every 40,000 years the earth's inclination of axis of rotation completes a cycle of changes in relation to the plane of its orbit. The existence of winter and summer are due to this inclination, hence any change will affect the climate. In addition to this, Huntington makes a case for variations in sun spots that cause fluctuations in the radiation of solar energy and hence in the convection of heat in air and sea from south to north. Other scientists believe that the changes in the icecap can be explained by geological phenomena like the opening or closing of the isthmus at Panama.

Von Konow makes an interesting case for this last conjecture. He writes that during the last glacial period the waters of the Equatorial Current flowed through the Caribbean into the Pacific, and there was no Gulf Stream as we know it today. This caused a drop of mean temperature to the north and a consequent extraordinary spread of the arctic icecap. This additional cold in the north created greater convection, which drew off to higher regions the normal heat transference from the earth. It is likely that, even with the icecap extending down over the continent, the part of North America free of ice may have had a warmer climate, due to the fact that with the Gulf Stream gone the cold Labrador Current did not come down our eastern coasts.

The final factor that helped form the icecaps is not disputed, namely, that the rise of new mountain areas like the Alps in Europe was favorable to the formation of extensive glaciers. Only when the now high mountain ranges have been leveled by long erosion, and glaciation has disappeared from the face of the earth, will the milder winds and currents of air and sea produce a more uniform and less revolutionary climate. Before that can happen we can expect with some certainty a renewal of the icecaps. But our own immediate climatic environment has become temporarily settled so recently that we need not worry about perihelions or the immediate creation of mountain ranges or the break-through into the Pacific. Nonetheless things are afoot that do affect us. Let's begin with the last retreat of ice only 15,000 years ago, and see what our climate has done since then.

It is obvious that as the icecap over northern Europe began to draw back the living conditions favorable to mankind's survival also increased — at first, probably, round the sea fringe of the European continent where forests began to grow. This story is told in the annual layers of sediment called "varves" laid down by the Baltic and other bodies of water which were then inland lakes near the retreating edge of the ice. By the year 12,000 B.C. the Baltic was well established as a huge fresh-water lake closed off from the warm currents of the Atlantic Ocean. The accelerated melting of the icecap after this time raised the level of the ocean. Between 8,000 and 7,000 B.C., at the time of the earliest Near Eastern civilizations, the Atlantic waters burst through into the Baltic. After another thousand years the land bridge between lake and ocean closed again, and did not reopen until some time between 5,000 and 4,000 B.C. In this Littorina period the waters of the North Atlantic were warmer than today, and heavy forests covered the seacoasts of northern Europe.

The climate from 4,000 B.C. on became warm and moist, dominated by the influence of the Atlantic currents penetrating into the Baltic. At this time the glaciers disappeared from the Alps, and the northern icecap had little influence on the climate. From 3,000 B.C. on for about ten centuries in this Atlantic period, mild and equable conditions reigned over Europe. Egypt and the kingdoms of the Near East were in vigorous expansion, and the Phoenicians were beginning to explore the western limits of their inland sea.

During the next millennium, after the warm moist Atlantic period, a warm, dry period held Europe. The lake dwellings grew up in the dried marshes around the Swiss lakes. This was the beginning of the Neolithic culture in Europe, and the so-called Bronze Age in the Mediterranean. As a matter of fact, the ability to smelt bronze from copper and tin and use it for weapons and utensils was probably brought by sea to Europe as the Phoenicians, pushing out from Gibraltar, sought the tin mines of Cornwall and the amber trade of the Frisian coasts of Denmark.

Then once again a radical fluctuation in the convection system of the Ocean River and its winds must have come on to increase the storm cycles and bring cooler weather and a much heavier precipitation. The times were bad. In the year 1275 B.C. the lake dwellers of Switzerland were suddenly flooded out. In the north, a few centuries afterward, the stormy and bitter stretch of years come down to us in legend as the Twilight of the Gods. This held on from 900 B.C. for about five hundred years.

In other chapters we have watched how the bold Mediterranean peoples, enjoying less drastic climatic changes, were pushing out through the Straits of Gibraltar both north and south on tentative explorations of the Atlantic coasts. The first thousand years of the Christian era opened warm and wet for Europe, and then turned warm and dry, with a corresponding stimulation in the Scandinavian and Teutonic countries that led to conquests and migrations. Before we follow the effects of the Atlantic storm cycles shifting north or south across Europe we can trace in some detail what a relatively slight improvement in the heating system of the Norwegian Sea and the Arctic accomplished for the Norse.

In 825 A.D. Irish monks sailed a day northward from Iceland before finding floe ice. Fifty years later a Norseman called Ingolf, pioneering at Reykjavik, spoke of the land being wooded from the mountains to the shores, and other early settlers spoke of tillage and a harvest of small grains. Annual drift ice, so common in our day around Iceland, was not mentioned in the early chronicles until 1200 A.D. The weather in medieval Europe for the most part was stormy and cold. This change caused the Norse to shift their course to the southward when they sailed to their Greenland colony. It also brought down the icecap and with it the Eskimo, who finished off the Greenland colony about fourteen hundred. Many catastrophes in Europe due to terrible storms and floods fall in these years. In the thirteenth century 80,000 people were drowned in Holland, and by the fourteenth century the inclosed Lacus Fleve — renamed the Zuider Zee — was open to the waters of the North Sea.

Various explanations have been offered for this change in the steady nature of the weather of our northern hemisphere. Huntington lays it to phenomenal sun-spot activity, especially in the thirteenth century, when solar radiation was supposed to have been exceptional. O. Pettersson has made a detailed study of cold Atlantic underwater waves, which oscillate between layers of water with marked density differences just as they do between water and air; he says that they were at a maximum in the fifteenth century. These thrusts of cold Atlantic waters into the Baltic herald a greater turbulence and mixing of cold and warm waters and hence an increased convection and storminess. They also pump into the Baltic with the colder waters great schools of herring, which normally do not penetrate beyond the Skagerrak off Denmark.

The object in tracing the history of these phenomena is to demonstrate how continuously, since records have been known, the currents of the sea and the weather above them have fluctuated through the years, and have thus changed the history of the welfare and expansion of civilized man in

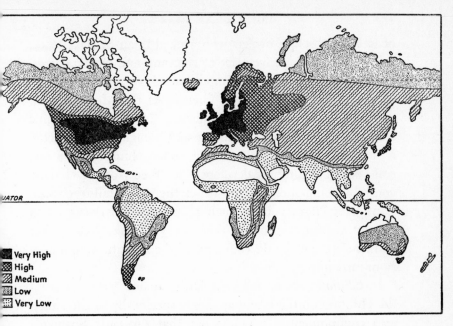

Very High
High
Medium
Low
Very Low

The Distribution of Human Health and Energy on the Basis of Climate.

northern Europe and Scandinavia. A parallel to this has been traced by Huntington in a study of Rome. He demonstrates the effect of climate on Mediterranean peoples when the cyclonic sequence of storm and rain through southern Europe and Asia Minor ran south of its present course. The polar front of opposing pressures and temperatures moved south from the 60° latitude to the neighborhood of the 40° line.

Roughly the optimum climatic times for the Mediterranean peoples ran with minor fluctuations from 1200 B.C. to 200 A.D. This was due to a plentiful rainfall and a more energetic climate. The rivers were full and watered the plains. Huntington states that the decline of Greece was due largely to malarial poisoning, because a declining rainfall left stagnant and ill-drained pools and swamps as breeding places for mosquitoes. After 200 A.D., when the Italian climate also deteriorated, agriculture fell off, farms came into the hands of wealthy absentee owners who worked them by slave labor, and wheat growing gave place to vineyards and olive orchards. The decline of the Roman Empire was also probably hastened by the rise of malaria, as in Greece. As the Mediterranean weather got softer and less stimulating, the energetic cyclonic zone moved into northern Europe and brought on great activity and invasions from the Gothic tribes. Huntington in several books has carefully developed this theory of the climatic control of human energy and hence the rise or fall of civilizations. Here it may be enough to mention his work as an interesting contribution to the history of the Ocean River and its effect on the development of the Atlantic community from early historic times.

In *Climate Makes the Man* Dr. Clarence Mills backs up the Huntington thesis and applies it specifically to the American environment. He points out that the early Spaniards coming into the soft Caribbean climate underwent a relaxation both physically and morally before they could become — in later generations — adjusted to their new environment, and that similar changes in Europeans meeting the stimulation of the North American climate have accounted for difficulties of adjustment. In other words, Mills holds that man is as much a pawn of climate as he is lord of creation. Certainly there is ample evidence to prove that mankind, responding to the cyclonic whip, has reacted to changes in this climatic sequence. Mills goes so far as to relate the terrific military energy of the Napoleonic period to a run of cold years in Europe between 1784 and 1817 and claims that succeeding years of revolutionary outbursts in 1830 and 1848 were detonated by the particularly vigorous nature of the weather in those years. Bruckner, of course, is another authority who correlates migrations from Europe to North America with the rainfall in Europe.

This brief résumé of the climate engine over the Ocean River and how it has affected the waters of the Atlantic and hence stabilized and extended climatic influence through the ages makes an interesting basis for an interpretation of the conditions now existing in and around the North Atlantic Ocean and the possible effects it may have on the future of our present Atlantic civilization. It is known that changes in the volume and warmth of the Florida Stream as it leaves the Caribbean are reflected in slight but nevertheless effective differences in temperature of the Irminger Current that runs from the north of Iceland down the east coast of Greenland under the colder and lighter waters of the Arctic Sea. Recent studies of this and other sources of information about the north all point to our entrance — during the past fifty years or so — into a warm trend along the polar front. A Russian scientist named Scholkosky says that the surface layer of cold waters in the Arctic is now only about 100 meters deep, or less by half than it used to be. The mean annual surface temperature of the sea has also risen since 1926 at Jacobshavn, Greenland, by more than two degrees This, accompanied by a retreat of the glaciers and the icecap throughout the north for the past several decades, is probably due as much to a a greater volume of the currents from the tropics reaching Arctic waters as it is to their slight rise in temperature. In the two years between 1927 and 1929 it was calculated that twenty percent more Atlantic water than normal reached the Norwegian Sea. This influx naturally influenced the climate on shore and the fishing conditions beneath the sea. Except for a brief relapse in 1934-35 and 1937-38, the persistence of this warmer period in the north due to the activity of the Ocean River has been reflected in the whole economy of the northern fisheries.

A. S. Jensen of Copenhagen has made a study of the recent change in the Arctic climate. Since 1919, he says, the cod have returned to the West Greenland coast and moved north to 70° of latitude; previous appearances of cod were noted in 1820 and 1840, but not since 1850. Together with the cod have come their natural food in the capelin and herring, as well as haddock, halibut, salmon, and even jellyfish. Meanwhile the more arctic forms of life, like the white whale, have moved back northward.

Fortunately many able scientists have been measuring all these signs of change in the north. Wagner and Scherhag tell us that from 1910 to 1930 there was a steady and constant increase in atmospheric circulation, i.e., in heat convection from south to north. Jensen attributes this stepping-up of the climate engine over the Ocean River to the strengthening of the subtropical high-pressure belt, while there has been a simultaneous increase of barometric minima along the north-polar front. This would cause an increased quantity of warm Atlantic air to stream in over Europe and the Arctic regions and bring on more oceanic or equable conditions. Coupled with this is the fact — according to Slocum — that there was a rise of four-tenths of a degree Centigrade in the temperature of the sources of the Gulf Stream. Thus air and sea, together complementing and sustaining each other, are at work today causing a definite shift toward a warmer and more beneficent north-temperate and Arctic climate. If this should continue long enough there well might be a sudden disappearance of the Arctic ice fields, and a return to the kind of climate that persisted for several centuries when the Norse found it easy going to Greenland and grains and forests grew in those lands.

We have marked the passage of great rivers of water along and below the surface, and the wind machine above them. The engine of the air and the Ocean River which it drives are well worth our attention, and the physical effects of wind and water have their own particular grandeur. But linked to them are the biological effects, the fierce and varied play of life within the waters and the great sea fisheries. It is therefore proper that we should turn our attention to the creatures now in our seas, and to the procession of life across and around the River that has resulted in the Atlantic community of man.

9

THE AGE OF FISHES

THE migrations of human beings across the Ocean River and the growth of human populations along its shores have their counterparts among the living creatures within the River itself. In many ways the two are interrelated, since the great Atlantic fisheries provide a substantial part of the food of Atlantic man and were an important factor in the pattern of exploration and settlement of the western shore. The fisheries in turn depend on the River, for the streams and water movements of the North Atlantic have an enormous influence on the lives and food of fishes.

The submarine life of the North Atlantic and its marginal seas has a unique importance in the history of science. Just as our knowledge of evolution in the ocean is based largely on ancient sediments laid down under the Atlantic waters when they flooded the Eurasian and North American continents, so our present day science of marine biology is founded on the discoveries made in the River and its depths during the early investigations of the pioneer Atlantic marine biologists and oceanographers. This scientific interest was greatly stimulated by the partial dependence of Atlantic communities on life in the River and the consequent necessity of sustaining and conserving the fisheries which this life supports. The success of early Atlantic investigations has prompted similar studies into all parts of the oceans, but even today marine biological research is at least as active along the Atlantic shores and in the waters of the River as elsewhere.

This salty cradle of life has been dominated by a procession of very different kinds of living creatures, so that there have been at various times an Age of Trilobites, an Age of Squids, and an Age of Reptiles. Today is a new Age of Fishes, which began when fishes displaced the swimming reptiles and inherited the ocean. Nevertheless, throughout all the ages there has continually flourished another and lower stratum of marine life without which the larger animals could never have existed. Plankton, as it is called, has been throughout these ages the very foundation of life in the sea. Migrations of fishes within the waters of the River and mysterious fluctuations in their abundance are influenced directly not only by changes in temperature, saltness, and flow of water, but also by the fluctuations in growth and movement of their plankton food which accompany these changes. Since the plankton consists mostly of small plants and animals without sufficient powers of movement to swim against currents, it is particularly dependent on the ocean circulation. It is worth our study for many practical reasons.

Unseen by travellers who peer overboard into the blue transparent ocean, but coming to life under the lens of the microscope, is a teeming world in miniature, fantastic and infinitely varied, a kind of miniscule botanical garden and zoo, and the very nursery of the ocean. Single-celled plants are fashioned in surrealist design or housed in delicately carved silica capsules. They may have intricately sculptured shapes with long spines, or carry in their bodies decorative oil globules to keep them from sinking. They are in a functional sense both the pasturage and corn land of the sea, for they vastly exceed in total bulk those larger marine plants, the seaweeds, even though plankton organisms themselves are often thousands of times smaller.

In the enormously varied zoo of the plankton the giants are jellyfish and Portuguese men-of-war, which trail their stinging tentacles behind them. Barely large enough to see are minute, many-legged crustaceans with voracious appetites, swimming in spasmodic jerks like strange monsters from another world, side by side with fierce-jawed arrow worms, long and streamlined. Plankton is the nursery of nearly all ocean life, for in it there float baby crabs with projecting spines many times the length of their bodies, and the young of spiny lobsters, flat, transparent, and leaflike, with spiderlike legs and eyes on stalks. Drifting helplessly along with them are large-eyed, transparent, newly-hatched fishes. These miniature monsters of the plankton live in part on each other, but the smaller of them are grazers, and feed only on the tiny drifting plants.

Some fishes are plankton feeders; and even some of the whales, largest of all living animals, live entirely on the drifting organisms in the plankton. In contrast to these are the carnivorous fish. They prey on other fish which are plankton feeders or which rely in turn for their food on plankton feeders. Thus directly or indirectly the richness of life in the ocean depends on the richness of its plankton growth, much as the food of mankind is limited by the success or failure of the corn crop and by the extent and richness of the pasture lands on which livestock graze. And so the Age of Fishes is still very much an Age of Plankton. Those who sought to find the secrets of how and why our fisheries are linked to the movements and pulses of the Ocean River soon found that plankton was a fundamental part of the answer.

Although plankton plays such a vital role in the life of the ocean, this was virtually unsuspected until as recently as about 100 years ago. It is true that from the earliest times men have noticed the occasional red, green, or yellow discolorations of sea water caused by excessive concentrations of plankton. Whaling skippers had long been aware that a good catch might be presaged by the appearance of the small, shrimp-like crustaceans, or krill, of the plankton. William Scoresby on his North Polar expedition in 1820 dipped up some discolored water and found that it contained great numbers of microscopic objects called diatoms. But it was not until 1847 that diatoms were first recognized as plants by the English botanist Sir Joseph Hooker, who, after exploring the Antarctic seas with Sir James Clark Ross, drew attention to their importance in the ocean pastures.

The first real advances in our knowledge of plankton were made possible by a very simple and obvious invention. Whereas early explorers were content to dip water from the sea in buckets or canvas bags in order to examine the plankton contained in it, the German scientist Johannes Muller in 1845, hit upon the use of fine gauze or silk nets that could be towed behind a vessel and so strain out the microscopic life. With a few improvements, this method of concentrating plankton is used in all modern scientific investigations of the drifting sea life.

The first organized expeditions for studying ocean life in the Atlantic were prompted not entirely by interest in plankton but partly by the desire to settle a controversy. It had long been assumed that the deep, dark ocean floors were muddy deserts of the ocean, completely devoid of life. When submarine cables were invented, however, and the recovery of broken cables showed undoubted evidence of marine life growing on them, it was decided to settle the mystery of the deep ocean floor once and for all. Edward Forbes, the great pioneer of oceanography, had much to do with fomenting a fever of interest, as a result of which H.M.S. *Lightning* in 1868 and H.M.S. *Porcupine* in 1869 were fitted out for deep-sea dredging under Wyville Thompson. The results showed unquestionably that there is fairly abundant and varied animal life even in deep water, and that only the plants are restricted, because of their need for light, to the lesser depths.

Just as the right moment produced a Columbus to crystal-
lize into a successful voyage the thoughts and speculations of
other men, so Wyville Thompson was the man to translate
into pioneer explorations the growing interest in the mysteries
of ocean life in the ocean. After the preliminary successes of
the *Lightning* and *Porcupine* cruises in the eastern Atlantic he
finally succeeded in organizing the greatest of all expeditions
in marine science, the voyage of H.M.S. *Challenger*. During a
period of three and a half years, between 1872 and 1876, this
2,000-ton corvette travelled nearly 70,000 miles in the Atlantic, Pacific, and Antarctic Oceans, collecting plankton with
the Muller net at varying depths, dredging sea life and rocks
from the bottom, and studying the changing chemistry and
physics of sea water. The scientific results of this famous voyage, which laid the very foundations of oceanic biology, were
of enormous importance; and so voluminous that the published reports of the expedition weigh nearly a quarter of a
ton. Among other things the *Challenger* expedition found that
Forbes was wrong in thinking the deep ocean floor to be completely barren of life. Many new and strange worms, sea
cucumbers, sea shells, and sea stars were dredged up from the
deep-sea bed.

The knighthood bestowed on Sir Wyville Thompson was
richly deserved. The voyage of the *Challenger* was only the
prelude to a whole series of scientific expeditions, just as
Columbus's voyage touched off a flood of commercial traffic
to the west. In the United States two Swiss naturalists, Louis
Agassiz and Louis François de Pourtales, did much to extend
marine biological research in the western Atlantic. Alexander,
the son of Louis Agassiz, was scientific director of the *Blake*
(already mentioned in connection with the investigation of
ocean currents), and later of the *Albatross*, which cruised the
Atlantic coast before proceeding to the Pacific. Notable contributions were also made by the German Victor Hensen, who

was first to use the name "plankton" and first to attempt accurate measurement of its importance in the ocean. His North Atlantic cruise of the S.S. *National* in 1888 was a milestone in plankton research; followed ten years later by another German expedition, that of the *Valdivia*. Next in order came the North Atlantic cruise of the Norwegian vessel *Michael Sars* under the direction of Sir John Murray and Dr. Johan Hjort, whose book, *The Depths of the Ocean*, is still one of the best-illustrated accounts of biological oceanography, as well as of the ocean currents related to it.

During the closing years of the nineteenth century and in the years since there have been so many expeditions for the study of ocean life throughout the world that it would be tedious to list them here. Mention must be made, though, of Albert Honoré Charles, Prince of Monaco, who used the proceeds of his famous Monte Carlo gambling casino to outfit yachts for scientific work in the Mediterranean and North Atlantic. We have already noted his part in studying ocean currents. He also contributed much to science from his research into the food of whales, and among other things made the discovery that the diet of sperm whales includes considerable quantities of squids. Though as a rule these are small, the contents of one whale stomach showed conclusively that there are even today in the waters of the ocean ferocious giant squids like prehistoric monsters. The true story of these deep-sea monsters completely overshadows such fictional devilfish or octopuses as Victor Hugo described in his *Toilers of the Deep*, for the incomplete arm alone of one of these squids was found to measure 27 feet in length. We know from later discoveries that they may grow to a total length of over 50 feet, or as long as whales themselves, and that they possess enormous arms with great hooked suction cups. Every now and then a whale is found with terrible scars on its body resulting from a fierce encounter with one of these colossal creatures.

The history of whale fisheries is one of careless exploitation which has driven a once important industry from the Atlantic to the distant Antarctic. The sperm whale or cachalot was at one time caught in nearly every part of the Atlantic, and the right whale flourished in the colder northern waters. As far back as the eighteenth century the United States alone outfitted over 700 whaling ships which hunted along with British and some Scandinavian ships from North Africa to the Arctic. By the middle of the nineteenth century the slaughter was so great that both sperm and right whale became almost extinct and the rorqual whales alone lived in undiminished numbers, largely because with their speedier movements they were able to evade the old type of hand harpoon.

This was a temporary respite, however. In 1860 the Norwegian Captain Sven Foyn invented a harpoon gun with which the faster rorquals could be taken. By this time the American whaling industry had practically disappeared, and the revival was almost entirely Norwegian. The renewed onslaught against rorquals soon decimated these unfortunate creatures in the North Atlantic, with the result that at the beginning of this century the fishery transferred its major operations from the coasts of Norway, Iceland, and the Shetlands to the rich virgin waters of the Antarctic. Today the North Atlantic is no longer so important to the whaling industry; but it is possible that with continued international control the northern herds of these giant animals may return to their former size and number.

Although in proportion to size there are many fiercer creatures in the ocean, the sperm whale is nevertheless a carnivore, and its long lower jaw is well provided with great pointed teeth, enabling it to catch the fishes and squids which go to make up its food. The right whales and rorquals are entirely different from the sperm. Instead of teeth, their upper jaws grow out into horny plates with long hairlike fringes of whalebone hanging down to form enormous sieves. Tons of water are taken into the mouth and then forced through the whalebone strainers by means of the huge tongue, which then scrapes the plankton off and thrusts it into the gullet. The horny fringe is thus a natural plankton net which serves to filter out the millions of small crustacea that make up the diet of both right whales and rorquals. The infinite numbers of tiny crustacea needed to sustain the large bodies of whales, weighing hundreds of tons, gives a measure of the prodigious quantities of plankton in salt waters.

Whales do not feed intensively all the year round although their rate of growth is colossal. In the summer they find their food in the colder subpolar waters in the form of great swarms of euphausids (small shrimplike crustacea with branching legs), still smaller crustacea known as copepods, and small drifting shellfish called pteropods. In the North Atlantic they may even strain small herring out of the water. In the winter they travel south, and at one time were the object of whale fisheries along the coasts of Portugal, North Africa, and the Azores. While wintering in tropical and subtropical waters they find little to feed on, since nowhere does plankton grow as richly as in the colder seas. During the winter their gargantuan matings take place, for they are in all respects mammals in spite of their fishlike habits and appearance. Few whales give birth to more than five calves during their lifetime, and the calves are helplessly dependent on their mother's milk during the first six months of their lives; thus it is not surprising that their reproduction could not keep pace with the inroads made by uncontrolled whaling. The modern 20,000-ton factory ships are equipped to handle together as many as 40,000 whales a year, which is uncomfortably close to the natural rate of replenishment.

The complex economies of the great civilizations that have grown up around the River are no more involved than the

economy of the creatures within it. Between the consumer and
the producer is an elaborate chain of distributors, wholesalers,
and retailers; and this has its undersea counterpart, which, as
we shall see later, is greatly influenced by the circulating
waters of the River itself. Besides the whales there are such
fishes as herring and menhaden which also feed directly on
the plankton. In turn they become the food of cod and other
carnivores. They strain their food from the water through a
sieve made of slender filaments, the gill rakers, which project
from the front side of each gill arch. Some bottom-feeding
fish, like haddock, soles, and plaice, feed on small shellfish,
starfish, and worms, but these in turn trace their food back to
the drifting life, and their own young are part of the plankton.
Even here, however, we have not reached the end of the food
chain; for we still have the further complexities of plankton
feeding on plankton. At the end of this long line of animals
eating still smaller animals we come to the microscopic plankton plants, the pasturage of the sea, the real producers.

We have already mentioned diatoms, which Sir Joseph
Hooker rightly took to be important among the food plants
in the plankton, but these are not alone, though in the cooler
waters they bulk large in the drifting plant life. In warmer
waters, as the diatoms become less plentiful their place is
taken by dinoflagellates, which have the same plantlike way of
feeding, but which are in other respects very different; for
whereas the diatoms are encased in an armor of silica the dinoflagellates either have a thin cellulose shell or are completely
naked. Though so small that their size is reckoned in thou-
sandths of an inch the naked dinoflagellates may sometimes
grow in such vast numbers that the sea is discolored for miles.
This was the cause of a lethal "Red Tide" that spread intermittently along the Gulf of Mexico shores of western Florida
during 1947. Though harmless in ordinary concentrations, the
myriads in the "Red Tide," as many as 60 million to a pint of

water, made the sea slimy to the touch and highly poisonous to fishes. Over 50 million fishes died as a result of this outburst of invisible plant life, littering the beaches with their decaying remains. Less harmful but more permanent is the growth of another type of microscopic drifting sea plant, *Trichodesmium erythraeum*, which is said to cause the color of the Red Sea and the sea of Baja California. Important as the diatoms and dinoflagellates are, there is reason to believe today that even smaller plantlike creatures, less than one ten-thousandth of an inch in size and passing through the finest silk nets, may in many places form the greater bulk of the seagoing pasturage, and that this nannoplankton, or ultraplankton, is the most productive food source of the oceans.

The detailed exploration of this great and complicated chain of sea life and its relation to the currents and drifts of the Ocean River has been partly carried out by the expeditions we have mentioned and by their more recent successors. The work begun from the heaving decks of exploring vessels could never have been completed, however, without the painstaking researches of men in the marine laboratories that developed side by side with them along the shores of the Ocean River. One of the first laboratories to be established and one of the most famous was founded at Naples in 1874; but scientific interest was already roused along the shores of other tributary seas and along the seaboard of the River itself. The Marine Biological Association of the United Kingdom opened its laboratory at the entrance to the English Channel at Plymouth in 1879, under the sponsorship of the great biologist Thomas Henry Huxley. Its contributions to our knowledge of plankton and of the complicated effects which water currents and the chemical makeup of sea water have on marine life have done much to lay the foundations of our present understanding of these problems.

The list of marine research laboratories that grew up in the following years covers many countries on both sides of the Atlantic and is associated with the names of many famous scientists. The fisheries of the North Sea and neighboring waters were the ultimate objectives of much of the research carried out at the German stations of Kiel and Helgoland, the British laboratories at Aberdeen and Millport in Scotland, and at Port Erin, Hull, and Lowestoft, and a number of important stations on the shores of France, Denmark, and the Scandinavian countries, such as those of Roscoff, Oslo, Bergen, Bornö, Copenhagen, and elsewhere. It was at Copenhagen in 1899 that the efforts of these countries and the disinterested internationalism of scientists resulted in the organization of the International Council for the Exploration of the Sea, devoted to the co-operation of European nations in marine research and particularly in the conservation of fishery resources.

It was not long before laboratories began to be established on the opposite side of the Atlantic and even in midocean, for a Bermuda station began operation in 1906. Today the principal eastern North American institutions for marine biological research extend from the research station of the Fisheries Research Board of Canada at St. Johns, Newfoundland, to the Marine Laboratory at the University of Miami, strategically located at the roots of the Gulf Stream. One of the most important is the Woods Hole Oceanographic Institution in Massachusetts, but there are many state and Federal fishery laboratories along the coast as well as university summer stations, museums, and other marine institutes which are steadily adding to our store of knowledge.

Less than a century ago life in the Ocean River was still a great unknown to biologists, just as 400 years before that the course and extent of its currents was a dark mystery to navigators. At first the scientists attached to the pioneer expeditions and laboratories were mainly occupied with discovering what manner of life existed in the open sea. With advancing knowledge the front of scientific attack soon shifted from the question of "what" to the questions of "how" and "why." Today it is mainly concerned with the intricate relationships among the different types of life, with the quantities and numbers and rates of growth in the food chain which are at the root of ocean economics, and with unravelling the complicated effects of water currents upon them.

We already have some rough answers, though our marine accounting is still in its infancy. Johannes Peterson of the Copenhagen laboratory has estimated that ten tons of plant or animal food are needed to produce one ton of fish. One ton of carnivorous fishes like codfish may consume ten tons of plankton feeders, as for example young herring, and these in turn may eat 100 tons of plankton. There may be still other links in the chain. The net result is that when a trawler brings back its catch each ton of seafood landed is the end result of a growth of considerably more than 1,000 tons of microscopic plant cells. The total annual world catch of food fish is something like 13 million tons, so that the plankton production is at least 13,000,000,000 tons in the comparatively small areas of the ocean to which commercial fishing is restricted. We do not know how many tons of cod may be eaten by a hungry New Englander, but it is clear that the plankton could support a good proportion of the world's population.

In these days of a rapidly growing world human population and a lagging food supply it is tempting to consider the possibilities of harvesting plankton directly, so that full advantage might be taken of the great food potentialities of the ocean. Scientists in several countries have in fact attempted to devise efficient methods of extracting plankton from sea water. Unfortunately, nothing practical has yet come of it. Plankton is fishy to the taste and not particularly palatable, but it would probably make excellent cattle food. The real difficulty, however, lies in another direction. The exceedingly small plants and animals that make up this drifting life are usually scattered throughout the water so that the task of concentrating them profitably, in large quantities, by filtration or otherwise, has so far resisted the inventiveness of man. The truth is that whales and fishes are so much more efficient than we are in collecting plankton and turning it into edible food that there is little immediate likelihood of man improving on nature.

There is still a further step in the long food chain that connects food fishes with sea water and the Ocean River itself: this lies in the invisible food needed as fertilizer for the small plant cells. Plants on land send down their roots into the soil and thus extract the chemical salts of nitrogen and phosphorus, the other fertilizer elements, and the minor growth elements needed to build up their tissues; only in the soil do they find such material. In the ocean, though, there is no need for food-seeking roots; the salt water is a gigantic hydroponics system, a bath of liquid fertilizer.

The chemical salts of sea water vital to the nourishment of plants — particularly the phosphorus and nitrogen compounds — are dissolved in very small concentrations, and are easily used up. The solutions used for hydroponics farming become weakened as the plants extract the chemicals for growth; the goodness of the soil is removed by excessive cropping so that it becomes impoverished unless periodically fertilized; and the ocean waters in like manner lose to the plankton their food chemicals. We have already mentioned the constant rain of dead plankton from the surface waters to the bottom. At increasing depths, by the inexorable processes of decay, this continual rain of microscopic bodies is turned back into fertilizer salts, just as a gardener turns kitchen refuse into fertilizer in his compost heap. Thus chemical pabulum is removed from the surface and accumulates in the deep, cold waters — the chemical reservoirs in the oceanic hydroponics system.

Here is where turbulence, rising and falling waters, and the conflict of cold and warm currents play their part in the economy of the sea, by replenishing the vanishing plant food. If the waters remained calm and motionless, the upper layers would be drained of their vital chemicals and life in the oceans would cease. Instead, replenishment of the surface fertilizer comes in many different ways, and the efficiency with which it is brought about has much to do with the yield and location of our commercial fisheries. The rivers, draining water from the land, also bring with them fertilizer leached out from the soil, and thus add continually to the fertility of coastal waters. This is one of the reasons why our fisheries are found in the shallow waters along the submerged edges of the continents, out as far as the edge of the slope where the sea floor runs from 100 fathoms or so to the deeps. But there are other reasons.

Plants cannot live without sunlight, and thus those in the plankton are able to grow rapidly only in depths of less than a hundred feet or so, depending of course on the amount of sunlight and the clearness of the water. It is therefore easy to see that only where the sea floor does not exceed this depth are the chemical foods released by decay at the bottom still available to plankton. In such shallow water there is no great danger of losing fertilizer, for it is brought back into circulation by plankton as fast as the dead bodies release it. Even in somewhat deeper water, though the plant life cannot grow rapidly in the lower layers, there are often mixing processes taking place that bring fertilizer back to the surface. When and where this happens we may usually expect to find a good plankton growth and therefore a good crop of fish.

In waters of moderate depth, as in the English Channel, the mixing of rich bottom water and depleted surface water is by no means continuous. There are sea seasons for growth just as there are on land, but for different reasons. The painstaking sampling of sea water, the making of chemical analyses, and the numerous detailed routine tasks that go to make up scientific research have shown that in spring a great plankton outgrowth takes place, using up the chemical food within the zone of active plant life. Toward summer the surface water becomes heated by the sun, but only in the upper layers — since water conducts heat rather slowly. These hot upper layers of water are lighter than those below, and therefore, like oil, they mix with them very poorly — particularly during summer when the winds are light and prevent the replenishment of surface fertilizer by mixing from below. During this time the rain of plankton carries chemical food down to the deeper water out of the zone of plant growth, until finally the surface supply of fertilizer is depleted and further growth is stopped.

As autumn comes and as the surface again becomes cooler, the different layers are able to mix again. The autumn gales may trouble the fisherman, but together with the flow of water they conspire to stir up the lower layers with their store of chemical food and so provide for a new growth of plankton at the surface. The second crop is shortlived, for light and heat begin to fail. As winter approaches the upper layers cool further, until they become heavier than the water beneath and tend to sink. This adds further to the mixing process, and fertilizer is restored to the surface. During the depths of winter, both the poor light and a temperature too low for rapid growth together with other factors play their part in holding back any new outburst of plankton until the warmth and sunlight of spring set the cycle of life once more on its rounds.

The Ocean River, with its branches and its tributary streams, acts like a gigantic pump, continually replenishing the depleted fertilizer in this natural hydroponic system from the deep sea reservoir. Wherever surface water is blown by winds away from the land, or where it streams apart in diverging currents, the underlying colder water, with its rich store of chemical food, is drawn up to replace it. The west coast of

South Africa is a notable example of such a place — and here is a major fishery. The seas off the west coast of Portugal and Morocco are likewise areas of up-welling waters that provide the nutrition for tuna and sardine fisheries. In the Gulf of Mexico the major fishing area of the Campeche Bank is also an area of divergent water flow.

One of the main reservoirs of the ocean is the deep Sargasso Sea at the center of the great Atlantic eddy. The blue surface waters of this central sea are like those of the Gulf Stream poor in fertilizer and therefore poor in plankton. Compared to coastal waters they are the deserts of the ocean. Drifting Sargassum weed provides a home for small fishes, crabs, and snails camouflaged by color pattern and by weird shapes to resemble the fronds of their hiding place, but the aggregate quantity of life is small. Beneath the surface, however, as the dying weed sinks down and as the impoverished plankton rains its nourishment into the waters below, the depths become richer in food, so that at a depth of three or four thousand feet — according to Hjort — a greater quantity of life is supported than in equal depths of the more easterly ocean. Sometimes the nutrient from this cold, deep Sargasso water may be brought back to foster life where the Gulf Stream eddies drag it to the surface. The arctic and antarctic waters, however, are the great sources of fertilizer, in sufficient quantity to nourish the huge amounts of plankton needed by the whales in their subpolar feeding grounds. From the arctic coasts and rivers of Siberia great quantities of fresh water drain into the sea, carrying with them the debris of vegetation and the raw materials for ocean food. Thus the Arctic Sea is a carrier of food material, while the less fertile Gulf Stream acts as a carrier of heat.

Millions of years ago the action of glaciers wore down the most ancient rocks of Canada, the Canadian shield, and carried great masses of rock and gravel to the edge of the continent, where they now form the floor of the wide, shallow submarine shelf of the Grand Banks of Newfoundland and the fishing grounds of New England. Here the arctic waters, well laden with detritus and rich in fertilizer, meet the warm waters of the Gulf Stream, and at this arctic front a great swirling and stirring of waters takes place — just as the cold fronts in the river of air bring about violent winds and storm. This turbulent mixing of waters provides the proper conditions of temperature and food for an outburst of plankton growth, and the crop of ocean pasturage in turn supports the greatest commercial fishery of the western Atlantic. The same beneficial effects of arctic fronts have much to do with the living wealth of fisheries elsewhere. The branches and tendrils of the River near Iceland, in the Norwegian Sea, and in the still more northerly Barents Sea, form growth-stimulating swirls of water and bring fertility as a result of their conflict with colder waters.

Now we begin to see how the Ocean River brings life to its fisheries by means of the perpetual conflict between the cold arctic waters and the great warm flood of the Gulf Stream, and how the pulses and changes in this ocean circulation have far-reaching effects on our sea-food harvest. When we can tell exactly how this happens, and when we can predict the effects of weakened or increased flow in the River, we shall be closer to predicting changes in the great fisheries and even in the weather. Were we able to foresee changes in this pulse of the ocean circulation, however, we should still be far from knowing their full effects on the commercial fish catches.

These changes work in a complicated manner and their results are sometimes paradoxical. The French scientist Le Danois, and with him the American Columbus Iselin, have suggested that a speeding up of the Gulf Stream flow may bring colder instead of warmer water to the Atlantic fishery grounds; it could happen in this way. When a current of water increases its flow — as we have shown in an earlier chapter —

the lighter, warmer water shifts to the right and the heavier and colder to the left. As the great North Atlantic circle of water speeds up it draws the warm water inward, toward the Sargasso Sea, but when the flow slackens the reverse takes place and warm water spreads outward over the surface toward the Arctic fronts. Though it has never been definitely proved, it is at least likely that a faster Gulf Stream may mean less warm water in the marginal seas of the northeast Atlantic.

Science still has much to learn about these complicated actions and interactions, but in the meanwhile there have been many occasions to remind us that they exist. Since 1929 the sea around Greenland has become warmer and codfish have moved in where they were scarce before. Warm and cold years in the Norwegian Sea affect the appearance and disappearance of shoals of fish; they alter the growth of trees and they change the harvest of the dry land. Coral reefs, typically tropical growths, exist in Bermuda far north of a limit beyond which they would quickly die were it not for the Gulf Stream. And in 1882 a change in the position of the Gulf Stream caused the death of more than a billion tilefish.

In the latter part of the nineteenth century a new fishery was discovered off the coast of southern New England, in waters between 50 and 100 fathoms deep on the western border of the Gulf Stream. The jubilant fishermen aboard their Gloucester schooners rapidly developed this windfall — and with good reason, for their lines and hooks brought in tilefishes of 10 to 50 pounds with flesh every bit as good as cod. In March of 1882 the fishery completely disappeared. Vessels crossing this part of the ocean reported dead fishes covering the surface as far as the eye could see during nearly two days of steady sailing. The terrific mortality took place over an area of 7,000 square miles, and estimates have placed the number of dead fishes at over one billion. At the time of the calamity there was an unusually strong run of the cold Labrador current. It therefore seems very likely that a sideways shift of the Gulf Stream and of the delicate balance between warm and cold currents had suddenly flooded the fishing grounds with unusually cold water, and this great and rapid change from more normal conditions almost annihilated the tilefish. Only now, after seventy years, are they beginning to return to their former numbers.

No other stretch of salt water has received as much attention from scientists as the North Sea, but even there the interaction of life and water is so complicated that we cannot yet predict the ebb and flow of fisheries with complete certainty. We do know that the Gulf Stream sends waters around the north of Scotland and then south into the North Sea, and that where these meet water from the English Channel there are great swirls and eddies. Where this happens rich bottom water is drawn to the surface, and there we have the great fishing grounds of the Dogger Bank and the Great Fisher Bank, where plankton grows thick.

Sometimes the natural effects of fluctuating water movements have been beneficial; and in at least one case they help us to forecast good and bad years in the fisheries. The herring fishery south of England at the mouth of the Channel seems to depend on the extent to which Atlantic water, bringing enrichment from the deeper layers, is able to push eastward and thus replace the less productive Channel water. The work of F. S. Russell at the Plymouth Laboratory has given us a rapid way of detecting these movements without the tedious necessity of chemical water analysis, and thus predicting the probable fluctuations in the fishery. He makes use of the fact that water currents carry with them, in a sort of forced migration, the plankton animals living in them. In Atlantic water — partly derived from the Gulf Stream — there lives one of the tiny, fierce-jawed, torpedo-like arrow worms known to scientists as *Sagitta elegans*. Its near relative, *Sagitta setosa*, on the other hand, is found only in less salty water, such as Channel water. The kind of arrow worm found in the waters off Plymouth is an important clue as to how far the Atlantic water has pushed its way eastward.

Before 1931 the arrow worms off Plymouth were *Sagitta elegans* and there was a valuable herring fishery there; in later years the herring fishery ceased. The plankton was poorer, and the water now contained *Sagitta setosa* instead of *Sagitta elegans*, thus suggesting that since 1931 Atlantic water had failed to enter the Channel and that the water that replaced it was too poor in phosphates to support the herring fishery. At the other end of the Channel, in the North Sea, a similar movement takes place at the northern boundary of the Channel water. Thus a study of arrow worms in the plankton off Plymouth helps us to predict in a rather general way both the Plymouth fishery and the fishery of the North Sea.

Plankton indicators — as organisms like *Sagitta* are called — are sometimes useful in tracing the path of ocean currents, though they must be used with proper scientific caution. Their tale of travel from far places is sometimes familiar to fishermen when they see in the cold Gulf of Maine waters or in the waters off European shores the Portuguese man-of-war or tropical kinds of jellyfish telling of their long drift from warmer latitudes. At times subtropical plankton is found in the scientist's silk nets as far north as the Labrador Sea. There are other cases, though, where plankton is able to escape from the drag of currents. If this were not so, many parts of the ocean might lose their rich pasturage, due to its continual drifting away in currents, without leaving behind a sufficient residue to breed new stock.

In the rich antarctic feeding grounds of whales there is a continual northward surface drift of the diatoms and crustacea during the summer. This does not lead to depletion of the plankton, however, because in winter the small organisms sink through the water into warmer, deeper layers, which are returning southward. Arriving again at their point of origin, the plankton now rises to the surface. Thus a regular cycle keeps the antarctic surface supplied with plankton.

Replenishment of plankton in tropical waters comes partly from the cooling and sinking of Gulf Stream water in the north and its return southward as a deep water flow. In the Gulf of Maine the work of Bigelow, Huntsman, and Redfield has shown that the breeding stock of plankton crustacea is maintained by a great circular eddy. This flow carries the eggs during their development around a great slow circuit which takes three months to complete. Johannes Schmidt of the Danish laboratory has found that the Icelandic cod fishery similarly depends on circular currents for its continued existence. When codfish lay their eggs they rise toward the surface and hatch there. The water currents around Iceland therefore carry the eggs of young codfish away from their spawning grounds off the south and west coasts. If the growing fishes were not returned to the spawning grounds there would be no future spawning, but fortunately for the fishery the currents complete a circuit around Iceland in a clockwise direction. When the developing codfish have drifted to the north and east coast they sink to the bottom, there to continue growth and to feed like their parents on bottom life. When they mature and the time comes to breed they return to the spawning grounds.

Many fishes undertake local migrations every year. Herring, menhaden, and pilchards — all plankton-eating fish — were probably coastal or fresh-water fish originally. They are normally scattered about in fairly deep water, but when ready to breed they gather in spawning schools in shallower depths. Whereas the herring are cold-water fishes, their relatives the shad are mostly found in warmer water, and their spawning migration brings them into rivers in search of warmth and oxygen.

Thus we see a great dynamic interlocking of the currents of

the Ocean River and of the complex patterns of life within it. The drift of water both aided and hindered Columbus in his voyage of exploration; and it plays its part today in the great migrations of fishes. Some of these great mass movements are dedicated to feeding and others to breeding. Some are local, like those of the Icelandic cod fishery, but others put even Columbus into the shade by the length of time they take and the danger involved. Their migrations are still in many ways a great puzzle to science. Not the least of these mysteries is how the fish is able to find its way along a well-defined path of hundreds or even thousands of miles through water that it may never have experienced before. The greatest of these travellers are the eels and the salmon, though the tunas follow them closely.

The most adventurous journey of all is that of the freshwater eel, which we have mentioned already in connection with the lost land of Atlantis. For many years men have wondered how eels were able to grow and multiply in rivers and streams and ponds, for nobody had ever seen their eggs or very young stages. Izaak Walton expressed contemporary opinion in 1653 when he wrote, ". . . eels are bred of a particular dew, falling in the months of May or June on the banks of some particular ponds or rivers . . . which in a few days are, by the sun's heat turned into eels." Even more curious ideas had their vogue, and the truth had not been discovered even when Pasteur exploded the old ideas of spontaneous generation, whereby life was supposed to arise from mud or putrefaction. The only clue was that suddenly, at certain times of the year, enormous numbers of elvers or young eels appear in the mouths of rivers and begin to swim upstream. The strange story of whence they come was not unravelled until 1922, when Johannes Schmidt, a Danish scientist, finally pieced together scattered evidence and found the solution to the mystery. Since, unlike Columbus, the eels keep no log books of their travels, and since we cannot follow their movements at sea directly, the evidence was indirect.

From the contents of plankton nets towed in various parts of the Atlantic Ocean aboard the *Thor* and *Dana,* Schmidt found that younger and younger stages of the tiny eels could be traced farther and farther back to the deep central part of the North Atlantic Ocean southeast of Bermuda. Transparent eggs about the size of a pea are found there in the spring about 500 feet below the surface, so that mating probably takes place near the deep-sea floor beneath. When the flat, leaf-like eel larva is first hatched it is only a quarter of an inch long. It is so different from the adult eel in appearance that when first discovered it was thought to be a new and altogether different fish, and was therefore named "leptocephalus." From the time of hatching these bizarre creatures grow slowly, and meanwhile travel on the long path toward fresh water. As a result of numerous measurements Schmidt was able to show that the baby eel takes three years to reach European waters. The American eel, a very close relative, breeds close by and to the southwest of the spawning area of its European cousins, but its journey to the American rivers takes only a year.

We cannot be sure, but it seems likely that the newly-hatched leptocephalus rising part way to the surface is caught by the Gulf Stream and thus carried in a slow easterly drift to the European shores. By the time it reaches there it has become of an age when it is strongly attracted by the fresh waters draining out of rivers, and it is old enough to swim against tide and current into the estuaries. Perhaps the rise of the American leptocephalus to a particular depth at a particular time places it within the grasp of somewhat different layers of water flow, so that when it reaches the time to change into an elver the ocean drifts have brought it near American shores. We can only surmise, for the complete evidence is still to be collected.

During the long transatlantic crossing the young eel grows

until it becomes three inches long, though still in appearance a typical leptocephalus. When it arrives at its destination in the river mouth it undergoes a great change. The leaflike shape disappears and it becomes narrow and round and begins to look like a miniature of its parents. In the rivers and streams where it takes up its home for most of its remaining life it grows to be a foot or more in length. Then, as much as twenty years later, it begins the journey back to the spawning grounds of the Sargasso Sea, where a new generation begins the long ocean circuit.

Eels return to their original deep-sea home when they are ready to breed, but salmon follow an opposite course. From the age of eighteen months or so they live on the floor of the ocean, where they feed on abundant red shrimps. At maturity they are impelled to seek the river in which they were hatched and to return to the headwaters for spawning. Still other fishes, like the tuna, confine their long migrations to salt water, but we are no better able to explain their uncanny ability to follow the same path, generation after generation.

The European tunny spend their winters in the subtropical Atlantic in deep water and grow there to maturity. During the spring they move northward by way of the coasts of Spain and Portugal, where they spawn. Large numbers of them enter the Mediterranean, but others follow the herring and mackerel schools and so reach the North Sea. We know little of the return of older fishes and of the first southward migration of newly hatched tunny to the subtropical deep waters.

The same is true of the bluefin tuna of the western Atlantic, which is believed to be a separate offshoot of the same species as the European tunny. It is rarely that any but scattered individuals of these giant mackerels are seen south of the Florida Straits. Somewhere about the end of May, however, the first schools begin to appear off Cat Cay in the Florida Current, directly opposite the Straits from Miami. They average 500 pounds, and offer a spectacular challenge to anglers who gather for the famous Tuna Tournaments at Bimini and at the fabulous Cat Cay Club. School after school of these fish pass by for two weeks or more, steadily driving northward in the current as if following a definite timetable. Later they are found off the coast of New England, where they feed on herring and mackerel. Finally in August they congregate in large numbers off Wedgeport, Nova Scotia, where they grow fat on the abundant food fish, and where competitors in the International Tuna Competition pit their skill and the strength of their rods and lines against the sheer weight of a fish that has been known to reach 1,800 pounds.

Schools of tuna have been seen off Jamaica during February, and isolated fish have been seen at other parts of the Caribbean Sea. It is probable then that they begin their long journey somewhere in this part of the West Indies, but just where they start and what path they take we do not know. Nor do we know when they breed, though their roe appears to be spent when they pass through the Florida Straits. Above all, we do not know what happens when they disappear from Nova Scotia. Perhaps the investigations now being carried out from Miami and Bermuda and Woods Hole will bring the answer.

Many of these journeyings — and those of other fish we have not mentioned — are in some way triggered into action by the breeding urge or by an urge to seek distant feeding grounds. The fishes themselves are undoubtedly guided in some manner by ocean currents, by changes in temperature and saltness, by the amount of oxygen or carbon dioxide in the water, or by the direction of sunlight. Just how these complex influences play their part has never been completely explained for any fish migration. The American bluefin tuna migrate along the slowly cooling length of the Gulf Stream, but since the temperature changes only by an infinitesimal fraction of a degree for each mile or so of the course there is nothing along the line of migration at any moment to point the way to cooler waters. These giant tunas migrate to waters rich in herring and mackerel and shad, but there is no sign on their way to tell them in which direction their food will be found. During a great part of their travel they are suspended in a great water stream out of sight of the land or the sea floor, and there is no easy reference in sight to tell them whether they are moving with the Stream or not. Recently it has been discovered that there are streaks or flaws along the direction of flow of the Gulf Stream; perhaps the tuna align themselves with these in their northerly exodus. Most likely — according to a few who have studied the mystery — they may be able to use the sun to direct themselves. These are all conjectures, and the certain answer is still to be found.

Scientists who devote their attention to the great sea fisheries are concerned not only with problems of migration, of food and growth, of the complicated effects of drifts and currents, of hot and cold, and of salt and fresh. All these are necessary preliminaries to the immediately practical question of how intensively we can carry our fishing without depleting the natural stocks of fishes, without reducing the average catch for each day away from port, and without bringing about a crop of smaller or inferior fish.

The ocean has a very much greater food potentiality than the land, and so far only a small part of this is being harvested. This has led in the past to false ideas about the "inexhaustible supply of food in the sea." It is true that each codfish will lay as many as 4,000,000 eggs, but there is a huge mortality among them. Eaten by the larger plankton carnivores and even by their own parents, these countless billions of eggs are greatly diminished in number before they have a chance to hatch. The young fishes, too, are the natural food of others. Thus there is a limit to the number of fish in any one part of the sea. As a result of heavy fishing the British and other European trawlers have gradually moved, over the past seventy-five years, from grounds close to shore into the North Sea, from there to the edge of the continental shelf beyond Ireland and Scotland, and even to the Icelandic waters and the waters around Greenland and in the Barents Sea, in a continuous fight to find fish in sufficient concentration to justify the cost of operation. It has been a vicious circle, for the fewer fish there are near home, the more elaborate and expensive the gear needed to operate efficiently and to compensate for the longer and longer periods spent in travelling to and from distant fishing grounds instead of in fishing.

Perhaps because they are direct plankton feeders and closer to the ultimate source of food, the herring stocks seem little changed by the effects of fishing. This is not true of the carnivorous codfish and plaice. About 70% of all the plaice in the North Sea have been caught, and both the average size of plaice and cod and the catch of these fishes per day away from port have dropped.

The discovery of the Grand Banks was, as we shall see in the Codfish Frontier, the start of a great new fishery. For a long time this seemed inexhaustible, but there are signs now that the inflexible laws of cause and effect apply to the fisheries of the New World as they do to those of the North Sea. This codfish frontier has provided a treasure more lasting than the gold and silver of the Caribbean frontier, but one which carries with it its own problems. The Ocean River is a self-fertilizing pasturage that needs no ploughing and seeding, but the harvest of fish must be gathered as a crop, with an eye to the proper yield, and not as an ore to be mined as quickly and completely as machinery and men can do it. We must perforce conserve what we have, for the ocean is our last frontier — there is no longer an unexploited New World awaiting exploration and development across the River.

10

THE TREASURE REVEALED

THE familiar rhyme tells us, "In fourteen hundred and ninety-two, Columbus sailed the ocean blue." But why then and not earlier or later? Certain men who make a mark in history find the time ripe for their adventure. But they also help to detonate the time by a specific act of daring and imagination beyond that of their fellows and are thus remembered.

The time was ripe at the end of the fifteenth century because the preceding two centuries had witnessed an increasing misery spread across Europe from Italy to England, this in spite of local centers of prosperity in Genoa and Venice. Wars, plagues, and poverty were the lot of the average citizen. The population of Europe is supposed to have declined a third since the days of Augustus. Besides disease, the general conditions of trade contributed to the poor state of Europe. In England and on the continent the simple fact that there was little or no winter forage or hay for cattle affected the diet, and forced men to search for preservatives like salt and spices, and to substitute fish for meat. Spices lay to the Far East, fish in the unknown seas. But there was a "Moslem curtain" between Europe and its former eastern trade routes. The Turks took Constantinople in 1453. They had overrun the Balkans, were pressing up the Danube, and threatened and finally took Syria and Egypt, bringing to a standstill the commerce of Venice and Genoa with the East.

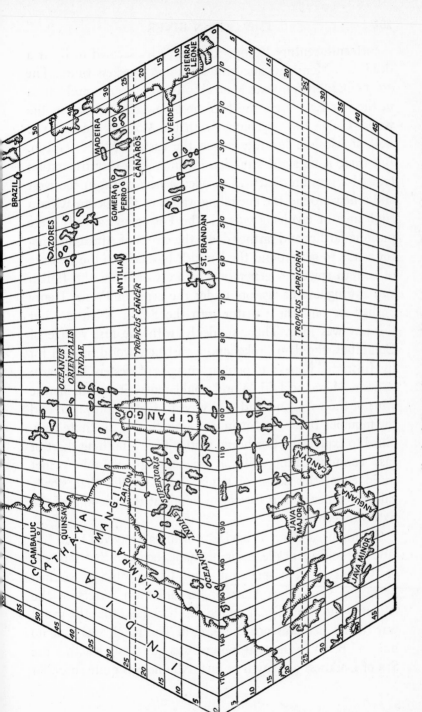

Sketch of Toscanelli's map, which was sent to Portugal in 1474, and used by Columbus in his first voyage across the Atlantic.

Fifteenth-century Europe in many ways seemed to be at a dead end. Men bemoaned the slack and hopeless times. The great crusading spirit was at an ebb. Turkey, nearby, and China in the Far East, were the two most powerful nations in the world. China had no contact with the West because of the wall of Moslem hostility across the eastern Mediterranean. But there is no static situation in time. This very frustration created a pressure that was to open a new world in the west and renew around the encircling waters of the Ocean River a fresh area of civilizing energy. The Portuguese already were pushing farther and farther down the coasts of Africa, looking for a way to get around the Turkish blockade to the treasure of eastern spices. A generation before Columbus the Italian and Portuguese navigators under the aegis of Prince Henry pushed beyond the equator into the South Atlantic — but the way was long. Then, suddenly, with the first voyage of Columbus, the dam broke; and a vast new world opened for the frustrated hopes and pent-up energies of western European nations. Here the Old World could renew its youth in the arms of the west, and find easy ways to China and Japan and the fabulous Indies. In Spain, the Church and the State combined to exploit the Caribbean world. Today, nothing short of easy communication with a neighboring habitable planet could equal this sense of a new lease on life that slowly gained momentum in European minds at the opening of the sixteenth century.

Columbus, a Genoese navigator who had traveled from Iceland to the Canaries learning his trade, believed that Japan — or "Cipangu," as he spelled it — and China could be reached by sailing straight west across the unknown waters of the Atlantic. Most intelligent men of his time held that the world was round; that was not the hazard. The pinch was that no one had put it to the trial; no one was quite sure whether the Sea of Darkness was myth or fact. No one was quite sure that the Coagulated Sea of the ancients might not catch and hold an adventurous craft in a clutch of doom. Columbus was a great sea captain, not only because he backed up Galileo in action but because he proved that the vast, slow-revolving pool of the Sargasso Sea was only skin deep in weed and no longer to be dreaded. In 1436 a chart of the Atlantic issued by Andrea Bianca called the Sargasso Sea the "Mer de Baga," the sea of berries. Centuries after Columbus popular tradition still held that lost vessels made their slow revolution in this sea of death and doldrums.

Several scraps of knowledge and of hearsay evidence were available to Columbus to buoy up his imagination as he faced the hazard of decision in planning his enterprise. He had sailed to Bristol and the French channel ports as a young man. Here were fishermen who were familiar with the open seas west of Ireland and north to the Iceland fishing banks. It is also probably true that Columbus himself had touched at Icelandic ports where men believed in the Norse adventures beyond Greenland to Markland and Vinland in the unknown west. But perhaps the most comforting bit of sea talk came to him right at home. For in the port of Palos lived an ancient mariner called Pedro Vasquez de la Frontera who had in 1452 made a voyage of discovery — according to Morison — with a Madeiran named Diego de Teive, under orders of Henry the Navigator of Portugal. These men had sailed into and through the Sargasso Sea, and heading north had discovered Corvo and Flores of the Azores group. Searching for Hi-Brazil, they had gone as far north as the latitude of Cape Clear, Ireland. Old Pedro Vasquez came to Columbus and told him to be of good heart for his venture, as he was certain that lands lay to the west of the Sargasso Sea. Unfortunately this poor man was murdered in a tavern brawl before Columbus returned to prove that his predictions had been right.

There is a kind of poetic justice in the fact that Columbus

outfitted in the Niebla district of Andalusia in the close neighborhood of the ancient seaport of Tartessos, where earlier
adventurers of an unknown race had traded into the wide
Atlantic two thousand years before Christ. This port was latei
known as Tarshish, where King Solomon bought gold and apes
and ivory.

The port of Palos in the Niebla region is only twenty-five
miles from the Portuguese border. Columbus, in outfitting
there, could use the best small seagoing vessels of his time,
the caravels of about fifty tons burden which had already
made voyages of some thousands of miles along the western
African coasts. They were lateen rigged and therefore could
point and make sail quickly, but were difficult to handle when
running before the wind. Columbus remedied this by a kind
of hermaphrodite rig, part square sail and part lateen. This
gave him handy, seaworthy craft that could make good time
in spite of their lumbering lines.

Before we set forth with the mature Columbus into the
roots of the Ocean River west of the Canaries we should
record one more evidence of the wide experience of pilots and
navigators of his time. There isn't much actual historical material here to justify more than a long surmise, but it tickles the
fancy. Unfortunately the Lisbon earthquake destroyed, for
all we know, other matter of this kind relative to Columbus as
a younger pilot. According to the notes of Ferdinand Columbus regarding his father, this was written: "I sailed in the
year 1477, in the month of February, a hundred leagues beyond
the island of Tile [Thule or Iceland], whose northern port is
in latitude 73° N. and not 63° as some would have it be; nor
does it lie on the meredian where Ptolemy says the west begins,
but much further west. And to this island, which is as big as
England, come English with their merchandise, especially
they of Bristol. And at the season when I was there the sea
was not frozen, but the tides were so great that in some places

they rose 26 braccia and fell as much in depth." Stefansson says that this was an open winter in the north. Columbus may certainly be off on his latitude, but the rest of the record fits.

We are following the Ocean River from east to west at its southern extremity beyond the Canaries. Others besides Columbus had planned western voyages but, most of them — like those of Nuremberg who planned to send Martin Behaim on a voyage similar to that of Columbus — favored too northerly a course. Martin would probably not have made it bucking the westerly winds from the Azores, but there is a surprising similarity between his basic information and that of Columbus, as Behaim's globe of the world illustrates. They both spoke of driftwood evidence of western lands. They both felt certain that Cathay lay just beyond a narrow Atlantic, and that the Orientals would rejoice to be subject to Europeans. They both drew heavily on Toscanelli, as he did on Marco Polo. Behaim's project, proposed for him by the German astronomer Muntzer to Dom João II of Portugal, was made in ignorance of the fact that a few months previously Columbus had already returned with news of the western world. The dual project shows how ready men's minds were for the venture — waiting only for leadership. Even Martin Alonzo Pinzon of Palos, one of Columbus' colleagues, who later betrayed his friendship, claimed that in the Vatican Library he had read of a voyage in earlier times by the Queen of Sheba westward to the islands of Cypangu or Japan. Whether rumor or fancy or fact now lost to light, the word was in the air, and the pull of the great unknown river of the ocean west of Gibraltar was as strong in men's minds as the current itself pulling at the great round-bottom craft lumbering from the Canaries into the sunset.

Columbus was a man of religious conviction and a man of persistent, obstinate purpose, so much so that after four voyages and fourteen hard years of covering the islands and

coasts of the Caribbean he died still apparently convinced
that he had discovered the Orient and that Cuba was a peninsula of the Asiatic mainland. The impress of Marco Polo on
the early fancy of Columbus might be said to be the dominant
color of his mind. Everything he saw had to fit his concept.

For men live by legend. The classic world lived on the
concept of the Mediterranean basin as the center of their
universe. The world beyond the Black Sea or the Gates of
Hercules at Gibraltar faded out into dread dark and a surrounding River of Ocean whence no man returned. We have
seen how the Phoenicians no doubt fostered this legend
while they dominated the earliest trade routes outside along
the Atlantic coasts. But men had dreamed of the Fortunate Isles and of Atlantis. The dream became a fact for them
because it was necessary to them. Man's mind cannot be contained by fear or the unknown. So the Fortunate Isles were
discovered in the Canaries. And Atlantis, once sought in the
air and the sun, is still sought beneath the waves by dreamers
and a few scattered scientists. Columbus, early in life moved
by the reports of Marco Polo, was possessed by his own vision
of the land beyond the west. He was also a man of persistent
purpose and action, well prepared to chase down what others
might have left to day-dreams.

There is something both grand and pathetic in his carrying
with him a converted Jew, Luis de Torres, taken along to
speak Arabic to the Grand Khan of Cathay when they made
landfall. His course from the Canaries had a similar logic —
that luckily panned out. They were the same latitude on Martin Behaim's globe as Cypangu, and it was known that easterly
trade winds blew pretty constantly in that area. What Columbus happily discovered was the persistence of these trades
clear across the ocean. What he failed to note was that here
also was the beginning of a similar drift of the seas from east
to west, forming the great equatorial current, the very root of

the Ocean River, that sped his caravels onward to the Caribbean.

There were late grumblings by the crew and a growing jealousy on the part of the lesser sea captains of his small fleet, but the first transatlantic crossing in the south was favored by wind and weather beyond the Canaries. As his craft slithered through the brown wrinkle of the Sargasso weed, Columbus records that the savor of the morning was like April in Andalusia. Eventually, by the subterfuge of false reckonings to calm the crew, and an astute change of course to follow the lead of migrating birds, the ships sighted Guanahani, now San Salvador, in the Bahamas, and after standing off all night they made a landing at daybreak. The story so often told need not be elaborated here. What was great good fortune for Columbus was the fact that he missed the ocean passage through the Bahamas which would have led his vessels into the full flood of the Florida stream and very likely left them wrecks beyond Cape Canaveral. No vessels of that time could readily sail against the Stream where the current off Florida makes as much as six knots. It was bad enough elsewhere in the Caribbean, as the Admiral himself recorded in his journal as follows: "You must not suppose there is anything wrong with the ships in the Indies because they can only sail down wind. The mighty currents running with the wind are such that nobody can sail on a bowline [point] in these waters . . . even lateen rigged Portuguese caravels can not do so. That is why vessels wait months in harbor for a fair wind."

What kind of a world slowly unfolded to Columbus in the course of his fourteen years of explorations? Certainly nothing that could resemble the Cathay of Marco Polo that he felt so sure was somewhere just down wind around the next headland. Instead of great cities rich in gold and alive with commerce, instead of learned dignitaries and well-organized civil ways of life, Columbus uncovered island after island inhabited by semi-naked Indians, some gentle and passive, others fierce, warlike, and cannibalistic. And beyond these islands were the low mangrove coasts, mosquito-infested and terrible to endure, like the rain jungles of the Isthmus. Slowly disillusion and defeat from sheer physical exhaustion, coupled with the terrific mental strain of an unfulfilled dream, broke his will. The pressure of brutal and inimical adventurers from his own homeland mounted year by year. Columbus was a poor administrator, and the same obstinate and uncompromising quality of mind that made his initial adventure succeed worked against him when it came time to organize his conquests. In the few years between the first discovery and the tragic fourth voyage in 1506 the West Indies were no longer the individual cruising grounds of Columbus and his companions. An increasing stream of tough, grasping, unimaginative, and determined characters came in on the heels of the firstcomers and tried to discredit them.

But the first New World Christmastide in Haiti — or Hispaniola as Columbus called it — took place in ideal surroundings at Ocoa Bay — which appeared so beautiful to the Admiral that he refused to describe it. And likewise the inhabitants gave all the appearance of sweet innocence and a readiness to be converted to new ways. They greeted the Spaniards with baskets of fruit and other produce of the land, tame parrots — and foolishly enough — presents of beaten gold ornaments. Las Casas reports that their behavior was singularly loving. Other descriptions sound as if these Arawaks were much like the Polynesians, a people at home on and in the water, easygoing, fond of singing and dancing, and unwarlike and amiable. Their sense of property was scarcely awakened, and the love of simple freedom was everything to them. Neither of these qualities spelt anything but doom when opposed by the fanatical, grasping ego of the Spaniards. The honeymoon in the Caribbean was brief.

Columbus heard the Arawaks speak of their interior country as Cibao, which to his excited mind was enough like the Cypangu of Marco Polo to make him up-anchor on December 24 and sail away down the coast looking for the Japanese Emperor in person. Instead, easing along the northern coast from Cap Hatien, at Christmas midnight the flagship of Columbus ran plumb on a coral reef, and the heavy Atlantic ground swell piled the *Santa Maria* hopelessly against the jagged rock. Christmas day was marked by a strange contrast. The pilot, Juan de la Cosa, fled the wrecked vessel, while the native Indians in their canoes helped salvage the cargo.

Here is a first picture of the western Paradise as seen by the great Italian letter writer Peter Martyr, who was called out of Rome to Spain "that he might collect these marvelous and new things, which should otherwise perhaps have lain drowned in the whirlpool of oblivion." It was written: "They saw certain men, who perceiving an unknown nation coming toward them, flocked together and ran all into the thick woods, as it had been hares coursed with greyhounds. . . . Shortly after a great multitude came running to the shore to behold this new nation, whom they thought to have descended from heaven. They cast themselves by heaps into the sea and came swimming to the ships, bringing gold with them, which they changed with our men for earthen pots, pins, hawks-bells and looking glasses. . . . at even tide about the falling of the sun, when our men went to prayer, and kneeled on their knees after the manner of christians, they did the like also. . . . They showed much humanity towards our men and helped them to unlade their broken ship and with such celerity and cheerfulness that no friend for friend or kinsman for kinsman, in such a case moved with pity could do more." Columbus went ashore as the guest of the chieftain, Guacanagari. Here out of the wreckage the Spaniards built their first home in the New World, the fort called Puerto de la Navidad, and Columbus sailed with part of his crew for Spain.

From here on the story of the Ocean River holds us in the West Indies as the new frontier of European transatlantic adventure. Down wind and down stream from the mouth of the old Mediterranean world, the warm, surging waters of the Caribbean foster a new kind of civilization for the white races — the civilization of slave labor and single-crop agriculture on a colonial basis that even the Romans had failed to equal.

It is natural that the first flood of westward European explorations should have taken a southerly route, following the lead of winds and waters rather than bucking the stormy head winds of the North Atlantic. It is also natural that Mediterranean people, once their fear of a southern hemisphere ablaze with heat had been dispelled, would seek the Indies in the land of sun. It follows that the nature and power of the Ocean River of the Atlantic was slow to be revealed, since its form and direction can be said to take obvious shape first at the Straits of Florida. Historically speaking, however, the discovery of the Caribbean waters and islands and the continent of the west took place quickly after the first assay of Columbus, although in a disorganized and fumbling manner.

The rulers of Spain were not impressed by the fact that Columbus came back from his succeeding voyages always asking for more men and vessels to push uncompleted discoveries. A few pearls and golden ornaments were not enough. He had not found, as he predicted, the great wealth of the kingdoms of Cathay or Cypangu. But the professional explorers kept enlarging the limits of the Caribbean world until Cortez in Mexico and Pizarro in Peru laid bare the infinite plunder waiting in those highly organized Indian kingdoms. Then at last men and ships poured into the Caribbean to the mainland, and in short order a few thousand tough soldiers and impoverished noblemen established by cruel conquest the first European colonial empire in the west. The State and the

Church — but the Church always subservient to the Spanish State — now moved in on the new settlements with dogma and law to try and establish a rigid absentee control. It can conveniently be stated that after Magellan in 1520 rounded South America and one of his ships complete the circumnavigation of the world, the day of the great professional explorers was soon to be superseded by the day of the politician, as far as Spain was concerned. She had found the jackpot and Cathay could wait.

But when Columbus first came back in 1493 to announce his great discovery there was no talk then of a New World. He believed, as did others, that he had come to the Indies of the Far East by way of the west, and that the challenge of Turkish control of the trade routes to China had been met. He returned on his second voyage to develop and push further discovery of the wealth of the Indies.

Columbus was now Admiral of the Ocean Sea, but with all his honors and titles the discoverer of the Indies could not keep an exclusive preserve. The year after he returned the second time to tell of Jamaica and the northern coasts of Haiti and of Cuba, which he regarded as the mainland, another expedition set out from Spain headed by Columbus' former captain, Pinzon, and two other pilots and navigators of good standing, Solis and Vespucius. In 1497–98 these men coursed along the shores of Honduras, made a close study of the Florida coasts, and before heading east to the Bermudas quite possibly may have cruised north along the American continental shores as far as Hatteras. This seems likely from the evidence of Cantino's map of 1502, which probably was based on this first voyage of Amerigo Vespucius. Meanwhile Vasco da Gama for the Portuguese was at this very time rounding the Cape of Good Hope to India — a voyage that would add tremendous stimulus to the Spanish search west for a short cut of their own to Indian ports.

Undismayed by the opposition of men at court and a certain lack of mineral wealth, Columbus at the turn of the century, sailed a third time and discovered Trinidad, Paria, and the Pearl Coast, but without great take of pearls. Immediately on his trail came Ojeda, La Cosa, and Vespucius again, opening the northern coasts of Brazil and exploring from Paria to Maracaibo. But others now made greater headway.

At the opening of the new century a Portuguese captain named Cabral, sailing for the Cape of Good Hope, made too much westing in the South Atlantic and hit the coast of Brazil between 12° and 16° S. Had Columbus never found the West Indies and opened the adjacent coasts, this would have been the discovery of the future Americas. In fact the exploration by Vespucius a year later, in 1502, southerly along the hitherto unknown coasts of Brazil from about 5° to 34° S. and thence to South Georgia Island 54° S., actually was the first voyage to bring a New World into public recognition. Columbus always insisted he was rediscovering the Indies, but with the publication of Vespucius' letter to his friend and patron, Lorenzo de Medici, the course of events that gave the name of America to the western continents came into being. Amerigo wrote: "I have formerly written to you at sufficient length about my return from these new countries. . . . it is proper to call them a New World."

The expression Novus Mundus caught on. A Latin version of the letter to Lorenzo was published in 1504. Eleven editions followed in Italy, and by 1506 eight German editions. In 1508 Johann Ruysch published a map of the world, fantastic in many respects, but for the first time replacing the conjectures of lands below the equator with an outline of the Brazilian coast called Terra Sancte Crucis or Mundus Novus. The earliest possible reference on a map to America as a name is attributed to Leonardo da Vinci in 1514, who gave the "wet" or oceanic interpretation of the western discoveries, making

Brazil a great island, Florida another island, and Newfoundland an island called Bacalar. The word "America" covers South America. Cypangu or Japan is shown floating just west of Florida, with no record of the Isthmus of Panama, though by this time that had been pretty well explored. This interesting map illustrates the slow interchange of ideas about the west. It also demonstrates one side of the controversy that made some cartographers always draw the new discoveries as part of a vast Asiatic mainland, and others, like da Vinci, hold to the ancient Antillian theory of a series of islands stretching west to Cathay. The globe of Orantius in 1531 and after that the Mercator map of 1541 show the two connected continents of the west, and for the first time extend the name of America from the southern continent to both the Americas.

Meanwhile, as Vespucius opened up the sea coasts to the south, Columbus made his final tragic voyage to the malarial regions of Honduras and Darien in 1503–4. Here Columbus' obsession with a sea passage to Cathay probably kept him from the discovery of the Pacific. He anchored in the Chiriqui Lagoon and there natives told him of the narrow isthmus. But harassed as he was, and blind to the importance of this news, he passed by the mouth of the Chagres River. Then, because of pressure from an unruly crew, he headed eastward in his wormy ships. Within sight of Cuba he was forced to scuttle down wind and beach his unseaworthy craft on the coast of Jamaica. Columbus' son Ferdinand thus describes their final landfall: "Having got in, and no longer able to keep the ships afloat, we ran them aground . . . shoring them up on both sides so they could not budge . . . upon the fore and stern castles cabins were built where the people might lodge, intending to make them strong that the Indians might do no damage; because at that time the island was not yet inhabited or subdued by christians."

After many months of hardship, and mutiny by some of

his men, Columbus was rescued and returned to Spain. From Jamaica he had sent a letter to King Ferdinand which shows his state of mental and bodily weakness. It reads in part: "I came to serve your Highness at the age of twenty-eight, and now I have no hair upon me that is not white, and my body is infirm and exhausted. All that was left to me and my brothers has been taken away and sold, even to the cloak that I wore, to my great dishonor. The restitution of my honor and losses, and the punishment of those who have inflicted them, of those who plundered me of my pearls and who have disparaged my Admiral's privileges, will redound to the honor of your royal dignity. . . . Isolated in this pain, infirm, daily expecting death, surrounded by a million savages full of cruelty and thus separated from the holy sacraments of the holy church, how neglected will be this soul if it here part from the body. Weep for me, whoever has truth, charity and justice."

This letter did not much move the king — it did not smell of success. Columbus spent the final few years of his life harassing the court in vain for adequate recognition of his services. His touchy temperament, his zeal for honor and worldly position and wealth, estranged a king never too sympathetic toward him. He died May 20th, 1506. Morison puts it well and briefly: "So died the man who had done more to direct the course of history than any individual since Augustus Caesar. Yet the life of the Admiral closed on a note of frustration. He had not found the Strait, or met the Grand Khan, or converted any great number of heathen, or regained Jerusalem. He had not even secured the future of his family. And the significance of what he had done was only slightly less obscure to him than to the chroniclers who neglected to record his death, or to the courtiers who neglected to attend his modest funeral at Valladolid. The vast extent and immense resources of the Americas were but dimly seen, the mighty ocean that laved their western shores had not yet yielded her secret."

It is common to attribute the naming of the two western continents, the Americas, to an accident of fortune. When we study the history of events this does not seem to be so accidental after all. In the first place we must always remember that Columbus did not intend or desire to find a new world; he was obsessed with the dream of opening a quick western route to the wealth of Cathay, the land of Marco Polo. Like so many Europeans of his day, he wanted to avoid or at least get around the Moslem Curtain across the East which shut off the land trade routes to the Orient — routes which were far too long, even when open. This drove the Portuguese around the Cape of Good Hope and the Spaniards to send Magellan around the southern tip of South America. Columbus and others refused to accept a blockade of new lands. They were determined to follow the slow beginnings of the Ocean Stream through the Caribbean and then keep on west through some unknown strait. At different times the Mississippi, the Chesapeake, and the Hudson were thought to be this strait, as were the Orinoco, Amazon, and La Plata in the southern continent. Amerigo Vespucius did a lot of looking for these straits.

A famous pilot named La Cosa was with Columbus on his second voyage. As Columbus returned a broken man to Spain in 1505, this La Cosa teamed up with Vespucius, who had now shifted his allegiance from Portugal to Spain, and they searched the Gulf of Darien looking for a passage to Cathay. They were not obsessed with any conviction that the West Indies were part of the Orient — Vespucius had already named the Novus Mundus. Again in 1507 Vespucius and La Cosa were back off the Darien coasts, but unlike Balboa they met no Indian chief to tell them of the Pacific just beyond the narrow cordillera; they were six years too early. For many years it was the habit of historians to belittle the part that Vespucius the Florentine took in western affairs. Today we know that his intelligent and persistent following of the courses opened by Columbus, and his insistence that these western lands were indeed a new world, gave him as good a claim as anyone to have his name perpetuated in history — especially since Columbus did not wish the New World recognized as such.

To show how spotty the mapping of the day was, it is interesting to note that for many years the coasts of Yucatan, when approached from the south, were considered an extension of Cuba. It is true that Ocampo in 1508 first sailed around Cuba and proved it to be an island, but the coasts of Yucatan were not accurately explored and mapped until 1517 by Cordova. A year later Grijalva explored the Gulf of Mexico, and the year following, Cortez, taking authority into his own hands, began the conquest of Mexico. This was the first step in a series of such conquests, opened in 1513 by Balboa's finding the Pacific, that caused a shift in emphasis from the West Indies to the main of the Americas and affected the economic and social development of the whole Caribbean area.

The decade of the twenties finally determined that the future of New Spain was the mainland of Central and South America. In 1526 Solis was killed at the mouth of the La Plata, but it was rumored, by those of his party who returned, that inland up the great rivers of the south was a mountain kingdom of vast wealth. Already between 1520 and 1526 Alejo Garcia had penetrated the cordillera from the eastern coast and visited the Inca governor in the neighborhood of the Potosi silver mines. Those of Garcia's men who escaped reported a civilized land of peace and untold wealth. In 1526 Sebastian Cabot and Roger Barlow, sailing for a combine of merchants of England, Spain, and Genoa, headed ostensibly for the Strait of Magellan and the west coast of Peru. Instead, they cut inland up the La Plata as far as Asuncion, and one of the party, Francisco Cesár, before returning to the Cabot camp at Holy Ghost farther down the river, reached the Andes and the edge of the Inca domain. These attempts to find and exploit the fabled wealth of the Incas are interesting to the study of the Caribbean only because they illustrate how the curiosity and energy of exploration was now passing out of range of the islands. Pizarro, cruising south from Panama, learned of the Peruvian empire in 1528, and wrote the final chapter to this quest when in 1536 he came to Peru by the most direct, practical route and opened the years of the fabulous looting of American treasure that for a time made Spain the greatest world power.

But this drive to the west drained the energy needed for the proper development of the Caribbean island empire. A sort of a frontier of aftermath, a "frontier of the rear" it might paradoxically be termed, developed for the West Indies. The Buccaneers temporarily took over to fill the vacuum that might better have been filled with hardy Spanish and European colonists; and after them, when sugar was introduced, came the flood of African slavery. Cortez, Alvarado, and Pizarro sealed the doom of the West Indies for centuries to come. The Spanish adventurers were neither maritime nor agricultural — they were looking for loot.

The roots of the Gulf Stream, the source of the great Atlantic gyre, were probably too warm, and gendered a climate too enervating, to have developed an effective European type of civilization, even if the main potential of energy had not suddenly drained through the Isthmus to Peru and up from the coast of Yucatan to Tenochtitlan and the Aztec treasuries. As with most historical phenomena we shall never know the reasons completely because we seldom find parallel opportunities for development, and therefore a means of measurement. But one thing was certain: by 1520 the news was out, and Spain could no longer maintain exclusive access to the wealth of the New World. The voyage of Sebastian Cabot to Brazil backed as it was by merchant adventurers of three nations, was a plain forecast of a new phase of exploitation. The State and the Church no longer held a monopoly. Verrazano — or John the Florentine as the Spanish called him — opened up wide prospects of new endeavor when he sailed for Francis I, and discovered the Hudson River. Here was fresh food for speculation as to a Northwest Passage. For many years the Chesapeake was called the Sea of Verrazano.

Let us first look briefly at the West Indian frontier, so lightly controlled by Spain that even her cultural influence was weak, though strong enough on the mainland to last to this day. In a short time Buccaneer authority came to equal civil authority. The pathfinders moved on westward and the exploiters and looters came following in, very much as the mountain men of our American Wild West opened up vast tracts of rich territory, then moved on and died as the squatters and traders and law-minded sharpers took over prior to the establishment of civil power. Like the later continental frontier, the island frontier had its romantic and picturesque heroes, its sordid villains and sharp lawyers. Here let us read a letter of Balboa from Darien; it is the eternal voice of complaint of the true frontiersman against the connivers and second-comers: "I entreat your Highness to command that no Bachelor of Law nor any other thing, unless it should be of medicine, may pass to these parts of the mainland [Darien], for no Bachelor comes here who is not the Devil, and they lead the life of Devils, and not only are they bad, but they even contrive how to bring about a thousand lawsuits and villanies." Balboa was aware of what the stay-at-home courtiers through their plotting had done to rob Columbus of his due.

Meanwhile, back in the islands after two decades of Spanish control, we have a sad picture of cruelty and disorganization. The Arawak population of almost a million happy, peaceable, and indolent souls decreased in the first fifteen years of Spanish conquest to fifty thousand, and on many of the islands even this pitiful remainder had not long to survive. The Spaniards, with their religious orthodoxy, and their strong sense of property and greed for wealth, looked on the natives as subhuman, or at best as children needing strong parental control. Even as educated and thoughtful a man as Peter Martyr illustrates the impossibility of any understanding between the races. He, who once chronicled the golden age, the living paradise of the islands, wrote the following: "The Indians are abandoned to drink and gluttony. They prefer to live in the woods eating roots and spiders to living with the Spaniards. They do not wish to be subject to anyone, but to be free to enjoy themselves in idleness. They smoke tobacco. No one would dig for gold without being driven to it. They have no business sense. They love to go about naked and they hold money and property of no value, excepting only food and drink. They will not work for wages; they take no interest in commerce, and have no conception of taxes or tithes. . . . If the Indians were set at liberty they would never become Christians; trade would cease because they would have nothing to do with the Spaniards, and the royal rents would cease, as the Spaniards would all leave the island." The other side was put quite simply by an Indian chief when he refused to be baptized before his execution. He said if he were baptized he would go to heaven. Heaven he was told was full of Christians. No, thank you.

So while professing — and no doubt sincerely — the saving of souls, the Spaniards devised systems for breaking the Indians to harness while the supply lasted. These two systems, one growing out of the other, were called the *encomienda* and the *repartimiento*. Both these terms, often but not accurately used for the same thing, were a carry-over from the Spanish feudal division of lands and responsibilities, but under harsh colonial conditions they soon reverted to what amounted to outright slavery. Columbus first instituted the *repartimiento* as a division of lands in Hispaniola to able and deserving proprietors. And with the land, as in feudal Europe, the present tenants of the land went along as workers, to be used and cared for and of course converted to Christianity. Thus, at least, in the mind of Columbus and the intention of the distant royal rulers, fixed responsibilities went along with the proprietorship of lands and the Indian "peasants." But where Spanish greed for gold and a disinclination for work in a hot climate met a similar Indian disinclination to work, plus no concept whatever of private property or ambition for wealth, the good intent of the regulation came to nothing. The Indians acted as slave labor, committed suicide, or were brutally murdered. The same abuse occurred under the *encomienda,* which was an allocation of enforced labor presumably for a limited time under definite terms of trust. It must be said that certain priests and landowners, notably Las Casas and the Friars Montesino and Vitoria, preached against this treatment of the Indians; but it was many years before any remedial laws were passed, and these were not carried out in the Caribbean. In a word, the conditions that might have established a separatist democratic society in the West Indies did not develop. Only in Darien under Balboa, himself a man of the people leading peasants and soldiers, was there any mutual sharing of work and government. The lawyers, as Balboa feared they would, soon put an end to this, for they cut off his head.

Paradoxically enough, the fear of Indian slavery and its resulting cruelty brought negro slavery into the islands, and Las Casas, the defender of the Indians, at least acquiesed if he did not actually recommend this extension of negro slavery as a solution. We can overlook this inconsistency in an otherwise farsighted Christian man on the grounds perhaps that the use of Africans, purchased already from a state of slavery, was an accepted practice, and further that they seemed acclimated and docile enough to carry on without the more obvious cruelties practiced against the Indians. At any rate, not until his later years did Las Casas admit the error of his first judgment. It is difficult, even for a good man, to think outside the pattern of his times.

Oviedo, an early historian, put the case against the Spanish occupation in a single statement. By 1535 the native population of the island of Hispaniola had shrunk from several hundred thousand to five hundred. Here was a rich domain waiting for development. Sugar and negro slavery went hand in hand. But before any safe and satisfactory plantation society could grow, the frontiers of anarchy produced by the draining of Spanish settlers to the mainlands had to be overcome. Cattle ran wild in all the islands. Tough, anarchistic individuals moved in to slaughter the cattle and sell the smoked and dried meat called "bucan" to the ships trading in the Indies. These "buccaneers" soon saw that they were mere butlers to the men of true fortune and wealth, the seagoers. So they in turn became "high-jackers" and took to the sea. A society of well-organized piracy with its headquarters on Tortuga, just north of Hispaniola, finally came into being, and these men were called "Buccaneers" after their original profession. So within a few generations after Columbus, the West Indies began to be a land of growing slavery and a seaway more and more dominated by freebooters.

Thus at the very start the failure of a healthy economic and social colonial system under the Spanish was forecast in the Caribbean. As Parry puts it: "The whole of the West Indies was an eager market for cloth, weapons, tools and hardware of all sorts, books, paper, wine, oil and slaves. Spanish producers could not or would not export these goods in sufficient quantities or at competitive prices. The Indies trade then was a standing temptation, not only to pirates and privateers, but to slavers, smugglers and illicit traders of all nations."

The downstream conquerors of the Mediterranean were doomed to lose out to the upstream migrations of northern Europe coming the hard way against the currents of the ocean and the rough Atlantic weathers. An occupation of proprietors in the south could never compete with the occupation of artisans and workers coming into power in the north.

When the first treasure ships from Panama and Mexico reached Spain and their treasure of hard cash was used throughout Europe to carry on the perpetual wars for religious domination then being waged, it was natural that big-time piracy should become attractive to other nationalities under the ready excuse of political or religious enmity toward Spain. We must always bear in mind that antagonism between Protestant and Catholic at the time of the Armada and the Spanish conquest of the low countries was a matter of life and death. European hatreds and rivalries were translated as a matter of course to the New World, and between the upper and nether millstones of this materialistic rivalry for power the gentle pagan world of the native Arawak was ground to nothing in a tragic brevity of time. Peter Martyr says of the native Cubans: "For it is certain that among them the land is common as the sun and water; and that Mine and Thine (the seeds of all mischief) have no place with them. They are content with so little that in so large a country they have superfluity rather than scarceness, so that they seem to live in the Golden World." Before the Spaniards came there was no overpopulation and hence little of the hunger and undernourishment we find today in the West Indies after three centuries of European civilizing influences. A lost world is now gone which once was free of material ambition and lust for property. We may well wonder how a returned Arawak might analyze the proud boast of the modern western man that his present involvement in mechanical complication is the highest standard of living the world has yet known.

It is certain the conquistadors of the early sixteenth century were not much bothered with scruple. Twenty years after Columbus found his paradise (at the cost of creating his own personal hell) here is the requiem of Peter Martyr: "A great number of them [the Indians] died of strange and new diseases which consumed them like rotten sheep. And to tell the truth our men's insatiable desire of gold so oppressed these poor wretches with extreme labor and toil, whereas before they had lived pleasantly and at liberty, given only to plays and pastimes, as dancing, fishing, fowling and hunting of little conies, that many of them perished even for very anguish of mind, the which (with their unaccustomed labor) are things of themselves sufficient to engender many new diseases." The way was now clear for the brief domination of a new kind of savage, the Buccaneer. For out of this native growth of the western world grew a kind of first government free of the European feudal pattern. From the hordes of the Brethren of the Coast, as their organization became perfected, both England and France made use of leaders like Henry Morgan and the Frenchman Le Clerc.

But there is also another side to the Caribbean development that came in an orderly fashion out of native Spanish roots that helps to balance this anarchistic savagery of the Buccaneer. The history of Las Casas, the greatest individual of the early Caribbean world, is in itself a history of Christian political and social progress in the West Indies and Central America that can be matched only later in the north by the militant liberalism of Roger Williams. Las Casas almost singlehanded was responsible for the perpetuation of the Indian culture that is so much a part of the Spanish-American culture of today.

His story is too well known in general to need great detail. To refresh our memories we can remember that he started out as a landed proprietor in Hispaniola. The maltreatment of the Indian population and its slavery and destruction moved him deeply. He was a man of great strength of character and a man of action. He stood out against the local governments and took his case to the king in Spain, and finally won new laws, which for a time ameliorated the worst conditions. But the economic forces of the colonial world were against him, and his greatest enemies were the local planters and exploiters of new wealth who had influential friends at court. This great see-saw battle went on for half a century. Las Casas lost out in the West Indies, but in Central America, after he had become a Dominican father, won notable triumphs. He ended as Bishop of Chiapas.

Arthur Helps wrote sympathetically of Las Casas: "In an age eminently superstitious he was entirely devoid of superstition. At a period when the most extravagant ideas as the divine right of kings prevailed, he took occasion to remind kings to their faces that they were only permitted to govern for the good of the people . . . at a period when brute force was appealed to in all matters, but more especially in those that pertained to religion . . . he contended that a missionary should go forth with his life in his hand, relying only on the protection of God and depending neither upon civil nor military assistance. Eloquent, devoted, charitable and fervent, a subtle and skillful manager of men, he was rightfully called the Apostle to the Indians." He had the capacities and the common sense and courage to see to it that his ideals did not exist in a vacuum; he went into action. The story of his peaceful conquest of the dangerous Guatemalan tribes stands in brilliant contrast to the brutality of Spanish conquests elsewhere. It stands as a symbol of the kind of colonial wisdom and human decency that somehow, in the face of greed and brutality, managed to effect a blended Indian-Spanish culture in Central and South America, succeeding in this respect where the English failed in the north.

In 1535 Las Casas composed a treatise that had great influence in the church. It was radical for its time, for it held to two propositions; one, that men were to be brought to Christianity only by persuasion; and the other, that it was unlawful for Christians to make war on infidels merely because they were infidels. The Spanish colonists who had captured Indian slaves by strength of arms naturally detested this argument. Las Casas, at this time in Guatemala, found himself derided for his ideas, and they dared him to attempt pacification of the warlike natives with only kind words. He was the man to take this challenge. He and other Dominican fathers began to master the Quiche language. Their intent was to tackle the most difficult of the border states, called "The Land of War," because in three attempts the soldiers had failed to conquer it. In 1537 Las Casas made a formal agreement with the governor to go into the mountains and pacify these Indians no other Spaniard dared approach. He and some others decided to risk all and visit the Land of War on a mission of conversion.

The Dominicans fasted and prayed. But Las Casas was both a holy man and a man of worldly wisdom and of many devices. First of all he had the story of creation, the loss of Paradise, the life of Christ, and the final redemption translated into simple Quiche verse forms and set to native music. It was a close thing whether Las Casas would be eaten or be well received alive; but in 1538 he won over the chief to complete the conquest by art and love where force had failed. Fortunately at this juncture Alexander Farnese, Pope Paul the Third, pronounced that the Indians were worthy of receiving the faith and demanded a halt to their enslavement and the taking of their possessions. With this help Las Casas penetrated even to Coban on new missions setting up pueblos for the converts. His final triumph was the willing visit of the wild chieftain Don Juan to meet Alvarado, his former enemy, face to face. A mutual liking sprang up between the warriors, and the peaceful conquest of the Land of War by Las Casas and the Dominican fathers was sealed.

Although this famous pacification in Guatemala might be considered the greatest thing of its kind in the field of practical affairs, this man of many parts and abilities now took a new phase of endeavor. In Spain on business with the King, he composed in 1541 his famous defense of the Indians and attack on colonial malpractice called *The Destruction of the Indies*. It was submitted to the King, but was not published for another twelve years. It was a bold and daring attack on the tyranny and cruelty of the civilian Spanish in the Indies and on Terra Ferma, as the mainland was called. So moving was this work that its direct effect in Spain was the writing of new laws against slave labor and injustice to the Indians. This made Las Casas probably the most generally hated man in the New World, as far as the Spanish proprietors were concerned. Before we close this account of a vigorous and saintly life we should note that this same book, *The Destruction of the Indies*, when published later in the century elsewhere in Europe, was used by Hawkins, Drake, and others as justification for their indiscriminate attacks on the wealth of the West Indies.

Las Casas in Mexico continued a dangerous life in trying to strike a nice balance of existence between the murderous hostility of the merchants and landowners on the one hand and the devout love of his half-savage parishioners on the other. In 1550 he went back to Spain and joined in a great debate on colonial church policy with Sepúlveda. The two antagonists were probably the most learned and able men of their time in Spain. The debate was without practical conclusion. It was the old battle between Christian ethics and the imperial theory that stronger and superior people could rightfully employ force to civilize the so-called heathen.

Even though Las Casas never won a clear-cut and lasting victory in his life-long struggle for justice for the Indians, he did much to ameliorate conditions in the New World and to sharpen men's consciences in the treatment of their fellow men. The result of his efforts in the more organized tribes of the mainland are visible today in the mixed populations of Spanish-Indian blood that have worked out a common destiny in Central and South America. It is difficult to raise a just comparison with the northern fate of the Indians under English conquest, because they were much less advanced socially than the Indians of Mexico and Central America. But in condemning the cruelty and brutality of the time among the Spanish conquistadors, men like the Dominican fathers Montesino, Vitoria, and especially Las Casas remind us of the slow triumph of justice over brutality in human relationships. They were the forerunners in the long fight for freedom that developed in the western hemisphere, ending in the great revolutionary movements of the two Americas. Spiritually they were the Bolivars and Washingtons of an earlier day.

11

THE HAND OF THE GIANT

"THUS far the explorations cover the little finger of a pigmy, since all that is known is the neighborhood of Uraba. What will it be when the whole hand of the giant is known and the Spaniards will have penetrated into all the profound and mysterious parts of the continent?" — Peter Martyr.

The companion of Columbus was speaking of Balboa's discovery of the Pacific. When shortly thereafter the civilized nations of Mexico and Peru with their treasuries of loot were revealed to the Spanish, and the news of rumored El Dorado came back to European ears, the first great American gold rush was on. Treaties, law, and respect for human life and decency were largely ignored while nations of men fought for the possession of life and treasure not their own. Adventurers from all over Europe were at first caught up in a current of anarchy where the freebooter and the buccaneer usurped authority. The forces of a wild frontier held sway in the early sixteenth century. Landless men in a strange environment greedy for wealth and property, hunters deprived of their hunting grounds, lawbreakers themselves hunted — all banded together, and were finally at the close of the century, forced to form a kind of confederation called the Brethren of the Coast. These men had at least a discipline and order amongst them-

selves that eventually was controlled and put to use by France
and England against the Spanish.

For the Spanish and the Portuguese, as we have seen, were
the natural heirs of western discovery, operating as they did
from their favorable position at the mouth of the Mediterranean where just to the south the Canary and Equatorial
Currents and favoring winds led westward downstream to the
Caribbean world. Nor did the Spaniards have much choice
of action. The Portuguese under the old papal decree controlled the African coastal route by way of the Cape of Good
Hope to the Indies; and in the Mediterranean behind the
western gates the Moorish pirates, backed by the Moslem
strength to the east, effectively blocked commerce on the
inland sea. This was conclusively demonstrated in 1538 when
Admiral Doria with a combined fleet from Genoa and Venice
was badly defeated by the Moorish Admiral Barbarossa off the
Dalmatian coast. So Spain turned west to get her treasure
from the Spanish Main; but since there also piracy on a growing scale was the problem, she fortified her ports and set up
heavily armed convoys for her treasure ships.

Piracy was an old, established trade applied to new waters
in the Atlantic. Just as Spain at home augmented the Moorish
fleet by her expulsion of the Moors from Spain, so in the
Caribbean, by attempting to suppress the cattle hunters or
buccaneers in the West Indian islands, she created a local
counterpart of the Moorish fleets but of European origin.
There was no simple category of pirates. Some were smugglers,
some were slave-runners, some were explorers not averse to
taking a little booty on the side, and others finally became
important organized enterprises seeking the concentrated
treasure of the Americas. All in all, it was a sporadic, lawless,
and anarchial beginning of what finally settled down into
oceanic commerce. Even monarchs used pirates to accom-
plish ends that were best obscure.

Now in the sixteenth century seagoing regiments of conquistadors, from grandee to jailbird, backed by the crusading
zeal of the Church and the imperial will of the newly con-
solidated Spanish kingdoms, poured along the pathway of
the trades and the roots of the River into the Caribbean.
Though the way was by sea this was not a migration of mariners or of a seagoing people, such as England was beginning
to unleash on the North American continent. The Spanish
were conquistadors, men who sought to control and exploit
rather than pioneer for themselves. Their government also
looked on the West Indies and the lands of the Spanish
Main as a region of inferior peoples and governments without
standing, fit only for conquest and rigid absentee control.
Part of this was due to the fixed class structure of Spanish
society and part to the fact that, when sugar was once introduced as the main crop in the West Indies, a great body of
slave labor seemed the easiest way to get a quick return on
the investment. As small as the white population was, even
those few began to dwindle as plantations increased. Only
Barbadoes, because of its earlier settlement, had a higher
percentage of white population. This inability of Spain to
colonize through its people or to adjust its highly legalistic
and narrow concepts of control to new conditions made the
eventual loss of her Caribbean empire inevitable.

The story of the British-Spanish battle for the Caribbean
is the story of the England of Elizabeth, a young nation
beginning to feel its strength, learning new techniques of
empire by firsthand experiment, while Spain, the older civilization with apparently greater weight of initial power and
wealth, proceeded into a new environment with fixed and
traditional habits of action. In the long run fresh improvisa-
tion defeated rigid immobility. Various elements contributed
to the English and French power. Some of it can be laid to a
new release of national energy by the Reformation. Some of

it was due to the training of able seamen and competent leadership developed by the northern fishing fleets of Newfoundland. The English government left room for men to rise from the school of experience and take charge, and to begin with recognized healthy separatism in colonial matters more than the Spanish government permitted. Spain tried to curb Pizarro; England elevated the pirate Henry Morgan to the governorship of Jamaica and knighted him, as the French did Le Clerc. Nevertheless, the weight of Spanish tradition, the combined power of an absolute theology and a legalistic monarchy, though it lost the West Indies, did mold for a time a solid empire on the mainland in Central and South America, and no amount of freshly improvised action by the British was able to destroy it.

Two things generally turn the tide of history one way or another at any given period: one is timing, and the other is readiness for new things or susceptibility to change. In the case of Spain, the times were ripe for a Mediterranean power to taste the first fruits of long years of preparatory explorations and scientific inquiry by the Mediterranean pilots and navigators. Spain, because she had at the right time a strong government that could exercise continued power, was ready to act. But actually by the very nature of that power she was also unable to adjust to the strange requirements of a situation beyond her experience. Spain had expelled the Jews, expelled the Moors, and successfully dominated the powerful nobles and large corporate powers within her realm, and her King reigned supreme at home. Naturally the home government had no intention of letting conquistadors and adventurers set up a new, ungovernable feudal aristocracy in the New World. As a result there was no great movement of individual enter-prise from Spain, but instead an export of judges, lawyers, priests, and administrators. Slaves filled the labor vacuum when the conquered Indians died or refused to work. Mean-

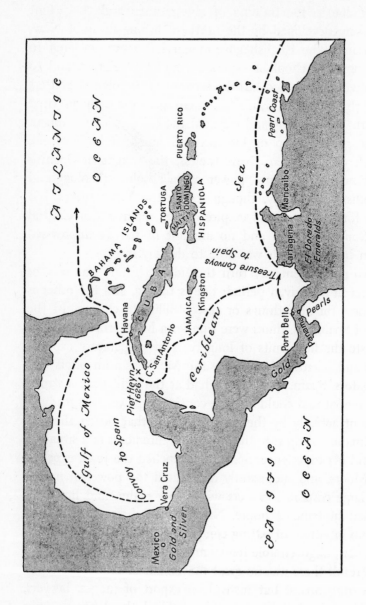

Map of the Buccaneer Hunting Grounds. From a photograph by Jan Hahn of the original map by Louis Renard, 1715.

while, as the colonies became strong, slavery and rigid absentee control from Europe laid the foundation for later revolt.

The picture of Spanish conquest is not any more cruel, considering the ideas of the time, than it was stupid and shortsighted. As a matter of fact there was constant debate on the moral issues of Spanish policy, led for the most part by the Dominican fathers discussing both sides of the question. Father John Mair, a Scottish priest in Spain, spoke like a good British imperialist of later days. He argued: "These people [the Indians] live like animals. It is evident that some men are by nature free and others servile. In the natural order of things the qualities of some men are such that, in their own interests, it is right and just that they should serve, while others, living freely, exercise their natural authority and command." Kipling couldn't have put it better. But opposed to this thought we find Father Montesino maintaining that the Indian tribes had equal rights under international law; and Las Casas, in his great debate with Sepúlveda, spoke out for the natural freedom of the Indians, urging that no command or proselytizing should take the place by force of arms. We have seen how in the pacification of the mountain tribes in Guatemala he risked his life to prove this point.

Actually the lines of development followed commercial opportunism for the English, and legal and governmental absentee control over colonial subjects by Spain. The economy of the time played against Spain. The British had piratical traders ready to bring European goods to dangerous markets, and the Spanish had neither the goods nor the type of trader. So Spain took treasure from the mainland conquests, and the British and the French and the Dutch "high-jacked" the treasure as it flowed to Europe and developed on the island plantations the new commodity of sugar.

Since our business is with the sea let us follow the ships. In 1537 two great raids by the French awoke Spain to her danger. An expedition from the French islands took Chagres on the Isthmus of Panama; and a larger fleet, organized by the powerful merchant Ango of far-away Dieppe, under the leadership of Verrazano, captured the returning Spanish treasure fleet. This forced Spain to organize the convoy system from American ports. The galleons of forty to fifty guns sailed every January to Porto Bello and Cartagena; and the Flota, also well armed, sailed for Vera Cruz early in the summer to avoid the hurricane season. Money began to pour back to Spain and enhance her power. But the raids kept on. François Le Clerc raided Porto Rico with ten vessels in 1554, and a year later Jacques de Sores pillaged Santiago de Cuba and Havana.

This news of good pickings in the Caribbean finally aroused the English to come in on the game with a show of force, though at first quietly feeling their way. The slave trader John Hawkins made his first voyage in 1563. John Davis wrote of him thus: "The first Englishman that gave any attempt on the coast of the West Indies being part of America was Sir John Hawkins . . . a man of excellent capacity, great government and perfect resolution. For before he made the attempt it was a matter doubtful and reported the extreme limit of danger to sail upon the coast . . . for the most part of us rather joy at home like epicures to sit and carpe at other men's hazzards, ourselves not daring to give any attempt." This need not have worried Davis for long. During the next four years Hawkins made additional voyages trading and selling slaves, and on his final and sadly unsuccessful attempt on Vera Cruz in 1568 he introduced a young lieutenant, Francis Drake, into his future career as scourge of the Spanish. Hawkins was the prospector for the great age of Elizabethan sea raids. The Queen herself, though always careful to repudiate any connection, took shares in his voyages. After 1570 the attack by the English, French, and Dutch on the Caribbean empire of

Spain began in earnest; the professionals were taking over. Even when France and Spain made peace by the Treaty of Vervins at the end of the century the territory south of the Tropic of Cancer was left out of bounds — anything went "below the line."

From Hawkins on through Drake and Morgan, the Englishmen attacking the Spanish domain knew just what they were after. The French on the whole even when operating "below the line," were a good deal more scrupulous of European treaty agreements than the British. Le Clerc, who was honored by the French king with a patent of nobility, seldom attacked in the Caribbean when France and Spain were at peace in Europe. Drake and his associates were not so punctilious. To illustrate the wealth pouring into Europe from the Spanish Main at the end of the sixteenth century, a contemporary letter written in 1580 describes Drake's loot as worth two million ducats. But another Fugger News Letter of the same period totals the wealth that still reached Spanish ports at close to twenty million ducats. Later in 1628 Piet Heyn, with 31 ships, 700 cannon, and a force of 3,000 men, captured the Spanish plate fleet near Cuba and returned 15 million guilders to the investors of the Dutch West Indian Company, which declared a fifty percent dividend.

Gold, glossed by romance or stated in terms of plain greed, called the tune in the Caribbean. The myth of El Dorado, the Golden Man, caught and held European imaginations. It originated in the practice of a Chibcha chief in the highlands of Colombia in dusting gold on his body and then ceremoniously washing it off in a lake. The alchemy of distance, strangeness, mystery, and greed soon created somewhere in the hinterland of the Andes, a golden kingdom shining with precious metal and alive with emeralds. The career of Sir Walter Raleigh is the story of the grip of this golden legend. By his time the country of El Dorado was called "Manoa," and Raleigh was to venture there and in this romantic, heroic, and vain endeavor to lose his fortune and his only son, and finally, through this ill success, his very life.

To show the strange mixture of almost religious awe, the challenge to heroic action, and the childlike lust for untold treasure, it is best to listen to Raleigh's own words of what he saw and of what he dreamed. Speaking of the falls of Caroli: ". . . and there appeared from ten to twelve overfalls in sight . . . which fell with that fury that the rebound of the waters made it seem that it had been covered over with a great shower of rain or smoke than had risen over some great town. . . . I never saw a more beautiful country, nor more lovely prospects . . . the river winding into divers branches, the plains adjoining without stubble, all fair green grass, the ground of hard sand easy to march on, the deer crossing on every path, the birds towards the evening singing on every tree with a thousand several tunes, cranes and herons of white and crimson, the air fresh with a gentle easterly wind, and every stone that we stooped to take up promised either gold or silver by his complexion."

Raleigh, alas, was better at describing the complexion of his mind and hope, like Columbus when he looked for the Grand Khan. Yet nothing could daunt the true Elizabethan spirit. Here is his final call to those who stayed at home: "The common soldier shall there fight for gold and pay himself, instead of pence, with plates a half-foot broad, whereas he beareth his bones in other wars for poverty and penury. Those commanders and chieftans that shoot at honour and abundance, shall find there more rich and beautiful cities, more temples adorned with golden images, more sepulchres filled with treasure, than either Cortez found in Mexico or Pizarro in Peru, and the shining glory of this conquest will eclipse all these so far extended beams of the Spanish nation."

There it is — romance, abundance, honor, national pride,

and conquest to the eclipse of Spain. That was the new dream of the new world that kept men's eyes to the west and made of the Ocean River a highway to future empire. But history often works on a smaller local pattern to prepare for the grand design of the future, and so it was in the Caribbean area. For the seeds of future revolt, of future separation from Europe, of a new kind of self-government and a new pattern of Spanish American culture were growing in small towns on the Main and on islands of the sea. No matter how wild the frontier or how free from absentee restraints of government it is a necessity of man to operate in some kind of order; and even among the wildest, most anarchistic of the frontiersmen of the Caribbean, the buccaneers, a sort of government evolved. Esquemelin saw it, and wrote it down first hand — how custom crystallized into law even among the lawless: "In council they agree upon certain articles, which are put in writing, by way of bond or obligation, which everyone is bound to observe and all of them set their hands to it. They specify what sums each one of them ought to have for that voyage, the fund of all payments being the common stock of what is gotten by the whole expedition; for otherwise it is the same law as among other Pirates 'No prey, no pay'. In the first place they mention what the Captain should have for his ship. Next the salary of the carpenter who careened, mended and rigged the vessel. This commonly is from 100 to 150 pieces-of-eight. For provisions and victualling they draw out 200 pieces-of-eight. Also a competent salary for the surgeon, usually 250 pieces-of-eight. And for the wounded or maimed, for the loss of a right arm, 600 or six slaves, for a left arm, 500, for a left leg, 400, for an eye, 100, and so it goes. They observe very good order among themselves, for in the prizes they take it is severely prohibited to everyone to usurp anything in particular to themselves." The pioneer adventurers had their own recruiting techniques. In the early days one Pedro Xemines promised his men: "Instead of mattocks, wenches pappies; for labor, pleasure; for hunger, abundance; for weariness and watching, sleep and quietness."

Combination among the buccaneers made a kind of Caribbean sea militia that the British, and sometimes the French, used in the seventeenth century. After 1655 the buccaneers generally sailed under commissions from the governor of Jamaica or Tortuga, and set aside a tithe or ten percent for the governor. Later in the centry this kind of freebooting had become such a native growth in these waters that Labat, a Dominican friar, could write of them as follows: "We were busy this morning confessing a crew of filibusters who had arrived with prizes captured from the English. The Mass of the Virgin was celebrated with all solemnity and I blessed three large loaves which were presented by the captain and his officers, who arrived at church accompanied by the drums and trumpets of their corvette. At the beginning of the Mass the corvette fired a salute with all her cannons. At the elevation of the Holy Sacrament she fired another salvo, at the Benediction, a third, and finally a fourth, when we sang the Te Deum. All the filibusters contributed thirty sols to the sacristy, and did so with much piety and modesty."

Père Labat was very much a man of the world. He could look with pleasant objectivity on the pirates, and even joined heartily in the social pastime of the islands, called "cochon boucane" — a kind of pirate picnic. "We forgathered," he recounts, "in a forest of poplars and all pretend to be buccaneers. Much rum is consumed and no water is allowed in the wine or spirits. I do not think it necessary to inform the reader that one of the essential things in a boucan is to drink frequently. The law compels it, (law du pic-nic) the sauce invites one to do so, and few err in this respect."

Although the English and the French and Dutch occasionally fought each other, the main prey was Spain with her widespread, unequally defended empire of pillage. The convoy of fleets began in the middle of the sixteenth century, but a hundred years later Spain was still rich and vulnerable, and though the French and the Dutch had their big strikes their success was sporadic. In the seventeenth century the English began to dominate the pirate trade. By 1660, after Mansfield had been captured and executed by the Spaniards, Henry Morgan took command. Sir Thomas Modiford, then governor of Jamaica, was a good friend and backer of those marauding against Spain. Sure of his backing, Morgan attacked Porto Bello, the great Spanish stronghold on the Gulf side of the Isthmus, and after reducing the fortifications returned to Jamaica with great loot, where he was immediately pardoned for having exceeded his commission. His well-known cross-isthmus march and sacking of Panama in 1671 was perhaps the classic example of boldness and a rich reward. Morgan was called back to England on the protest of the Spanish government, but ended up Sir Henry, Governor of Jamaica. In 1688 he died in his bed fat and unrepentant, and was happily interred at Port Royal.

Things had so changed in the Caribbean that it was no longer the Spanish sea, but under the control of England through the power vested in the Governor of Jamaica. Instead of pursuing Spanish gold from the Main of Mexico, the colonial British were searching for sunken treasure among the islands and the shoals; and the sugar planters were establishing an orderly society on the land. A notable example typifies the new order in the Caribbean. Up in the province of Maine, off the Kennebec at Woolwich, a farm boy of eighteen, William Phips, got tired of tending sheep and made his way to Boston, where he studied to be a ship's carpenter. He came back to Woolwich and near Montsweague on the Sheepscote River set up a small shipyard. Indian troubles drove him out and away to sea. He drifted down to the Caribbean and became familiar with the islands and the buccaneers trading there. He located a sunken treasure ship in the south Bahamas, and persuaded the new Governor of Jamaica, Lord Albemarle, the son of General Monck, to outfit a search. After two attempts, in 1687, they found the treasure, which amounted to about 300,000 pounds sterling. Albemarle, who was much in debt in England, kept all but 16,000 pounds, which went to Phips. He then sailed for England, and was knighted by the king and made Sheriff of New England under Andros. When that unpopular governor was deposed, Sir William Phips came back as a friend of the colonists and led the successful expedition that captured Port Royal from the French. He failed in subsequent attempts against Quebec and Montreal, but used some of his treasure to pay off the colonial expenses of the expedition. He was appointed royal Governor of Massachusetts in 1692, the first native son to attain this honor — illustrating the growing importance of the colonies in relation to the mother country. Phips was a sea captain and knew his own mind. He tolerated, as did Governor Fletcher of New York, the use of New England harbors by Caribbean buccaneers and pirates; trade was the important thing. But he was unfitted for his position; he fought with Fletcher and was called back to England where in 1695 while awaiting trial, he died.

It is pertinent to quote Haring on the conditions at this time along the western seaboard: "In the North American colonies these new pirates still continued to find encouragement and protection. Carolina had long had an evil reputation as a hotbed of piracy, and deservedly so. The proprietors had removed one governor after another for harboring the freebooters but with little result. In the Bahamas, which belonged to the same proprietors, the evil was even more flagrant. Governor Markham of the Quaker colony of Pennsylvania allowed the pirates to dispose of their goods and refit along the banks of the Delaware, and William Penn showed little disposition to reprimand or remove him. Governor Fletcher of New York was in open alliance with the outlaws, accepted their gifts and allowed them to parade the streets in broad daylight. The merchants of New York, Massachusetts and Rhode Island, who were prevented by the navigation laws from engaging in legitimate trade with other nations, welcomed the appearance of pirate ships laden with goods from the East; provided a ready market for their cargoes, and encouraged them to repeat their voyages."

Here is the same story of the same mistake Spain first made in trying to control the remote commerce of the Caribbean. England, now growing in a similar position of power, likewise chose to ignore the rights and needs of the native New World colonies, and thus encouraged the spirit of revolt and lawlessness that gradually took form as the American Revolution. The western continent was growing up and beginning to feel its muscle. The tide of empire pouring in from north and south along the Ocean River was developing native commercial power in the west. The names of pirate, privateer, or merchant were not delicately distinguished from each other in the growing cities of Charleston, Philadelphia, New York, Newport, or Boston. The "hand of the giant" was opening wide.

But now we must look at the second phase of the maturing economy of the west — the growth of negro slavery in the Caribbean. There are two ways of looking at the rapid speed-up of historical development due to the opening of the resources of the west. Spain as an empire missed the boat because of her rigid immobility, due to an absolutist political concept of the king and the unbending power of the Church fathers remote from the scene. England built her power at home and as an empire on what her enemies would call the rise of piracy and the slave trade. Actually, England at sea and at home was moving with a new release of nationalistic energy. She became great as the Atlantic Ocean, the Ocean River of the west, emerged out of the unknown; for her sailors, explorers, and fishermen, untrammelled by a rigid church or a jealous concept of kingship, moved out freely on the tide of the future. It is only just to remember, when we see how the English inaugurated the slave trade as a successful commerce to the Caribbean and the southern colonies, that the English were also the first to condemn slavery and make attempts to control the trade. We have seen how Hawkins initiated the English contraband trade in slaves in the Caribbean with the connivance of the local Spanish colonial authorities. From then on, as sugar plantations grew on the islands, nothing could stop it. White adventurers went on to the Main looking for gold. The native Indian populations on the islands were soon dead and gone under the harsh breath of European lust for property. Africa filled the gap so well, indeed, that Haiti and Jamaica today have populations almost completely of African descent. This negro predominance was inevitable for two reasons. The Spanish colonizer did not come to work the land himself; his concept of rising in life was not through day labor. Also he was perhaps lazy, certainly proud, and the climate did not suit him. After 1518 the crown recognized the need for imported labor and created contracts and licenses called "asientos," which in turn were farmed out by the favored holders to actual slave carriers. But here again the heavy hand of absentee government placed such imposts on these commercial privileges that it actually encouraged illicit contraband trade.

It might have been possible, of course, for the West Indies to have remained in the hands of white European settlers if there had been concerted action by European governments to that end. But no such long-term policy was likely, for several reasons. First, the European governments were most of the time at each other's throats in religious and imperial-istic wars; and secondly, the proper use and development of land through diversified small holdings had no chance to take hold in the West Indies as it did on the North American con-tinent. All reason and judgment on the part of both govern-ments and settlers was lost in the greed for quick wealth in gold, silver, and other commodities that could be wrested from the natives. And unfortunately the African slave trade, long developed and systematized by Mediterranean peoples, was ready at hand to solve temporarily all the deficiencies of the West Indian sugar economy.

To begin with, the Spanish crown farmed out the slave trade to the Portuguese, then the French and Dutch, and finally to the British Royal African Company, in "asientos" or licenses. This somewhat expensive and complicated remote control naturally encouraged contraband slave trade, and finally, when the labor-hungry sugar plantations of the islands really got going in the seventeenth century, blew the market wide open. The Spaniards made a general mess of their island possessions because of their particular preoccupation with the vast riches of Central and South America.

Jamaica, potentially one of the richest islands of the west, had been in the hands of the Spanish for a century and a half when the British conquered it in 1655. In 1611, after a hun-dred years, the Church took a census. There were 696 Spanish men, women, and children on the island, 107 free negroes, only 74 surviving Indians of the many thousand original inhab-itants, and about 600 negro slaves — all in all a mere handful. The present population of Jamaica — woefully overpopulated — is 1,364,000. As the Spanish population decreased the freed slaves, plus the Indians, formed a community in the back country and called themselves "Maroons." Spanish rule had little control. As early as 1526 immigration from the island to the Main had been forbidden. When the English, under

Admiral Penn and General Venables, came ashore in 1655, some 8,000 people took to the hills. The British, never able to subdue the Maroons completely, finally made peace treaties with them, giving them freedom and property on a reservation. Even today in Jamaica you have this subdivision of modified authority called the Kingdom of the Maroons.

With the English, the buccaneers moved in and used Jamaica as a port of repair for raiding the Spanish treasure fleets. At the same time sugar plantations were established and the slave trade necessarily flowed in to fill the labor vacuum. From a statistical standpoint the answer by 1780 was self-evident. Jamaica supported 30,000 whites (and "white" was open to local definition), 10,000 free colored, 1,400 free Maroons in the hills, and 250,000 slaves, in a total population of less than 300,000. That tells the story of the kind and quantity of population increase in the West Indies at the time of our Revolution, with some natural but not greatly different variation in the smaller islands.

The above figures of the tremendous population increase and the plantation growth in Jamaica, as in other Caribbean islands, spelled one thing — sugar. The Dutch traders, able, ubiquitous, and transitory in the New World, first brought the art of commercially successful sugar making to the Barbadoes from Brazil in 1640. Long before this, of course, Columbus had introduced sugar cane from the Canaries, but the Spaniards had made little real progress as planters. In the seventeenth century the French and English, stimulated by the Dutch merchants, made over the derelict Spanish island empire with sugar and molasses. The Barbadoes, Jamaica, Haiti, Antigua, and other islands prospered immensely. The French West Indies in particular specialized in the manufacture of refined sugar because their home government placed no restrictions on the trade, and Haiti had some of the best soil in the Caribbean. The Dutch meanwhile, though driven out of Brazil, acted as middlemen in the sugar trade and in marketing slaves which the plantation economy demanded.

So Charles II of England chartered the Royal African Company to take the slave trade away from the Dutch, and also inaugurated restrictive navigation acts with all the English colonies to damage further the free commerce at which the Dutch were such masters. This led to eventual troubles with the colonies of the North American continent, and brought in such a flux of African slave labor to the Caribbean that from the middle 1600's on the white population of the islands began to dwindle. Sugar created a temporary prosperity at the cost of increased slave trade, impoverishment of the soil, and heavy-handed absentee controls that bred increasing trouble with the Atlantic seaboard colonies to the north. The Caribbean sugar economy brought in the Yankee traders and created commercial rivalries with England that came to final settlement in the Revolution, which in turn set off the slave revolts in Haiti and elsewhere.

Who were the people strange to the American continent that were forced against their will to populate the West Indies? They came in misery and chains down the long easy reaches of the equatorial roots of the Ocean River. Did the white men of the north who bought and paid for their inexhaustible labor make them slaves? Did John Hawkins think up the slave trade to enrich himself and his countrymen? Nothing so temporary as that. The institution of slavery had developed from the time of earliest history in the Mediterranean world. It developed around human beings as the spoils of war. The western slavers translated this into transactions in merchandise, but all they had to do in order to do business was to placate the coastal rulers and local African kings, for the slave trade was thriving in Africa before the first black man was ever transported west, and the rulers of this trade were the Africans themselves.

When Portuguese first opened up trade along the African coasts, before the discovery of America, they had intermarried with the negroes, and mulattos had attained positions of importance under the Portuguese rule. This habit of freedom prevailed, at least among the ruling class. The European nations, neither by force of arms nor by efforts of penetration through conversions to the Church, ever got beyond the slim foothold in Africa first established by the Portuguese. Traders had to obey local kings, wait on their pleasure, and pay adequate port duties. Africa saw to it that the path of empire, at least in the early days, turned down the Atlantic current to the west and away from themselves.

The Negro, coming to the West Indies as a slave, has today, by his adjustability and by sheer weight of numbers, virtually taken over the islands. To quote Wyndham in his study of the slavery question: "As a result of his slavery, the Negro acquired a position in the world to which he would not have attained had he remained free. He was of tougher fibre than the Indian. His capacity for survival was greater. He was more independent of circumstance, less vulnerable to misfortune. His inexhaustible vivacity was his strength . . . it was an outward and often audible sign of resiliency which was the fulcrum of his self-defense, and the point of vantage from which he invaded the cultural and economic territories of the whites. His revolts did not serve him so well as his unchangeableness, coupled as it was with a degree of adaptability, which, while not submerging his special characteristics, increased his power of influencing his new environment."

The contemporary white settlers felt this pressure, but naturally did not analyze it in any such dispassionate way as Wyndham has. Their contemporary reactions explain the economic and social basis of troubles of adjustment not only in the islands, but also in North America. The prototype of all such complaints was well put by Cervantes in the mouth of one of his Spaniards against the Moors: "Their only thought is how to scrape up money and keep it . . . by perpetual getting and never spending, they get the greater part of the money in Spain into their hands. Consider how numerous they are and how they increase . . . neither sex take monastic vows but all marry and multiply. They have no servants, for they all wait upon themselves, etc., etc."

This economic and social complaint was carried over into the New World. The Spanish Bishop of Oaxaca wrote home in 1544: "Your Majesty may be reassured on the way the Indians are treated. They are so protected that they dare even to maltreat the Spaniards. . . . These Indians own properties, many are rich and all possess goods of which their ancestors were ignorant. In fact, all the money of the country is in their hands . . . and they sell goods at such exorbitant prices that living here is impossible. Everything is topsy-turvy."

And finally from the island of San Domingo in 1755: "These people are beginning to fill the colony and it is a scandal to see them increasing in numbers continually among the whites, and overtaking them in opulence and riches. . . . Their low standard of living enables them to save their earnings each year. They pile up capital. They become arrogant because they are rich and in proportion to their wealth, etc., etc."

So we see from the beginning the established Indian of the mainland and the Negro in the islands began taking over from a white population that was enervated by the climate, not used to the hard manual labor necessary to a new frontier, and too proud to adjust to conditions his own eagerness for quick wealth had superimposed on the islands. And yet the Spanish, French, and English governments, according to the lights of the times, did try to recognize in law the inevitable mixture of races and the social and economic adjustments that had to take place. They did this, at least, until the pressure against the old-time white minorities became too acute and the colonies themselves instituted repressive legislation.

In Jamaica in 1733 all persons were considered white who were three degrees removed from exclusive Negro ancestry, and such people possessed full free privileges. The degrees of ancestry from Negro to white were called mulatto, quadroon, and mustee. The Spanish inserted more complicated variations of degree, and also distinguished between Negro and Indian mixture of blood strain. Similar distinctions were recognized also in Virginia; until 1691 Negro-white marriages were legal in that colony, and until 1723 free Negroes and mulattos had the vote. But the story of growing economic pressure repeats itself in Virginia as elsewhere. In the fifty years between 1670 and 1730 the slave population increased from 2,000 to 26,000; and this also forced a growing class of dispossessed poor whites, and the laws protecting the free Negro or the Negro of mixed blood were revoked.

The temptation to dwell in the Caribbean with the first great turn of the Ocean River is great. But the Stream carries us on into the Florida Straits, leaving behind in the eighteenth and nineteenth centuries a free Negro republic in Haiti, a Negro British colony in Jamaica, a Spanish-dominated island of Cuba of mixed bloods and inheritance, and the outer islands divided among the British, French, and Dutch. One main thing stands out. Spain missed her bid for empire in the islands, and as a whole the European migration to the west in the seventeenth and eighteenth centuries failed to take root in the Caribbean, where the original slaves by number and in adaptability outlasted the white conquerors. Africa, not Europe, won most of the islands; though without political sovereignty except partly in Jamaica and totally in Haiti. And the gentle, nonbelligerent, sensuous Arawaks, never understanding the zeal and lust of the European for property, simply disappeared from the face of the earth.

In the eighteenth century the pioneer era of opening the North American continent was over. A new and enthusiastic rush of Europeans, partly French but predominantly English, poured across the Atlantic seeking new homes — and by "homes" they meant freehold lands and freedom for mind and spirit. This new century and this new impulse was Protestant and rational, well suited to start the great expansion of material growth and prosperity across the waters that the later invention of the steam engine and the cotton gin so much accelerated. Commerce increased all along the North American seaboard, particularly in New England. As early as the end of the seventeenth century the English home government was worried about this. The minutes of the Privy Council record: "New England is become the great mart and staple by which means the navigation of the Kingdom is prejudiced, the king's revenue is expressibly impaired, the price of home and foreign commodities lessened, trade decreased, and the King's subjects much impoverished."

Here is the same European jealousy and concern with the growth of power in the west now transferred from worrying about the Negroes in the Caribbean to the codfish Yankees and their able merchant marine. So the pressure was put on by various Acts of Trade aimed at curbing too much independence in the colonies; and the Yankees answered back when the Massachusetts Assembly declared: "We humbly conceive, according to the usual sayings of the learned in the law, that the laws of England are bounded within the four seas and do not reach America . . . and not being represented in Parliament we have not looked to ourselves to be impeded in our trade by them." From now on the die was cast, and in commercial terms — though as like as not argued on a very high level of morality. It was no longer conquer and convert; it was liberty of action and freedom of trade for a New World people becoming more and more self-sufficient and self-confident.

The Indian frontier in the eighteenth century was pushed back beyond the Alleghenies. The sea frontiers of the adventurous sons of New England girdled the globe. Now at last the northward sweep of the Ocean River was coming alive with their trading vessels, seeking not only the Caribbean waters but the far spice islands of the Indian Ocean and Indonesia.

12

THE CODFISH FRONTIER

WHEN the new western world opened to the races of Europe, no single nation or people had any organized plan, nor were they efficiently prepared in any way to take advantage of the greatest opportunity for expansion ever offered to civilized man. It is not an unusual picture in history to see blind and preoccupied rulers leave the hazard of new adventure to bold individuals. The opening of the Atlantic, the discovery of the rich world of the Ocean River, and the wealth of the shores westward seem slow and tardy business as we look back into history. But there was nothing slow about the exploitation of the New World once man's natural aversion to an unfamiliar notion was overcome by the clink of gold and the holy odor of codfish. The only thing lacking was order and law.

Perhaps if Henry the Navigator had lived a century later the Portuguese under his enlightened leadership might have been the heirs to the western world; but they had already turned the Cape for India. So the fierce energy of Spain consumed the peace of the native Caribbean, and the French and the tough English seadogs moved in on the codfish banks. Though these things happened almost simultaneously at the beginning of the sixteenth century, the immediate pay-off fell, as we have just seen, to Spain.

The English nailed it down in the north more slowly. Theirs was the hard way, but it stuck. Just when the first fishing barks came to the new continent and found the cod swarming the Grand Banks and the Gulf of Maine, we do not yet know. Sailing north and west of the Ocean River was a foggy and mysterious business, but a business well established long before either Columbus or Cabot officially made landfall and history. Over against the difficulty of bucking the prevailing westerly winds and the turbulent waters, the opening of a way to the northern continent was broken by landfall of no greater interval than a moderate two days' sailing. The Norse in their relatively small but seaworthy craft discovered this, as we know, about the year 1000. The hardest stretch from Norway to Newfoundland was possibly the reach from Norway itself to Iceland. In those days, as we have explained, the weather was a good deal more moderate in northern waters, and there is no report of floe ice blocking the small craft that made their way from Iceland to Greenland and thence to Labrador and probably as far south as Cape Cod.

From Norse days onward the tradition of the northern voyages was largely founded on a desire to trade in lumber and naval supplies and fish, and not the wild adventure after pearls and silver and gold. But at both ends of the North Atlantic a common search for a passage to India also drove men westward. After the Norse voyages were cut off, how long a lapse there was before other fishing or trading vessels pierced the foggy curtain of the northeast coasts, no man knows for sure. There are many ships' logs and no doubt other unexplored documents, possibly of Bristol, or St. Malo or Dieppe or Honfleur or the Basque ports in the Bay of Biscay, that may hold the key to our knowledge of pre-Columbian discoveries; nothing new has yet been read. But we do know that in 1480 an expedition captained by John Lloyd left Bristol looking for Hi-Brazil and western lands and was gone nine weeks. Again in 1491 and 1492 Bristol merchants outfitted ships to make the same search. These were commercial men, not idle dreamers, and they very likely had some circumstantial evidence to warrant the expense. It is said that the father of the two Corte-reals, João Vas, as early as 1465 on a voyage from Terciera in the Azores discovered the Baccalaos shores. All these early voyagers, including Cabot and the brothers Corte-real in 1500, first made landfall at Greenland and then stood west and south as the Norse had done some centuries before. And they were all a little vague about just what these new lands were, most of them believing that they had come on a continent that was one with Asia and the realm of the Grand Khan. So persistent was the dream of Columbus.

As far as we know for certain, the first after the Norse to open up the Codfish Frontier was Giovanni Caboto, a Genoese working for the English. He was immediately followed by the Portuguese. But shortly after these voyages at the close of the fifteenth century, the codfish fleet that had long worked the waters around and west of Iceland was well established off the Grand Banks of Newfoundland. The fishermen did not wait for government grants to get started, and they came from all the eastern Atlantic countries — from Bristol, from the French ports of Normandy and Brittany, and in the south from the Basque country and the Portuguese ports. The fleet was international. It held together for a while in more or less peaceful enterprise and mutual help, in spite of shifting allegiances and troubles fomented by the home governments.

But once the undersea wealth of the Newfoundland fishing grounds became established in Europe for a population in great need of fish, the efforts of the various governments to explore and stake a claim to the American Atlantic seaboard accelerated during the sixteenth century. The professional explorers and pilots began to take over, and men of many nations sailed the waters of the Ocean Stream — for the most

part unaware of its influence once they had come north of the
Florida Straits. The years of this century saw the Spanish
power broken with a rise of French and Dutch sea power, combined with the domination of the British in the Caribbean,

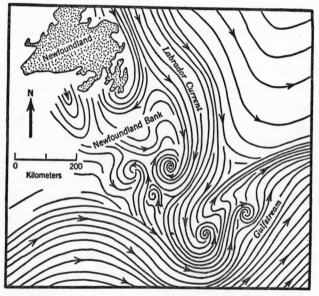

The beneficial mixing of Labrador Current and Gulf Stream waters over the
Grand Banks.

due largely to the great reservoir of trained and tough seadogs
bred in the rough battle of the Newfoundland fisheries.

Before going into the further development of the Codfish
Frontier as a new offshoot of the English race, we might take
up briefly the course of the explorations from 1500 on — when
European governments were obsessed with the notion that a
waterway could be found either directly through the barrier of

the western world or around the northern bounds of it. In 1498, the year after Cabot's memorable voyage to Newfoundland, the Spanish ambassador in England wrote this message home to his king: "It is seven years since those of Bristol used to send out every year a fleet of two or three or four caravels to go search for the Isle of Brazil and the Seven Cities, according to the fancy of the Genoese." Here the fancy of the Genoese comes obviously from Cabot, and was apparently in working order as early as the fancy of that other Genoese, Columbus.

But another and still unresolved note is struck by Cabot himself when he states: "There are plenty of fish and those very great, as seals and those which we commonly call salmons: there are soles also a yard long, but especially there is a great abundance of that kind which the savages call Baccalaos." This was great news to governments which at this time compelled people to eat fish as often as every third day; but of greater interest historically is the bald statement that the native Indians spoke of cod by the common Basque name of "Baccalaos." McFarland, in his basic history of the northeast fisheries, writes: "The conclusion has been made (by Parkman) that the fishermen of France must have visited these regions long before the voyage of Cabot. Local traditions have laid claim to the discovery of the banks of Newfoundland by the fishermen of Normandy and Brittany before 1492. . . . Such ports as Dieppe, Saint Malo, Honfleur and others had already furnished men and leaders for voyages of exploration and discovery . . . they had already visited the Canaries and the coast of Africa." To quote Parkman: "If, in the original Basque, *baccalaos* is the word for Codfish, and if Cabot found it in use among the inhabitants of Newfoundland, it is hard to escape the conclusion that the Basques had been there before him." We have no specific proof to back up this likely-seeming conjecture, but such proof may well exist in the early microfilm records from French seaports now in the Library of

Congress, or in various other maritime libraries whose store of manuscript material has not yet been thoroughly studied. The principal point of interest in this study of the Atlantic is to see how widespread in European ports was the half-knowledge of a waiting western world beyond the Ocean River.

The Portuguese interest in the new fishing grounds was stimulated by the voyages of the two Corte-real brothers from the Azores. Gaspar and Miguel both lost their lives, disappearing into the fog-bound waters of the Grand Banks, but not before they had extended the search of the coasts in looking for a Northwest Passage to Cathay and the Indies. Theirs was the first important effort, after Cabot, to solve the impossible problem of finding an open way by the back door of the west to eastern riches. The history of the opening of the Atlantic waters and the mapping of the North American eastern seaboard is the story of many such trials by men of all the coastal European nations. And while the land of the cod was revealing itself in the northeast, other explorers from the Caribbean were diligently pushing north from the roots of the Stream beyond the Florida Straits.

The chief credit for exploration during the first half of the sixteenth century on the Codfish Frontier belongs to France under the leadership of Henry IV. But before this Vespucius for Spain and Verrazano for Francis I had put the Atlantic seaboard on the map. The voyage of Vespucius is important because it is likely that the information he gathered in 1497 was used five years later by Cantino in the first reasonably accurate map of the North American coast. Cantino's map shows Cuba as an island, calls the West Indies for the first time the Antilles, and has the position of Newfoundland carefully indicated. Vespucius made his way north through the Florida Straits, riding the current of the Stream after a voyage to the Honduras coast. Like many others, he was searching for a break in the continental landfall. With him were such experienced navigators and explorers as Solis and Pinzon, the companion of Columbus on his second voyage. These three seem to have cruised along the coast as far north as the Chesapeake and then returned east by way of Bermuda.

In 1500 Jean de La Cosa, one of the best pilots and cartographers of his time, and pilot for Columbus on his first and second voyages, made a map of the northeast coasts based on reports of Cabot's discoveries. It is a little vague, as it had to be, but it gives what probably was the Gulf of St. Lawrence and parts of Newfoundland. The neighborhood is labeled "Sea Discovered by the Englishmen." It indicates that the Cabot voyages may have extended from Labrador to Cape Cod; it also indicates that any accurate knowledge of these coasts did not yet exist. Men were still often unable to distinguish between islands and promontories, or whether a large bay might not be the long-desired passage to the Indies.

Cabot and his Bristol men were the first to prove they had been to the Grand Banks. They reported the cod there so plentiful that they could be hauled out of the sea in baskets; but the English were slow to take advantage of this good news. It might be used as a persuasive argument for prior knowledge that the Norman, Breton, and Basque fishing fleets established themselves on the Banks by 1504, when there was report of only a single English vessel there. Two years later Jean Denys of Honfleur cruised through these same waters, and further extended the mapping of the St. Lawrence Gulf. In 1521 Alvarez Fagundes made a more careful exploration of the St. Lawrence region for the King of Portugal, but the Portuguese were so involved in the exploitation of their new wealth in the Far East that they did not push the matter.

Francis I of France was not content to let the Spanish and Portuguese have the Pope of Rome divide the world between them; he ironically pointed out that he also was a direct heir of Adam. The King at this time — about 1520 — was much

impressed by the exploit of the Florentine navigator and captain Verrazano, who resided at Dieppe. Verrazano made his
first great killing in the capture of Spanish treasure from
Mexico; he captured the returning fleet of Avila while in the
employ of the merchant Ango of Dieppe. As a result of this
exploit Verrazano was commissioned by the King in 1524 to
search the northern coasts of America for sources of new
treasure, at the same time keeping his eye open for a short cut
to the Indies. This was the first well-planned attempt to locate
the Northwest Passage. Men's minds were turning this way
because the reported hardship of Magellan's circumnavigation
of the world proved that there was no quick or feasible way by
the Patagonian Straits. Verrazano put on the map a mythical
sea called for many years by his name. As he sailed northward
by the Carolinas, the inland salt sounds of Pamlico and Albemarle, to say nothing of the Chesapeake a little to the north,
gave him the impression that here might be found a way into
the Pacific waters. So we have for a few decades the so-called
Sea of Verrazano. Beyond this the Florentine pushed into the
Hudson River and beyond to Narragansett Bay. Northward
from there he is said to have seen from his ship's deck the
peaks of the White Mountains of New Hampshire. But he
found no answers to the Northwest Passage or gold mines for
his king. The idea of the Sea of Verrazano, however, stuck in
men's minds for almost a century after this voyage, and was
so recorded on many maps. Verrazano returned to Dieppe a
hero, but his place in the sun was short. He went forth two
years later, once again a captain for the great merchant Ango
of Dieppe, on a voyage to the East Indies for spices. The Spanish, still burning under the insult of the capture of their treasure fleet, waylaid this great pilot and hanged him for piracy.
Many of the great adventurers thus died violently — Gilbert,
Raleigh, Magellan, Roberval, Balboa, and others.

By 1550 the coasts from the Caribbean to the Gulf of St.

Lawrence became a connected reality, and the Europeans were ready to believe that this was really a new world and not a part of the kingdom of the Grand Khan or an extension of the Indies. The French continued to go on with an intelligent study and exploitation of the northern waters and the lands beyond the eastward turn of the Ocean River. Also in 1527 a certain John Rut of Bristol vainly searched the waters around Labrador for the Northwest Passage; but at this time the real initiative westward lay with the French. In the 1530's, Jacques Cartier explored the St. Lawrence looking for a short cut to India, and found the entrance to the future empire of colonial France, penetrating as far as Montreal. Cartier was from St. Malo, and his enterprise was calculated to strengthen the fishing interests of that port with a solid settlement on the shores of Canada. But nothing consecutive was accomplished by the French Government to this end, because of wars at home and the bitter winter weather of the North American continent. As usual, certain exceptional individuals kept up the effort. Roberval in the 1540's made vain attempts to make a settlement stick. Under Roberval was a man of tougher breed and wide experience at sea, Jean Allefonsce, from the Biscayan town of Saintonge. He took one of Roberval's vessels and sailed southward looking for the mythical Sea of Verrazano. He came down Long Island Sound and penetrated the Hudson far enough inland to taste its freshness. He thought at least that this great river must connect with the St. Lawrence somewhere near the Indian metropolis of Hochlega. He called the vicinity of New York "Norembega." In 1540 a French blockhouse was built on the site of Albany to protect fur-trading interests. Roberval, though a great disciplinarian and an eager explorer, failed because he was not a practical man; nor did he get consecutive backing from his government. He was later murdered in a street fight in France, and his companion Allefonsce was lost at sea.

And still the English had not realized the opportunity of the new western discoveries — though there is a little hint of the growing importance of the sea in English life. In 1539 Fletcher of Rye, a shipwright to Henry VIII, invented the first successful fore-and-aft rig, and was able to tack his craft close-hauled to the wind. This revolutionary advance in the maneuverability of a vessel did much to give the smaller English fleet an advantage over the Invincible Armada of Spain in 1588, when Drake sailed out of Plymouth.

We have seen that the British, slow to follow up the discoveries of Cabot, left the initiative to France. The conservative English fishermen kept going back to the nearer grounds in the neighborhood of Iceland; but the bolder adventurers moved in against the Spanish in the Caribbean, as Hawkins did to found the slave trade in those waters.

The French had by no means abandoned their Caribbean adventure because of their new interests in the north, but at this particular time they were no match for the last flare-up of Spanish power. The story of the early attempts by any of the European nations to settle permanent colonies just north of Florida along the Stream were all tragic. In 1562 Jean Ribaut, a Huguenot, explored the St. Johns River in Florida, then called the River of May, settled there for a while, and later established a fort at Port Royal in North Carolina. Unfortunately for the French, the Spanish at this time had an admiral of exceptional ability and ruthlessness, Menendez, who attacked Ribaut's men and murdered most of them. In 1667 the French under deGourges attacked and sacked the little town of St. Augustine in revenge, but four years later Menendez rebuilt the fortifications; and the last French bid for continental power in the southern part of the continent had failed.

In the second half of the sixteenth century the English began to take serious notice of Newfoundland and the Banks.

France at this time was involved in a series of civil wars that dried up her available resources for overseas settlement on the American continent. England now began to wake up to the importance of the western world as a place for Englishmen to settle. We have the record of the brave but ill-run attempt by Sir Walter Raleigh, in the Carolinas at Roanoke Island, to duplicate the colonial efforts of France, and the similar expedition by Raleigh's half-brother, Sir Humphrey Gilbert, to take over Newfoundland for the British in 1583. Gilbert exhibited the same courageous and romantic flare for adventure as Raleigh. He landed among the fishing fleet near St. Johns, raised the English flag, and with a flourish of bugles announced future empire. He declared that here the unemployed and loose-of-foot at home could be shipped to labor usefully to enrich the mother country. Sailing for home, he boarded the smallest and most unseaworthy vessel of his little fleet, the *Squirrel*, in order to share all danger equally with his crew, and in a great storm in the Bay of Biscay he went down, shouting over the waters to his comrades on *The Golden Hind*, "We are as near to Heaven by sea as by land!"

From now on the opening of the American northeast coast to English enterprise was undertaken by more competent navigators and by the tough fishing fleets of the west country of England. The merchants of Devon and Bristol now engaged their interest to exploit the Codfish Frontier. These fishing interests, however, were directly opposed to those who wished to make permanent settlements in Newfoundland or Nova Scotia. The merchants did not want the year-round competition of resident fishermen against the seasonal venture of the fleets to the Banks. They did not want any civil authority established on the shores and in the bays where the fishing admirals seasonally established their own autocratic rule. This battle — a kind of mercantile civil war — did much to settle the future struggle for power between the New England colonies and the mother country by delaying the growth of the maritime colonies, while settlers poured into Maine and Massachusetts and built a native marine power there on the great fisheries of the Gulf of Maine. Meanwhile, even though the attention of the new and powerful merchant class in England was finally centering on the lowly cod, the idea of quick wealth by a new passage to the Indies still persisted. In testimony to this, Martin Frobisher made three voyages west from Greenland searching for the Northwest Passage; and John Davis explored the strait named after him as far as 72° N. latitude at about the same time that Gilbert and Raleigh were failing to settle Englishmen in Nova Scotia or the Carolinas.

But no one had yet the vaguest notion of the great revolution of the Ocean River, although they were aware of the Labrador Current. The testimony of Peter Martyr, first printed in 1516, spoke of the westward course of waters in the Caribbean and the southwesterly course of the Labrador Current. Of Cabot's observations he wrote: "As he traveled by the coasts of this great land which he named Baccalaos, he saith he found the like course of waters towards the west, but the same to run more gently and softly than the swift waters which the Spaniards found in their navigations southward. Wherefore, it is not only more likely to be true, but ought also of necessity to be concluded, that between both the lands hitherto unknown, there should be certain great open places whereby the waters should thus continually pass from the East unto the West, which waters I suppose to be driven about the earth by the incessant moving and impulsion of the heavens." Not yet feeling sure that the North American continent extended unbroken from the Isthmus of Panama to the Arctic, no one could yet conceive of a great circular turning of the west-running waters. So there was nothing possible for men to seek but a passage through the land to the eastern seas.

While explorations continued along the North American

coasts and men laid plans for profitable settlement there, the real progress in the western world was along the sweep of the Ocean River where it cut north and east at the edge of the continental shelf off the codfish Banks. By the end of the six-teenth century an annual fleet of over two hundred vessels from France, Portugal, and England at the end of winter bucked the headwinds and March storms of the North Atlan-tic to load with cod for the Catholic markets. From time to time pirates or raiders of one nation against the other stole cargoes of this "Poor John" in order to pre-empt the early market. The merchants of the west country in England fitted out vessels and sometimes let men go along as crew to share in the catch — what was termed "on their own hook." But these shipowners continued to frown on any attempt at a permanent settlement along the shores of Nova Scotia or Newfoundland.

Other men meanwhile turned their attention to the shores just west of the Ocean River. In 1602 Bartholomew Gosnold, formerly with Raleigh, sailed from Maine to Cuddyhunk off Cape Cod and came home with a cargo of sassafras and cedar wood. Martin Pring followed the next year, cruising the waters of Massachusetts Bay. And George Weymouth in 1605 ran from Cape Cod to the Kennebec and wrote such glowing reports of the Maine coast that in 1607 Popham sent out his colony to the mouth of the Kennebec that lasted one brief, unhappy year. But the English were working up to it; in the next few years new projects came thick and fast. The year of the Popham colony John Smith settled Jamestown in Vir-ginia. For the French, Champlain landed at the site of Quebec the following year. In 1609 Henry Hudson explored the Hud-son River for the Dutch, and in 1614 opened up the great bay and future fur-trading empire which bears his name; then was cruelly marooned, with his son, to perish in those icy waters.

Six years before the Pilgrim fathers arrived from Holland, John Smith cruised the New England waters, gave the region its present name, and returned to write a real-estate panegyric of the new country. This same year, 1614, another northern visitor from Virginia, Captain Argoll, attacked the French settlement of Sieur de Mont at Somes Sound in Mt. Desert, and raided Port Royal in Acadia where the French had settled four years before. It is also sadly interesting to note that Sir Walter Raleigh, the great romantic searcher after wealth and honor in Virginia, the Carolinas, and at last in Guiana, coming home to England in final defeat, was beheaded in 1618 for having stirred up trouble with Spain. Kings recognized only success. Two years later, without any of the grand dreams or bold individual scheming that marked the sixteenth century's courtly adventurers, the humble, ill-prepared, but persistent group of Pilgrims made the first really permanent English settlement north of Virginia. Fishermen had been wintering along the coast off and on for almost a hundred years, but the Pilgrims were the first who came to this region to found a home.

This Plymouth settlement, and the ones to follow shortly after at Boston and Salem, marks the beginning of a force that was eventually to challenge and finally control the codfishing Banks, "the silver mines of the sea," where the Ocean River and the Labrador Current combined to create the basic wealth of early New England. Meanwhile the merchants of western England were still doing their best to prevent colonization in Newfoundland, and thus indirectly helped New England prosper. Perhaps this is the place to draw a picture from the early records of what went on offshore and onshore by the Grand Banks.

Actually the first effective colonization of the western world north of the Caribbean was seaborne — the international working colony of the Brotherhood of the Banks on the Codfish Frontier along the northeastern course of the Ocean River. The French, under Champlain, were penetrating the waters of the great St. Lawrence River to found the beginnings of their inland empire. The English were coming in at Plymouth and Boston and Salem along the coasts of New England handy to the lasting wealth of the New World — cod. Between fur and cod the French very shortly had the wrong end of the stick. Meanwhile they made a settlement in the valley of Acadia in Nova Scotia, the same place whose people, later transported as English prisoners, were resettled in the bayous around New Orleans as "Cajuns." But the business on land did not prosper as did that of the sea.

The persuasion of a vessel full of cod was more eloquent than the romantic exhortations of men like Lescarbot, who pleaded with his king for companies of settlers, or Nicolas Denys, who tried to prove the north a temperate land by showing that Acadia in latitude at least was in the same weather belt as the Midi of France. Both men left out the one explanation they could not know of—the great Atlantic current system that brought warm winds and waters to western Europe and left the maritime provinces at the mercy of the fogs and cold waters of the Labrador Current. It is true that Lescarbot was one of the first to note the beginning of the Ocean River in the Caribbean, but he did not connect it with the offshore currents of the Grand Banks. Men were loth to winter on the northeast coasts; only at sea was there enough quick wealth to warrant the hardships involved. And there at last the rivalries and contentions of the European homelands reached out into the community of the Banks, even as men like Captain John Smith, Admiral of New England, was writing some of the best early real-estate promotion for Massachusetts: "Who can desire," he said, "more content that hath small means than to plant and tread that ground he hath purchased by hazard of his life? What so truly suits with honor and honesty, as the discovery of things unknown, erecting townes, peopling countries, informing the ignorant, reforming things unjust, teach-

ing virtue and gain to our native mother country. . . . And is
it not a pretty sport to pull up two pence, six pence and twelve
pence, as fast as you can haul and vere a line; he is a very bad
fisher cannot kill in one day one, two or three hundred cods,

Drawings from an early illustration showing the Newfoundland cod-fishery.

which dressed and dried be sold for ten shillings a hundred . . . if a man work but three days in seven, he may get more than he can spend unless he will be exceedingly excessive. What sport doth yield a more pleasing content, and less hurt and charge, than angling with a hook and crossing the sweet air from isle to isle over the silent streams of a calm sea, wherein the most curious may find profit, pleasure and content. Therefore honorable and worthy countrymen [he con-cludes] let not the meanness of the word fish distaste you, for it will afford as good gold as the Mines of Guiana or Potassie, with less hazard and charge, and more certainty and facility."

Captain John Smith, with his immense gift of common sense, correctly gauged the true wealth of the New England coastal waters, but he did put it a little on the easy side. It is time we took a brief look at the actual set-up along the shores in from the Banks and see how those that mined the silver of the deeps handled their difficult if profitable task. All nations wished to dominate the fishing wealth of the Stream's edge along the Banks. Roughly there were certain things favoring the English. The French and Spanish colonial systems were developed largely under strict governmental control, and after the brief Huguenot supremacy in France no colonization was permitted other than Catholic. The English was much more a straight commercial enterprise, without particular emphasis on Church or State; time played into English hands when the day of the traders superseded the day of the gentlemen adven-turers.

Just as the Mediterranean poured its vessels west and south along the Equatorial Current under the favoring trade winds to the Caribbean, so the rough and clouded waters of the Channel each year in February and March assembled a fleet of vessels great and small, outfitted for the western fisheries of the Banks. Newfoundland was the new hunting ground for west England and the French seaports. The cod challenged the herring as the great staple fish. The French fleet, as a rule, got off to an early start. Both fleets had to buck the roughest waters and the most cantankerous weather in the northern hemisphere, but the captains and the men were long trained in a hard school and their ships were rugged — they averaged from sixty to three hundred tons burden and carried small boats and gear for a six months' journey over and back, if necessary; though some, leaving in winter, made a point of an early catch for the Lenten markets. This was "wet cod," salted but not dried.

We cannot do better here than go to first sources and give a brief account of the fishing as reported by Nicolas Denys in 1672, in his *Natural History of North America*: "It is necessary that a captain who sets out from France for this fishery should make preparation in provisions for six months at least. After that they go to take on their salt at Brouge, Oleron Ré, or Brittany . . . which makes up almost all the rest of what the ship can carry. This fishery consumes much salt. There is need, further, of lines eighty fathoms in length, eight to ten for each man. A much larger number of hooks are required. There is also needed for each man twelve to fifteen leads of six pounds weight each, also knives for dressing and splitting. After she is equipped she sets sail and goes, by the Grace of God, to find the Grand Bank. Having arrived there, all the sails are furled and the ship is prepared for this fishery. The tiller of the rudder is attached on one side, so the vessel remains almost as if she were at anchor, though she drifts nevertheless when there is a wind. Some now throw over their lines and others build a staging along one side of the vessel outside. Upon this staging are placed the barrels; these are half-hogsheads, which reach to the height of the waist. Each fisherman places himself inside his own. They have also a large leathern apron which extends from the neck to the knees. The lower end of the apron is placed over the barrel outside, in order to insure that the water, which the line brings with it drawing up the cod from the bottom of the sea, shall not run into the barrel . . . the lead must not reach the bottom by two fathoms. He catches only a single cod at a time, and in order to know the number that he takes, each fisherman has a little pointed iron near him, and at the time he removes the hook from the cod, he cuts the tongue from it and strings it on this iron. Each fisherman has two lines. A good fisherman is able to take as many as three hundred and fifty to four hundred per day, but that greatly tires the arms. If they did this every day they would not be able to stand it.

"There are ships that will be fortunate enough to complete their fishery in a month to six weeks, others will be three to five months. None ever anchor upon the Banks but have a little square sail by day at the stern that keeps them into the wind to prevent drift. For the night they set their mainsail all on one side that they may drift all alike and avoid collisions. The Grand Bank is rarely without mist or fog, which is sometime so thick that one cannot see from one end of the ship to the other."

The persistence of the maritime ports of France and England in developing the fisheries of the New World was as heroic as any exploit of the conquistadors to the south, though the small monetary gains involved added nothing much to the incentive. Fortunately for France and England, the very nature of the hazard was a challenge that kept the enterprises alive. After weeks of buffeting the winter's-end westerly gales along the reaches of the Atlantic drift, one day at long last the small vessel would smell the cold fog of the Banks and see the first gulls drift in with their sharp crying and perch on the spars. In spite of the rivalry of nation and nation and the desire for each captain to fill and pay away for home and the early markets, a remarkable amount of teamwork was necessary to avoid the dangers of fog and drifting ice, and sudden northwesterly gales that came ripping off the cold continental plains.

This teamwork even extended to the shore stations where the ships that fished on into summer in the Newfoundland waters made for land to establish huts and drying stations for the stockfish or Poor John. The lucky vessels that caught the big green cod of the Banks in early season salted wet and drove for home. But the majority of the fleet took their catch to land and sun-dried and salted the split fish for carriage to the southern markets of the West Indies and the Mediterranean. As this fleet drew near to land, the captain would lower away a ship's boat with his best oarsmen and a sail stepped forward. This rough regatta of single boats raced for the shore, hardly pausing to eat until they found a cove or harbor suitable for the sheds and drying frames. The law of the fleet each season gave command in any cove to the first comer; the captain of the vessel whose boat got in first was admiral of that territory, and assumed complete control even over any local inhabitants who might have presumed to squat there. A kind of rough but absolute frontier justice prevailed among the fishermen as a self-contained group.

But the merchants back home who paid for the ships and gear were not pleased to see any kind of settlement on the shores of Newfoundland or Nova Scotia. They knew that men who lived there the year around had an advantage in the fisheries, pre-empting the harbors and avoiding the high costs of transatlantic fetch and haul. And for a while they were successful in preventing the colonization of the maritime provinces. From their point of view colonial enterprise was detrimental, for as a result of it the English fishing fleet of 250 vessels in 1605 had decreased by 1670 to a mere 80. So the Lords of Plantations in England determined to depopulate Newfoundland, and the dwellings of the settlers were systematically wrecked and burned. The military nature of the new policy is well illustrated by the fact that in 1676 a fleet of 202 ships, each carrying twenty guns and eighteen boats, made the Banks, escorted by two ships of war, and the total value of the fish and oil brought home was £385,000 sterling.

Sabine, in his report on the situation, wrote: "The triumph of the English merchants over their fellow subjects in this lone and desolate isle, was as complete as that of a warrior who storms a city . . . as a class the 'Admirals' were both knaves and tyrants."

Here we have a classic example — fortunately of only a temporary nature — of the English reverting to a strict governmental control of far colonies such as the Spanish used with such ill success in the Caribbean.

As a result of this quarrel in the north, the New England fishermen moved in on the Banks with over 600 vessels and 4,000 seamen. Only half as many men as employed by Britain caught an equal number of fish. The growth of the New England population and its skill, daring, and independence, outpaced the application of similar preventive measures until the mother country was unequal to the task. As for the whole history of the misbegotten policy in Newfoundland, Edmund Burke said in 1766: "The most valuable trade we have in the world is with Newfoundland," but he also broke out in anguish over the costliness of the policies in these words: "Good God! What sums the nursing of the ill-thriven, hard-visaged and ill-favored brat has cost this wittol nation. Sir, this colony has stood us in a sum of not less than seven hundred thousand pounds." This was a fair indictment of a policy that helped England lose all her American colonies by an inability to read the course of natural events, namely, the population of a wilderness and the harvesting of the wild waters of the sea by Englishmen transplanted to new strength and independence.

At the end of the seventeenth century the shores of North America were growing a people from Europe who would and did turn about toward the tracks of the Ocean River and build their strength on it with codfish and trade spanning the world. The age of the domination of sea power was at hand. As Parry puts it: "The ships which sought the northern passages and opened the trade with Russia; the expeditions which began the settlement of North America; the English and the Dutch fleets which defeated the navies of Spain, were largely manned by sailors trained in the hard school of the Banks fisheries." These victories opened up the New England mainland to a flood of English artisans who were dissenters from the ruling religious group in England, and were finding it increasingly difficult as well to earn an honest living in the disrupted economy of the mother country. The merchant class in England, wishing a greater trade in Caribbean sugar, Virginia tobacco, and New England codfish, set up stock companies to forward the development of colonies. It was these private enterprises that attracted and initially supported the settlers in New England, and that by their nature encouraged the settlers to grow in independence. This was in complete contrast to the state-governed and -supported type of colonial enterprises sponsored by Spain and France. The English companies, unfortunately, never made much money in the west, as they did for instance in the East Indies. Colonial trade, all too soon for the profit of the sponsors, began to flourish on its own and free itself from control. The Barbadoes was the first colony to prosper. Slavery brought a sudden source of cheap labor to the sugar plantations, and the exports from the Barbadoes to England, as we saw in an earlier chapter, by 1650 were greater than those of Virginia and larger still than exports from New England.

But a group of shrewd and independent leaders soon began to put Massachusetts in the running. The strict monopolistic policies of Richelieu in Canada limited the rapid development of French colonies in the north. At his death in 1642 there were only 3,000 Canadians, against 20,000 settlers in Massachusetts alone. Toward the end of the century the English had peacefully elbowed the Dutch out of New York and New Jersey. The Dutch had never made serious attempts at colonization in America; they played a successful game of middleman. With superior crews and better-designed vessels they ruled the carrying trade of the Atlantic for many years. To end this the English devised various acts against free trade that were intended to channel American export and import to English vessels and English ports. In return, the British protected the colonies against France in Canada and the pirates of the high seas — piracy being a real hazard. In 1679 Algerian pirates captured thirteen Virginia vessels off the mouth of the English Channel.

But as the New Englanders became more independent they began to resent the increased trade restrictions of the mother country. The Yankees were inclined to take protection for granted; and meanwhile they built ships thirty to forty percent cheaper than the English. Hard work, rocky home acres, and small capital outlay, plus the protection of the British Navy, thus more than offset a limitation of capital. Smuggling and illicit trade with the pirates themselves became frequent and went unpunished. The law of supply and demand, the less complicated bargaining of free trade, put custom and expediency above the artificial restraints of English law. There was a new breeze blowing along the western side of the Ocean River that smelled of codfish and timber and a new self-sufficiency for the transplanted British artisans meeting the challenge of the New World.

In closing this brief survey, again let us sum up by quoting from Parry's book, *Europe and a Wider World*: "By the end of the seventeenth century the general lines of the final struggle for power and trade in America were already apparent. The Dutch were beginning to drop out, weakened by unequal wars in Europe. The power of Portugal was localized in Brazil. The Spanish empire seemed on the verge of collapse, although it was to outlast the others as an imperial unity. Of the major fighting competitors each had its weakness. The English empire obviously suffered from lack of unity and discipline, but the French empire had the more serious defect of lack of people."

At the beginning of the eighteenth century, though Spanish America seemed far ahead of the northern colonies in culture, trade, and inhabitants, the northern colonies were ready with their vast undeveloped resources at sea and in farms and forests to receive the sudden flood of migration from Europe that presently began. In addition, the free spirit of Protestantism, independent by nature and linked with the growing mercantile classes in England, had a great advantage over the restricted, Catholic, state-controlled immigration policies of the French in America. The great Ocean River slowly swirling from the west to make its rounds of the Atlantic world was now surrounded not only by the active civilization of seaboard Europe, but by a new and tremendously vital transportation of Europeans all along the western boundaries of the Gulf Stream. This fresh development guaranteed a new lease of life to western Christian civilization as an Atlantic common culture — much as the Mediterranean had fostered the older parent culture of classical and medieval times. By 1700 the Atlantic world of today was coming into being around the full circle of the beneficent waters of the Ocean River.

13

SAIL AND THE STREAM

I T TOOK nearly two hundred years to stabilize in European minds the picture of the New World. The cloudy but persistent rumors of an island paradise, beyond the unexplored waters of Hi-Brazil and St. Brandon's Isle and the Seven Cities of Cibola, gave way to the gentleman explorers and the Italian scientific navigators who pushed through and beyond these dreams to the actual boundaries of a New World. The ambitions of royal governments to settle controlled areas and milk them for the European masters in turn faded out. The strength of European aggression and conquest of the far side of the Ocean River at last fell into the practical and tenacious hands of men bent on bettering their lot by piracy, smuggling, or legitimate trade, which might honestly be summed-up as commerce. Commerce required settlement and development. Men vigorous enough to exploit a wilderness soon discovered to their backers at home that they were also strong enough to set up shop for themselves. Europe in the seventeenth century extended its power to surround the Atlantic world, and at the same time saw the growing divorce of this new growth from its original European control.

In the Caribbean, sugar remained as a great colonizing force after the first drain of Indian treasure had flooded Europe, just as tobacco and cotton dominated the economy

of the southern states of North America. In the north, cod
was always king, and in itself acted as a lever to pry gold from
the Catholic countries of the Mediterranean. The nature of
sugar planting in the Caribbean encouraged slavery, which in
turn acted as a brake on any healthy development of European civilization there. The rugged and resourceful nature of
the northern fisheries, coupled with a poor and rocky coastal
soil, developed the transplanted Europeans into individual-
ists of fresh invention, and kindled a commercial energy that
inevitably conquered the initial flood of southern gold. On the
codfish was built a new merchant marine; on the codfish the
separatist in religion became the new liberal in politics; on
the codfish a tough and cantankerous race of transplanted English in New England furnished the drive and culture that
pushed across the continent to the Pacific coast and united
a vast region under free institutions. Men cannot endure the
joint rigors of life at sea or the common dangers and sacrifice
of settlement in a strange wilderness without hammering
into being a common tolerance and respect for each other
as men. One might say that democracy is healthier for having
one foot in the sea.

Superficially, there was no obvious reason why the Portuguese or the Spanish should not have claimed and conquered
the lands of the Codfish Frontier. As a matter of fact, the
English were the slowest to exploit these difficult riches of
the sea; and shortly before Sir Humphrey Gilbert claimed
Newfoundland and Nova Scotia for his country, the Spanish,
Portuguese, and French vessels on the Banks outnumbered
the British. Perhaps the ultimate outcome is best hinted by
the report in 1524 of the Spaniard Gomez, who sought a
northern passage to the Moluccas: "It must be true," he said,
"that animated organized creation is scattered with a sparing
hand in these dreary climates." And our old friend Peter
Martyr wrote: "What need have we for these things that

are common to all the people of Europe. To the South to the riches of the equinoctial — not into the cold, frozen North." People migrate and home governments are most interested in the kind of a New World that is already familiar. Spain looked for "organized and animated creation," and the quick exaction of tribute. Basically the English looked for trade by hook or crook and would go anywhere and do anything to forward that end — and in so doing would give wider freedom to individuals than would the more highly centralized Catholic societies of France and the Iberian peninsula.

In the previous chapter we spoke of the first colonizing of the northern coast of the New World as seaborne off the fishing Banks. This same image might well be extended — that for the first two centuries of European knowledge of the New World in the north, the whole development was largely seaborne and a true child of the Ocean River, for the cod built the shipping and the shipping freed the colonies and built the solid commercial foundation for the sudden continental expansion and growth of capitalism.

But let us keep to the sea and follow the ships. They began to carry England's strength in the reign of Elizabeth, and it is convenient to consider the seventeenth century as the beginning of her Atlantic conquest. Before that we saw how Henry VIII and after him Elizabeth were the first to recognize the continuing need of naval and commercial fleets. They helped organize navigation schools where the use of the quadrant and telescope were taught, and maps were made using Mercator's projection. The century after this beginning gave no evidence of carefully planned or organized sea power; but the privateers and adventurers in increasing numbers raided the Caribbean. Cromwell in mid-century sent one fleet against the Algerian pirates and with another took possession of Jamaica. The commerce to the West Indies increased rapidly as the spread of English sugar planting, particularly in the Barbadoes, called for traders. In the north likewise the English colonials on the mainland of New England showed a sudden spurt of growth, especially at sea — at the expense of the neighboring maritime provinces of Newfoundland and Nova Scotia, where the west country fishing interests were strong enough to prevent settlement by Englishmen. The civil wars in England gave New England a chance gradually to shift the center of power on the fishing Banks to the colonies themselves, for America possessed the natural home ports. More than this, the future Yankees had learned by hard necessity the art of manning and handling their ships with a new efficiency that was still foreign to the English.

At the end of the century the war between England and France in Europe, and the colonies and the French in America, came to an end with the Treaty of Ryswick. This would have left the American colonies in a bad way if their commerce had not been so well founded. The French claimed Nova Scotia and all the surrounding waters, and began running out all but their own nationals; New Englanders were told to keep south of the Kennebec. The stubborn commercial interests in England pursued the shortsighted policy of monopoly so far in Newfoundland that they very nearly wrecked the fishing there by establishing the visiting fleet "admirals," who not only took command over the inhabitants but actually burned and destroyed their property. Boston at this time had an active fleet of close to 200 seagoing vessels fishing the Banks in spite of the French, and was developing a great trade with the Barbadoes. New England merchants, vending their cured cod to Bilbao, reckoned a fifty percent return on their money.

We can see why the British colonies were outstripping the mother country. First, their warfare with the French was casual and not too destructive of commercial development. Secondly, the home ports were near the Banks and allowed both winter and summer fishing. Thirdly, New England was well situated for the triangle of trade between North America, the West Indies, and Europe. In this round-the-ocean voyage cheap salt for the fisheries could be picked up at the Canary Isles — together with the good local wine. The ships trading directly from the Banks to the West Indies and the Canaries as carriers of fish but not actual fishermen were called "sack boats," probably because they hauled back to London the "sec" wines of the Canaries. A writer of this time says: "Ye New England traders were the key to the Indies (carrying beef, pork, fish, bisket and lumber) without which Jamaica, Barbadoes and ye Charibby Isles could not exist."

In the 1700's the community of the Atlantic, nourished by the warmth and the undersea riches of the Ocean River, began to come into its own. Its western shores were fully explored, and its dominant triangular trade routes from England to the colonies, to the West Indies and back again to Europe, in spite of the artificial interruptions of attempted absentee control, operated either legitimately or by smuggling and semi-piracy. Along with this commercial growth a natural improvement in the techniques of an ocean civilization developed. In the Caribbean the pirates gradually became the planters and traders, if not governors like Sir Henry Morgan. Invention forwarded the art of sail; lines lengthened, taking away the awkward tubbiness of vessels, the high poops were removed as trade became paramount over warfare, compass variation was mastered in navigation, and capstans and winches made for economy of manpower. Just after the turn of the eighteenth century the steering wheel was introduced, and the first schooner was launched at Marblehead.

This added vigor naturally bred stronger commercial competition between England and her fast-growing colonial empire in the west. The stage was set for the gradual tightening of this competition and the ultimate and inevitable Revo-

lution. Spain had failed in the west because she imposed an
absolutist control over her colonies. France under Colbert, in
spite of a military build-up at sea, failed because she either
would not or could not export her population to the west.
England, in spite of an increasingly jealous and shortsighted
policy, won out for the time being in the west because her
working people and skilled artisans brought with them the
backbone of European culture and gave it fresh impulse and
development without the constant interference of the home
government or a state church.

But along with this commercial growth — as is always true
in any period of intense and energetic development — both
political and religious thought also developed with increasing
vigor. In Massachusetts the Congregational system of church
government laid the foundation for town meetings and the
basic democracy of small communities. In Rhode Island Roger
Williams demonstrated the possibilities of political and
religious liberty, for in himself he represented the best of the
new impulse stirring in England. He was a close friend of
Milton and Sir Harry Vane. It is worth noting that Vane as
a young man got his training in Massachusetts, and was
appointed governor there at the age of twenty-four; later in
England he came to the aid of Parliament, and administered
the Royal Navy. These men helped mold the earliest New
England tradition. Pastor Robinson of the Pilgrims had
expressed this clearly when he said, "We are not over one
another but with one another." A Connecticut preacher had
declared as early as 1638: "The choice of the public magis-
trates belongs unto the people by God's own allowance";
and the pattern of the Connecticut system was largely adopted
later as a model for the Federal Constitution.

On both sides of the Atlantic world a new spirit bred from
the release of energy and from the new horizons of human
expansion due to the westward opening opportunity marked

the passage of the seventeenth century. John Locke in England carried forward the plea for freedom of mind provided
property was well protected, and others spoke of the natural
law and hence the natural rights of man. Given ideas with a
wider and more material horizon, in a world of endless
opportunity for the exercise of individual initiative, and a
vigorous racial stock to people the newly opened lands, the
political independence of the American shore from Europe
was inevitable. It came a little earlier than it might have,
because England was caught in the control of a stupid and
nearsighted political policy that involved her with France
and the colonies at the same time. While the British Government dragged its feet, history picked up speed: the speed of
new invention, fresh opportunity in a world of endless
resource, and better and quicker ways of transacting commercial operations. The aggressive commercialism of New England, according to Innis, which contributed to the breakup
of the French empire, pushed relentlessly on to the breakup
of the first empire established by Britain. New England took
all the molasses obtainable from the British West Indies and
even then only half met her wants. This close contact with
the Caribbean colonies likewise bred in that quarter a new
spirit, which Bryan Edwards described thus: "The leading
feature is an independent spirit and a display of *conscious*
equality throughout all ranks and conditions. The poorest
white person seems to consider himself nearly on a level with
the richest, and emboldened by this idea, approaches his
employer with an extended hand and a freedom, which, in
the countries of Europe, is seldom displayed by men of the
lower orders of life towards their superiors."

The British Government, feeling that the western men
beyond the Ocean River were getting ahead too fast for
England's good, by 1763 fell into the error that had hurt the
colonial enterprise of both Spain and France — a too severe

absentee control where actual control was not fully enforce-
able or even warranted. She put on the Molasses Act, which
restricted trade between New England and the West Indies
to British colonies alone, and cut off fishing in the Straits of
Belle Isle and Labrador from the New Englanders. This tax
on molasses cut into the profits of the three-cornered oceanic
trade on which New England's prosperity was founded;
molasses from the West Indies, turned into rum at a profit
in New England, which, mixed with some other export goods,
was taken to Africa and turned into a profit in exchange
for slaves, which were carried to the West Indies and sold —
at a profit. England found it difficult to get her hand deep
enough into this bulging Yankee pocket, since the colonial
vessels traversed the free ways of the Ocean River. Actually,
the commercial restrictions, though resented as such, were not
as important as the idea that England could reach out and tell
the Yankees how and where they could trade.

These restrictive policies of the Government were not reflected in the feeling of the common Englishman, who was
at heart an individualist and a free trader like his Yankee
cousin. Adam Smith, writing at this time, said: "In her present
condition, Great Britain resembles one of those unwholesome
bodies in which some of the vital parts are overgrown, and
which, upon that account are liable to many dangerous dis-
orders. . . . The expectation of a rupture with the colonies,
accordingly, had struck the people of Great Britain with
more terror than they ever felt for the Spanish Armada or a
French invasion. It was this terror, whether well- or ill-
grounded, which rendered the repeal of the Stamp Act, among
the merchants at least, a popular measure. In the total exclu-
sion from the colonial market, was it to last only for a few
years, the greater part of our merchants used to fancy that they
foresaw an entire stop to their trade; the greater part of our
master manufacturers, the entire ruin of their business; and

the greater part of our workmen, an end of their employment." Here we have an excellent testimony that the common people and the practical people of England, as they did during our Civil War, understood better than the traditional statesmen the common bond in the business of mutual self-preservation that existed on both sides of the Atlantic.

In mid-century the Barbadoes alone consumed goods annually valued at £100,000 sterling. Huske, an English writer on *The Present State of North America,* put it this way: "It is from the American colonies our royal navy is supplied in a great measure with masts of all sizes and our naval stores, as well as our merchant ships; it is from them we have our vast fleet of merchant ships and consequently an increase of seamen; it is from them our men of war in the American world are on any occasion manned, and our troops there augmented and recruited; it is from them we have our silver and gold by way of Spain, Portugal and Italy, in payment for their immense quantities of fish, rice, etc.; it is from them we have all our tobacco, rice, rum and sugars, dyeing and other valuable woods, cotton-wool, ginger, indigo, whale and cod-liver oil, beaver, furs and innumerable other articles." Well, there it is. The child had grown at a tremendous pace, history was at the gallop, and the American world just west of the Ocean River was now a member of the Atlantic community to be reckoned with.

As far as the commercial growth and general recognition of American independence went, the War of 1812 might well be considered as part of the Revolution. England was loath to recognize the birth of a new western nation in world trade. Fortunately for the United States, with the advent of the Napoleonic Wars involving England on the continent after 1790, the Atlantic carrying trade took more and more to American bottoms. England at that time was using half of all American exports and the West Indies was taking a third.

The continental nature of trade began to show up with increasing exports of wheat from Baltimore and flax seed from New York to Ireland. Congress aided this new opportunity to develop the American merchant marine with a differential shipping tax of fifty cents a ton for foreign shipping and six cents for American. Help was needed. The little port of Gloucester had lost a third of her men during the war. There was also a bounty paid fishermen of five cents a quintal for dried fish and the same per barrel for pickled fish. The jockeying by government for commercial advantage had begun, and was to last until Andrew Jackson, representing the continental needs of the people as a whole rather than the mercantile class, in 1830 re-established the principles of free trade.

Along with this new seaborne prosperity in New England, the British seaports flourished mightily after the Revolution. The port of London was badly congested with an annual turnover of more than 3,500 foreign voyages to handle, and Liverpool had more than 4,000 vessels clearing port; over 100 of these were slavers. A local report reads: "The great annual return of wealth may be said to pervade the whole town contributing to the support of the majority of the inhabitants. Almost every man in Liverpool is a merchant, and he who cannot send a bale will send a bandbox. It will therefore create little astonishment that the attractive African meteor [the slave trade] has so dazzled their ideas that almost every order of people is interested in a Guinea cargo."

But there was a dark side to this picture of commercial progress for the newborn republic. With no naval force worthy of the name we became a prey to all the other seagoing powers; there was only one international law at the time: Might makes Right. We bought off the Barbary pirates of the Mediterranean with tribute of ships and supplies; we could not so buy off the French and British. They captured our vessels and the English shanghaied our sailors at will. The official British policy was quietly and persistently hostile. Lord Sheffield wrote in 1784: "It is not probable that the American states will have a very free trade in the Mediterranean; it will not be to the interests of any of the great maritime powers to protect them from the Barbary states. They cannot protect themselves, they cannot pretend to a navy."

The inconclusive War of 1812 to 1815 helped to settle the status of the new nation by convincing Europeans that the Americans were determined to fight for their liberties. After this conflict had petered out, the new growth of the American merchant marine reflected for the first time the impetus of world-wide commerce. Codfish was no longer king.

The art of shipbuilding and ship handling followed the new demands of world trade on both sides of the Atlantic, but the Yankees made greater progress and held this leadership of the sea until the age of steam, when England once more took the lead and has held it ever since. This cannot be laid to the type or quality of the English seafarers. The handicap to the development of English shipping was the conservative attitude of the Government and the natural conservatism of the English moneyed classes. A naval architect, Captain Gower, in 1796 designed and built at his own expense a four-masted barkentine that in some ways anticipated the narrow and deeper lines of the future clippers. The ship outsailed anything the other English builders could put in the water, and was officially tested and proved out by the Admiralty. But the Navy wouldn't have her; she was too modern. The French also at this time built a ship, *L'Invention*, with similar lines, designed by Thibault of Bordeaux. She made the voyage from Gibraltar to Virginia in thirty-seven days; and after falling into British hands sailed from the Channel to St. Johns in twenty days. For 1800 these were fast passages, better than anything previously on record. But the authorities who might have forwarded the adoption of this improved type of vessel did nothing; they left it to the Yankees. Basil Lubbock writes: "The merchantmen of Napoleon's wars were what the sailors call a heavy-working ship . . . this was entirely owing to two pet theories of British seamen, that weight meant strength and that big, clumsy looking blocks took away from a vessels smartness. The Americans fell into neither of these mistakes. Their ships could be worked by half the men required on the English vessels owing to the fact that they used smaller ropes and bigger blocks so that their running gear worked easily." The wide Atlantic horizons and the challenge of a New World had already begun reacting on men. Oversea Britons, sharpened by a new climate and fresh opportunity, were developing experimental, mobile, and curious minds. Nowhere was this better illustrated than in the race during the first part of the nineteenth century for mastery of the sea, first with the American schooner, then the packets on the New York-Liverpool run, and finally the crowning triumph of men against the sea, the Yankee clippers.

About 1835 the British Parliament, worried over the manifest loss of trade to the Americans, set up a commission which reported in part as follows: "The committee cannot conclude its labor without calling attention to the fact, that the ships of the United States of America, frequenting the ports of England, are stated by several witnesses to be superior to those of similar class amongst the ships of Great Britain, the commanders and officers being generally considered to be more competent as seamen and navigators, and more uniformly persons of education, . . . while the seamen of the United States are considered to be more carefully selected and more efficient, that American ships sailing from Liverpool to New York have preference over English vessels both as to freight and to rate of insurance, and higher wages being given their equipment is maintained in a higher state of perfection; as the American shipping has increased in late years in the proportion of more than twelve per cent per annum while the British shipping have increased in the same period one and a half per cent per annum."

Europe's stepchild of the west was coming of age at the beginning of the nineteenth century for two reasons. Her fresh and inventive use of the sea paths of commerce had developed, along with the original codfisheries of colonial days, into a world-carrying trade on fast and efficient bottoms that could not be matched elsewhere. And back of this, new seaports like New York, with the Erie Canal leading into the trans-mountain west, and Baltimore, with her roadways and new canal pouring inland wealth through the Alleghenies, brought a fresh supply of truly continental goods like flour and hides that were needed in the world market. No wonder the packet ships of the '30's and '40's, followed by the magnificent China clippers, were a glorious testament to the final conquest of sail over the storms and currents of the Ocean River.

This is how it came about. The shore fishing off the New England Banks near Cape Cod was carried on at first by crude ketches that did not handle too well. The Chebacco boats — early name of Essex, Mass., where they were built — followed this design for offshore fishing both winter and summer. They were not very big but chunky, with two masts, the foremast well forward. They used square sails that could be snugly trimmed. They were seaworthy and safe but slow. From this design they developed the short-sterned "pinkie" in the early nineteenth century. It had a raking sternpost and an extension of the bulwarks aft raised up as a rest for the boom. A parallel development from the blunt two-masted craft of an earlier day were the square-sterned schooners sometimes called "dog-boddies" and "heel-tappers." They in turn took on sharper lines, and the raked masts of the Chesapeake clipper schooner. The best of these innovations that were to evolve into the Gloucester fishing schooner were built at New London and at East Boston by Samuel Hall about mid-century. They had loftier rigs and were about a hundred tons burden.

At this same time the transatlantic packets were being built and the big, deep-bodied, steep-sided clippers were coming off the ways in Boston and New York. It would be impossible to classify this sudden flowering of swift ships in exact categories. Many of the so-called packets were almost on clipper lines, and there were many deviations from the strict descriptions. In the main the packets were shallower and had blunt, full bows, while the larger and more elegant clippers had more rake to the masts, steeper sides, greater draft, and hollow rather than bluff bow lines. But it is still a matter of open debate whether it was superior design alone, or more skillful, harder-driving masters, that made the difference in the average speed of these vessels. At any rate they had so developed in reach and speed that now the trade of the Atlantic began to take on a world-wide nature. Vessels set out from Salem to open up the spice islands of Malaya, and Boston vessels rounded the Horn to start the profitable fur trade from the Pacific Northwest with China. The ship *Rajah* of Salem as early as 1795 came back from Sumatra loaded with pepper and paid a profit of 700 percent. The answer to this new success was to be found both in the kind of men and the kind of ships developing on the eastern American seaboard. At the age of twenty-one Richard Cleveland of Salem wrote: "I had now the gratification of uncontrolled action. An innate love of independence, an impatience of restraint, an aversion to responsibility, and a desire to have no other limits to my wanderings than the globe itself, reconciled me to the endurance of fatigues and privations which I knew to be an unavoidable consequence of navigating in so frail a bark." It should be noted that the commander of Cleveland's ship to the spice islands was nineteen.

Just as the sailing vessel was developing into its climax as the great clipper of 1850, the handwriting was on the wall of what was to follow — namely the complete eclipse of sail by steam as master of the turbulent waters of the Ocean River. Once more sea supremacy went back to the English. With the opening of the western lands after the War of 1812 the surplus population of young men in New England and on the eastern seaboard no longer needed to look to sea for fortune and advancement. In fact, ready wealth by development and speculation in western lands, and the sudden rise of western cities and inland commerce, offered opportunities that could no longer be matched at sea. The masters of the great American packet boats and clippers still were Americans, as were most of the officers, but sailors and "Liverpool packet-rats" were often shanghaied to fill a crew — the hard discipline and low pay did not appeal to young men with a new transmountain continent opening to the westward.

Also at this time the first ocean steamers were being built, and only the British with their advanced skills in iron and steel then knew how to build them well. Five years before the first American clipper began to set new records for sail the British had two steamers in transatlantic operation, the *Sirius* and the *Great Western*; and as new rivals for the carrying trade the Inman Line from Liverpool to Philadelphia was a commercial success without a penny of government subsidy. It is true that the invention of the screw propeller — which according to Anderson gave the death blow to sailing men-of-war — was followed almost at once by a great though transient advantage to merchant sailing vessels when steam tugs allowed easier maneuvering and a quicker turnaround for the biggest sailing ships in harbors and narrow waters. The flowering and the eclipse of the great days of sail belonged to America for

the brief period of a few decades only; by the time of the
Civil War it had passed. Only on the Grand Banks a thousand fishing vessels, many of them the new fast Gloucester
schooner design then developing, still held supremacy for the
Yankees in this original field.

We have briefly outlined the influence of the Ocean River
on the development of sail from the first discoveries to the
final glory of the great clipper ships. But we cannot go into
the story of the vessels, because the ocean itself is the focus
of our story. By the nineteenth century the pathways of the
sea for trade and immigration to the western side of the
Atlantic were well established. It all began with the fishing
colony of the Banks with the Yankees in charge. Then these
same Yankees pioneered the trade with Malaya and the spice
islands. Vessels from Salem and Boston rounded the Horn
to buy furs along the shores of the Pacific Northwest and
resell them to the Chinese. Next the fast, scheduled Black
Ball packets between New York and Liverpool showed the
first sign of other than New England ports taking leadership
in transatlantic shipping. Almost simultaneously Griffith and
McKay launched the clippers — the largest, swiftest, and most
beautiful vessels man had ever seen, which dominated the
China trade and the transportation to the California gold rush.
Then Australian clippers, copied from these American vessels,
began to give the English a fresh grip on world trade, and
the English pioneering and mastery of steam finally brought
that country supremacy in the Atlantic trade routes.

With this new speed and regularity of ocean traffic, the
troubled peoples of Europe found readier access to the newly-
opened western lands of the United States, and the final racial
unity of Europe and the western continent grew in strength.
After the earliest English settlers in the eighteenth century
Germans from the Palatinate poured into Pennsylvania.
When the lead in fishing interests transferred to New Eng-

land, Irish came down into Boston from the maritime provinces of Canada; and after the War of 1812 various waves
of a new German immigration poured in from the Rhineland,
due to hard times in Europe. The Scotch-Irish, following the
flax trade, came into western Pennsylvania. In brief, the pull
of the Atlantic world made the west a land of opportunity
for the harassed and surplus populations of western Europe
prior to the Civil War. Free land in the west was largely
the impetus at this time, just as industrial development and
the black prairie soil later brought in new groups of immi-
grants from Europe and the Mediterranean.

Until the nineteenth century the collection of information
and the study of the Ocean River that so greatly affected
sailing the Atlantic was slow and almost casual. We have seen
how Franklin got the Stream mapped in 1769 from information gathered by Folger and other whaling captains of Nantucket. He then interested younger men in following up the
thermal charting of the great Stream at America's front door.
In fact, the thermometer was often of more use in navigation
to the American captains, even into the early nineteenth
century, than the chronometer, which they regarded as too
expensive. But even before Franklin, a few scattered individuals were laying the foundation of navigational studies in
America. At the beginning of the seventeenth century Benjamin Hubbard of Charlestown, Mass., published *Orthodoxal
Navigation* — ignored at the time, but the first attempt to
chart a great circle course across the Atlantic. Lawrence
Wroth, in his pamphlet *Some American Contributions to the
Art of Navigation,* writes: "Hubbard's chief contribution to
the practice of sailing upon the great circle course was the
construction of a chart which he called a new and true Para-
doxal Chart. That chart represented the superficies of a
spherical triangle embodying one eighth of the surface of the
earth. Upon the chart thus constructed he laid down eighteen

great circle courses. . . . Disregarding its exactness or inexactness, we are able to say of him that he gave development in his book to the principle now universally followed in laying down a great circle course upon a chart of the Mercator projection."

After Hubbard a certain Captain Cyprian Southhack made numerous charts of New England waters, and in 1720 published *The New England Coasting Pilot*. His charts for some time to come were included in *The English Pilot, Fourth Book*, and did much to start a more thorough coastal survey of American waters.

Just about the time of the Revolution Bernard Romans, a Dutch engineer who became an officer in the Continental Army, made some interesting charts of Gulf and Florida waters, published in New York in 1775, with several copper plates engraved by Paul Revere. Romans also published *A Concise Natural History of East and West Florida*. But interesting though they are these studies did not add much to our knowledge of the Stream. What was perhaps the first American notation of the great current was made in 1735 by Captain Hoxton of Virginia, who noted a strong northeast current and gave directions how it might be avoided.

At the time Franklin was getting Folger to measure the Stream with thermal observations, William Gerard de Brahm, a pioneer in the settlement of the south and a man of wide education, published in 1772 *The Atlantic Pilot*, which gave descriptions and charts of the Gulf or Florida Stream at its inception off our southern coasts. This chart, together with the work of Franklin and his grandnephew Jonathan Williams, might well be considered the true start of oceanographic science on this side of the Atlantic. Captain Truxton worked with Williams, and in 1799 their combined data were published in a book called *Thermometrical Navigation*, ". . . tending to prove, that by ascertaining the relative heat of sea water

. . . the passage of a ship through the Gulf Stream, and from deep water into soundings, may be discovered in time to avoid danger."

Meanwhile in Boston John and William Norman were publishing *The American Pilot* from 1791 to 1794. In 1796 Edmund Blunt of Newburyport issued *The American Coast Pilot*, edited by a Captain Lawrence Furlong. In 1800 Blunt brought out John Hamilton Moore's *New Practical Navigator*. The interesting thing about this book was the editor, a young Salem sea captain, Nathaniel Bowditch, who made several hundred corrections in the text. When a later and fully corrected issue came out in 1802 Bowditch had practically rewritten the book, correcting over eight thousand earlier errors and enlarging the chapters on astronomy, mathematics, and sailing directions.

Here at last, through the natural genius of Bowditch, the sum of navigational knowledge collected laboriously during the sixteenth, seventeenth, and eighteenth centuries — particularly of course the eighteenth — was brought together and amplified into what has truly been regarded as a new masterwork. With Bowditch at hand and the later addition of the British Admiralty compass in 1840, together with the chronometer based on Greenwich time, modern conquest of the Atlantic and the mastery of the great waters of the Ocean River had come to pass. An exact reckoning of longitude and the ability to sail at night were now possible. Commerce could hold to advertised schedules.

With the nineteenth century the seaborne conquest of the oceanic western frontier along the courses of the Gulf Stream assumed for the most part its modern form. Slavery was on the way out, independence from European domination was largely accomplished; a world commerce free from piracy was established, and the economic, political, and social problems of the Americas had a western land pull that for the next hundred years overshadowed traditional or present day ties with the mother countries of the Atlantic community. Before we close this brief, condensed survey of the world of the Ocean River, a summary seems called for of the balance of forces and their future development around and within this heart land of western civilization.

14

THE ATLANTIC AND
WESTERN MAN

IN OUR foregoing chapters we have tried to keep the focus on man and his fate as he is affected by the natural law of the widespread yet interrelated world of the Ocean River of the Atlantic. Anatole France has well expressed this humanistic view of science. What is admirable, he says, is not so much that the field of the stars is so vast, but rather that it is man who has measured it. Adhering to this point of view, consciously or unconsciously we find ourselves swimming upstream against the flood of acquiescence in the second law of thermodynamics, which so much dominates the scientific mind.

The law sounds formidable and final, and it most certainly predominates in all natural phenomena. Put simply, it states that though there is a constant volume of energy in the universe, this energy, changing from one phase to another, tends always to reach into lower potentials and become more diffuse. If this can also be applied wholesale to man then we certainly fit the pattern espoused by Spengler and his kind; and the all-too-human question "Where do we go from here?" is vain indeed, for our potential of survival is everywhere in retreat.

Fortunately, the scientists themselves, being human, have evolved an escape from this deadly leveling of creative force. Clerk Maxwell in the nineteenth century invented a demon which somehow manipulated the inevitable laws of chance to account for creative evolution; in our own day this scientific nickname for the God of our fathers has been "Anti-Chance." Anti-Chance accounts for continuing evolutionary phenomena in what might seem to be a universe automatically doomed to a dispersal of living energies. For man, as far as we know — unlike other animals — can will himself to live or die for an idea; no other animal is consciously torn between the two great instincts that drive individuals and their governments, the fight for absolute power opposed to the equally strong instinct for co-operative effort. As we observe the inhabitants of the stream below water, we see that the fish swim in vast schools for mutual protection but also that the shark and the barracuda operate as very rugged individuals. Man, aware of himself in relation to his natural environment, has exerted choice and disciplined his instincts in a conscious idea or ideal of social self-preservation, and has evolved from hard experience the Christian precept of brotherhood, which in its political phase has expressed itself most effectively in the dogmas of democracy. For western man this is the mainspring of our present life; and was historically the dominant characteristic of the growth of our western civilization as it spread to the Atlantic and the stimulating environment of the Ocean River.

So today all facets of learning, from pure science to the broad interpretations of history, are seeking a kind of unity in nature and man, for in spite of all setbacks a natural and mutually beneficial teamwork is clearly becoming not only possible but obligatory if our western Christian civilization is to go on prospering as a way for men to live together with dignity, security, and more than a promise of the pursuit of happiness. Science, so far from being antagonistic to our instinctive beliefs, by bringing them into the light of day has clarified the rhythms and laws by which we live, and made an ultimate solution much more likely — provided man can assume the necessary intelligent disciplines to conform to them.

Lord Acton, in describing what he calls "Universal History," has set the sights for the modern student: "The recent past contains the key to the present time. All forms of thought that influence it come before us in their turn; we have to describe the ruling currents, to interpret the sovereign forces that still govern and divide the world. By Universal History I understand that which is distinct from the combined history of all countries, which is not a rope of sand but a continuous development, not a burden on the memory but an illumination of the soul. It moves in a succession to which the nations are subsidiary . . . according to the time and degree in which they contribute to the common fortunes of mankind." He further points out that modern history begins with the sixteenth century a new phase of human development, both in scientific research and in the realm of ideas. His presentation can scarcely be improved on: "The modern age did not proceed from the medieval by normal succession, with outward tokens of legitimate descent. Unheralded, it founded a new order of things, under a law of innovation, sapping the ancient reign of continuity. In those days Columbus subverted the notions of the world and reversed the conditions of production, wealth and power; in those days Machiavelli released governments from the restraint of law; Erasmus diverted the current of ancient learning from profane into Christian channels; Luther broke the chain of authority and tradition at the strongest link; and Copernicus erected an invincible power that set forever the mark of progress upon the time that was to come. . . . It was an awakening of new life; the world revolved in a different orbit determined by influences unknown before. After many ages persuaded of the headlong decline and impending dissolution of society, and governed by usage and the will of masters who were in their graves, the sixteenth century went forth armed for untried experience, and ready to watch with hopefulness a prospect of incalculable change."

From the standpoint of modern science and of our social and political adjustment and growth in the invigorating atmosphere of a new world, the second important factor growing out of this vast new opportunity for man is the almost terrifying speed-up of his extension of material power. Western man no sooner got used to the gifts of new fisheries, huge forests, and a virgin soil already cropped with the Indian maize that saved the lives of the first-comers, before fresh invention and growth in commerce and the art of sail brought the riches of the world to create the wealth and power of the Atlantic seaboard colonies. Meanwhile the stored treasure of the Aztec and Inca empires had poured back into Europe, also establishing there great mercantile enterprises that were in a few generations to feed greater expansion based on the invention of the steam engine and on the industrial revolution. Speed of expansion and invention accelerated, and released the revolutionary optimism and ideas of progress that rejected colonialism in the west and shortly thereafter put an end to human slavery.

As in all periods of fresh and renewed vigor in human development, the impulse was felt in all the affairs of men. Method, idea, spiritual insight, and political invention all leaped ahead into new and untried fields. The ocean, once a barrier, became a way for safe world communication, and the wave of westward immigration of European peoples spanned the Ocean River from east to west. This has been the greatest movement of peoples and cultures since central Asia poured its refreshing hordes into the Mediterranean world, and the science of the Arabs penetrated to the early universities of Europe.

At first, of course, the romantic, the greedy, and the personally ambitious poured in on the heels of the trail-breakers;

but as the New World became settled civil authority and social organization inevitably followed. Then the fresh realization of power, and a feeling of complete separateness and independence from the older countries, brought on the colonial revolts and the breaking of political ties. But all this was only a preliminary to the process of settlement. In our own time the frontier of westward-marching Europe has for some time been a thing of the past. The period of western adolescence is over; and the western child, now in full maturity, has been forced to look on the parent continent of Europe and re-estimate the relationship. The hard necessities of mutual protection, mutual trade, and — not least — the mutual unity of scientific investigation which is beyond and above nationalism, are forcing a modern reinspection of the community of the Atlantic peoples. The time of separate exploitation of human and natural resources has passed into a time where the study of the common stewardship of resources is forced on the peoples of the west.

In 1909 Henry Adams, using the idea of "phase" as expressed in science, tried to give this idea an interpretation as a measure of historical change from one period of equilibrium or static period of society, through dynamic change, into another such relatively static period. He was preoccupied to discover how much the laws of scientific change in matter could be applied to the affairs of men and the realm of ideas that govern men's actions. He makes an interesting comparison of how ideas obey the scientific laws of attraction, acceleration, and volume. For instance, the attraction of a New World in the west stimulated the imagination and thought of philosophers, statesmen, and merchants; the exploration and development of the resources of the west accelerated intellectual activity, and awakened from inertia the minds of multitudes of Europeans who otherwise might have been held in the static concepts and hopeless attitudes of the medieval world before the stimulus of the west was felt.

Although Adams used a different idiom from Lord Acton, it is interesting to follow his exposition of the speed-up we have been talking about in the historically recent affairs of men since the time Columbus ventured forth into the realms of the Ocean River. Europe, he points out, in the fifteenth century was in the deadly grip of medieval inertia except for scattered individual minds that were forcing a search for new patterns and a new lease on life. The dammed-up forces of communication and freer thinking were typified in the invention of printing by Gutenberg, by Galileo's thesis on the shape and unity of the earth, and by Bacon's earlier insistence — in the face of excommunication — that the truth lay in a methodical and fearless study of accumulated facts. This grew out of the fresh stimulus of classic Greek thought with all its unorthodox curiosity that flooded into Europe with the Renaissance.

The beginnings of acceleration in the pace of man's self-development from 1500 on to 1700 can largely be accounted for by the factors we have just mentioned — applied, of course, to the new horizon of the western world. The maximum movement possible to the world of the Church of Saint Augustine was suddenly exceeded from there on with each succeeding century, as first steam was harnessed and finally electrical energy came in with the dynamo. The pace of action and thought keeping up with invention or ahead of it has forced our modern world at such a speed of material progress that, according to Adam's theory of "phase" in history, very few years remain to modern man to readjust and resolve his tremendous evocations of power into fresh patterns, now that the lid has been lifted off Pandora's box by the splitting of the atom.

The mechanistic extensions of individual power have outraced both our emotional adjustment to this power and our ability to devise social and political controls to handle it in our own best interest. Adams in 1910 predicted that by 1940 the world might well have come to a dead end in its ability to handle its own affairs; and that once more a phase of historical advance might futilely grind to a stop in general blind confusion. The exact date doesn't matter; but his diagnosis is important, though far from hopeless, for with the end of each phase of development the seeds of a fresh way have been planted. Which way the human race turns when it comes to an apparent dead end of social or economic adjustment has never been predestined or inevitable for all men. The whole point that Adams, Acton, and at present Toynbee as social historians are trying to make is the perpetual necessity of man to meet new challenges with fresh ideas and free adaptation to the changes of his environment. Our study of life within the waters of the Ocean River, and the history of the River's influence on the lives of men and around its shores, fall into this pattern.

In the preceding chapters we have tried to chart the Ocean River in relation to our present scientific knowledge of the life within its waters and the forces that shape its course and drive its currents. We have also sketched historically the influence of the River on the great movement of European peoples in their conquest of the last frontier, that of the New World. That kind of conquest is now a thing of the past on this planet. Let us briefly retrace these forces through their various phases of expansion. They are represented by the histories of Spain, Portugal, France, Holland, and England, all countries with open access to the life-giving influence of the Ocean River.

Spain, consolidating her power at home in fixed and autocratic patterns, discovered the pot of gold at the western end of the rainbow. With some interference she brought her treasure back to Europe and supported armies and built armadas in a bid to dominate Europe. When this bid failed her power failed, because she had not successfully colonized either the

Caribbean or Central and South America. For a while the flood of her conquest swept from Florida to the Mississippi, and from there through New Mexico into California. She introduced sheep, cattle, and the horse to the western continent, and set up a great agrarian domain. But Spain failed to establish new and fresh forms of government to hold this domain. She failed also to hold her communications across the waters, because she could not learn the skills of maritime power. As a result, mixed Spanish-Indian cultures grew to independence on the mainlands. The Caribbean was lost both to other European powers and to the endurance of the imported African peoples to survive slavery and outbreed their masters.

For a while the Dutch made great progress in the Caribbean, and planted colonies in North America; but the Dutch were weakened by wars at home and by inability to transport and plant their people in sufficient quantity to look out for themselves in the New World. The Dutch were masters of trade for part of the seventeenth and eighteenth centuries, with better ships, better sailors, and a better organized and more adaptable commercial system. They prospered financially but failed as colonizers — except in the Far East, where they took over the countries Portugal first opened to trade. Portugal itself, having done more than any other nation to explore and exploit the routes to the East around Africa, was not strong enough to face the competition of her European neighbors.

France, next to England, had a great opportunity to hold possessions in the west. Her sailors and navigators were native to the Atlantic. She held power for a while from the Grand Banks to the headwaters of the Mississippi, and thence in the western lands southward to Louisiana and New Orleans. But a combination of military exhaustion at home and the inability to export populations lost her these domains.

England remained as the dominant Atlantic power because she was only partly entangled in the self-destructive rivalries of European wars, and because as a nation her power grew with the flood of new energies released with the sixteenth century. England's people followed England's conquests; and England took to the sea and dominated the world of the Ocean River and ultimately built her great nineteenth-century empire on that sea power, which in turn gave her control of the commerce of the world by her strategic grip on the thoroughfares of trade. Her loss of the American colonies proved a political loss rather than a long-term commercial handicap; it did not affect her wealth.

Today it is plain that the original thrust and power of these European nations of the eastern borders of the Ocean River has run full course and receded eastward, again leaving in the west a transplanted world of European blood, European ideas, and traces of European culture, all made over by a strange and powerful environment into a related but separate civilization. For a while this new world of America, successfully in revolt from all European ties, thought of itself as independent of the old countries; all sights were set to the west. But there was an end to west. The frontier of free land, endless natural resource, and room for an expanding population is just about over. We in the west have come in our day to the end of a four-hundred-year period of expansion; we face either a progressive phase of a growing western civilization, or the final phase.

What does our study of the nature and resources of the Ocean River bring to light? The westward migration from Europe has come to an end. There is no longer a free movement of surplus populations, because there is no more free land north of the Caribbean; and the resources of the western world have been so exploited that the promise of quick wealth for energetic and ambitious people has been radically restricted.

And now the west as well as the eastern borders of the Ocean River face an immediate problem — particularly in the Caribbean — of overpopulation in relation to economic opportunity. These are the static or negative factors. But the great advance in scientific knowledge and the new techniques of science foreshadow a new frontier of economic opportunity in the lands bordering and even in the depths of the Ocean River itself — with one all-important proviso: that science is put to disciplined use, not only in expanding fresh resources of food and raw material, but in governing and controlling a beneficial and selective growth of populations. Two dreams are gone: one, that Americans have escaped from the competitions and problems of Europe; and two, that Europeans by a westward leap can find a new world of promise ready to hand. On both sides of the Ocean River the natural way out of this dilemma is to study the available resources of the Atlantic common to all the inhabitants of its borders. This demands a partnership of science and government beyond the narrow concept of temporary, nationalistic advantage. We can hark back to Robinson's advice to the Pilgrim fathers: "We are not over one another but with one another."

This is not a matter of political slogans, but a common practical problem that involves the uses of our new weapons of science in social, industrial, and political fields alike. The dinosaurs and other huge animals of a once lush environment had to meet a changing world, but failed because they had become fixed and unadjustable in their development of size alone. All animals of land or sea fail when they cannot meet new situations with fresh patterns of behavior; the animals that survived the long sea change of prehistory were those that could adapt themselves to new circumstance. An eminent scientist, Joseph Needham, puts it this way: "The law of evolution is a kind of converse of the second law of thermodynamics, equally irreversible but contrary in tendency. We are reminded of the two components of Empedocles' world, friendship, union, attraction; and strife, dispersion and repulsion."

Just how can modern man face reduced available resources, the disappearance of available free frontiers and overpopulation? Today, assuredly, we have all the knowledge and "know-how" necessary to defeat the disease, poverty, and hatreds due to an unequable use and distribution of the world's available wealth. But so far we have not found satisfactory uses for this knowledge. It lies neither in the sometimes advocated extreme of *laissez-faire* industrial exploitation nor the rigid police state of dictatorship. The scientists tell us of the unexplored resources of the Ocean River itself. Nature and man have through the ages reduced much of the concentrated mineral wealth of the land to the dilute revervoir of the sea by erosion, floods, and even the wasteful processes of our modern industrial world. If science can develop the techniques of handling the dilute but prevalent solutions of food and minerals everywhere present in the salt sea, a new frontier of common wealth is available to mankind, a technological frontier. But obviously this cannot occur unless the other problems, both social and political, are likewise met in a scientific and co-operative spirit. This demands of the Atlantic peoples a willingness, first to look with open eyes on the new problems they face, and then to submerge their differences and face as free peoples the task of common survival; to organize without economic slavery to protect individual freedom under democracy without the killing touch of mediocrity.

This can be done by free communication among the peoples of the Atlantic communities. A sharing of ideas and scientific techniques has in the past given us weapons for survival. Physics provided the thermometer, engineering the vessels, and mathematics the understanding of the Coriolis force, all of which have helped build oceanography as a scientific teamwork in the service of mankind. Long ago the Roman emperor Justinian decreed that the ocean was a thing common to man, like air or rain water. We have seen that the ocean was at one time a dread barrier to physical travel, and was even considered beyond the realm of rational study. Then we saw the ocean become a way for expanding the range of man's growth, and a new path for intercommunication among peoples. Recently men have fought to dominate the ocean surfaces as a means to national power. Today, science is looking beneath the waters of the Ocean River and studying its rich life, its resources of chemicals and minerals, and is rediscovering a frontier that moves and lives, and that may well be of paramount importance if it is used as a "thing common to man, like air or rain water." Its fisheries have been exploited but yet may be farmed; the study of its currents that help control our sea and air climates may well lead to a full knowledge of the forces that guide the powers of sea and air; ocean chemistry may radically expand our industries.

Meanwhile each year the scientific advances in medicine face the world with a population increase of 21,000,000 people — 21,000,000 additional mouths to be fed, bodies to be clothed, souls to be assured a full chance of a good life. If we release forces that make for uncontrolled fertility without evolving social and political means to handle this force, we face a danger to man's successful and continuing evolution no less threatening than the blind use of atomic energy. Each of these dangers is also an opportunity for fresh advance. But one thing is certain: inertia or fear to face this challenge to world-wide cooperative effort will bring defeat. All the means are at hand for a solution; and no small part of the solution lies in keeping in focus a concept of the Ocean River as a scientific, social, and political unity — a new frontier for western man.

BIBLIOGRAPHY

Chapter 1

Coker, R. E.: *The Great and Wide Sea*, University of North Carolina Press, Chapel Hill, 1947.

Herdman, Sir William: *Founders of Oceanography and Their Work*, Edward Arnold, London, 1923.

Russell, F. S., and Yonge, C. M.: *The Seas*, Frederick K. Warne & Co., London and New York. Reprinted 1944.

Chapter 2

Baker, H. B.: *The Atlantic Rift and Its Meaning*. Copyright 1932 by H. B., B. P. and C. G. Baker.

Daly, R. A.: *The Floor of the Ocean*, University of North Carolina Press, Chapel Hill, 1942.

Du Toit, A. L.: *Our Wandering Continents*, Oliver & Boyd, London, 1937.

Gamow, George: *Biography of the Earth*, Mentor Books M27, New American Library, New York, 1948.

Kuenen, P. H.: *Marine Geology*, John Wiley, New York. 1950.

BIBLIOGRAPHY 2

Ryder, T. A.: *Mother Earth*, Hutchinson, London and New York, 1947.

Chapter 3

Hussey, Russell C.: *Historical Geology*, McGraw-Hill Book Co., Inc., New York and London, 1947.

Pearse, H. S.: *The Emigrations of Animals from the Seas*, The Sherwood Press, Dryden, New York, 1950.

Chapter 4

Donnelly, J.: *Atlantis, The Antediluvian World*, Harper and Bros., New York, 1910.

Forrest, H. E.: *The Atlantean Continent*, H. F. and G. Witherby, London, 1933.

Spence, Lewis: *The Problem of Atlantis*, W. Rider & Sons, Ltd., London, 1924.

Termier, P.: *Annual Report of the Smithsonian Institution*, 1915.

Whishaw, E. M.: *Atlantis in Andalucia*, Rider & Co., London, 1930.

Chapter 5

Beazley, C. R.: *Dawn of Geography*, 3 vols., P. Smith, New York, 1949.

Rawlinson, G.: *Phoenicia*, G. P. Putnam's Sons, New York, 1889.

Torr, C.: *Ancient Ships*, Oxford University Press, London and New York, 1894.

Chapter 6

Brown, Lloyd A.: *The Story of Maps*, Little, Brown & Co., Boston, 1949.

Marmer, H. A.: *The Sea*, Appleton, New York, 1930.

Pillsbury, J. E.: *The Gulf Stream*, Appendix No. 10 to Report for 1890, U. S. Coast & Geodetic Survey.

Chapter 7

Coker, R. E.: *The Great and Wide Sea*, University of North Carolina Press, Chapel Hill, 1947.

Colman, John S.: *The Sea and Its Mysteries*, Bell & Sons, London, 1950.

Russell, F. S., and Yonge, C. M.: *The Seas*, Frederick K. Warne & Co., London and New York. Reprinted, 1944.

Sverdrup, H. U.; Johnson, Martin; and Fleming, R. H.: *The Oceans*, Prentice-Hall, New York, 1942.

Chapter 8

Brooks, C. E. P.: *Climate Through the Ages*, E. Benn, Ltd., London, 1926.

Huntington, E.: *World Power and Evolution*, Yale University Press, New Haven, 1919.

Mills, C. A.: *Climate Makes the Man*, Harper and Bros., New York, 1942.

Tanehill: *Hurricanes*, Princeton University Press, Princeton, New Jersey, 1950.

U. S. Agricultural Dept.: *Climate and Man*, Year Book of Agriculture, 1941.

Chapter 9

Coker, R. E.: *The Great and Wide Sea*, University of North Carolina Press, Chapel Hill, 1947.

Colman, John S.: *The Sea and Its Mysteries*, Bell & Sons, London, 1950.

BIBLIOGRAPHY 4

Graham, Michael: *The Fish Gate*, Faber & Faber, London, 1948.

Herdman, Sir William: *Founders of Oceanography and Their Work*, Edward Arnold, London, 1923.

Meek, Alexander: *The Migrations of Fish*, Edward Arnold, London, 1916.

Ommaney, F. D.: *The Ocean*, Oxford University Press, London and New York, 1949.

Russell, F. S., and Yonge, C. M.: *The Seas*, Frederick K. Warne & Co., London and New York. Reprinted 1944.

Chapter 10

Asciniegas, Germán: *Caribbean, Sea of a New World*, Alfred A. Knopf, Inc., New York, 1946.

Haring, C. H.: *Spanish Empire in America*, Oxford University Press, London and New York, 1947.

Helps, Sir Arthur: *The Life of Las Casas*, Bell & Daldy, London, 1868.

Morison, S. E.: *Admiral of the Ocean Sea*, Little, Brown & Co., Boston, 1942.

Chapter 11

Edwards, Bryan: *History of Jamaica*, James Humphries, Philadelphia, 1806.

Esquemelin, J.: *Buccaneers of America*, Dutton & Co., New York, 1924.

Haring, C. H.: *The Buccaneers in the West Indies in the XVII Century*, Methuen & Co., Ltd., London, 1910.

Parry, J. H.: *Europe and a Wider World*, Hutchinsons University Library, London, 1949.

BIBLIOGRAPHY 5

Wyndham, H. A.: *The Atlantic and Slavery*, Royal Institute of International Affairs, Oxford University Press, 1935.

Chapter 12

Biggar, H. P.: *The Precursors of Jacques Cartier, 1497–1534*, Ottawa: Government Printing Bureau, 1911.

Fiske, John: *New France and New England*, Houghton Mifflin, Boston, 1902.

Innis, H. A.: *The Codfisheries*, Yale University Press, 1940.

Lescarbot: *History of New France*, Edited by H. P. Biggar, Harper & Bros., New York, 1928.

McFarland, R.: *A History of New England Fisheries*, University of Pennsylvania Press, Philadelphia, 1911.

Chapter 13

Albion, R. G.: *Square-Riggers on Schedule*, Princeton University Press, Princeton, 1938.

Spears, J. R.: *The Story of the American Merchant Marine*, The Macmillan Co., New York, 1910.

Morison, S.: *The Maritime History of Massachusetts, 1783–1860*, Houghton Mifflin Co., Boston, 1921.

Wroth, L. C.: *Early American Navigators*, John Carter Brown Library, Providence, Rhode Island

Chapter 14

Lord Acton: *Lectures on Modern History*, The Macmillan Company, London, 1950.

Adams, Henry: *The Degradation of the Democratic Dogma*, The Macmillan Company, New York, 1919.

Cook, R. C.: *Human Fertility*, William Sloane Associates, New York, 1951.

La Blache, Vidal: *Principles of Human Geography*, Constable, London, 1926.

INDEX